DEVON AND CORNWALL RECORD SOCIETY

New Series, Volume 52

DEVON AND CORNWALL RECORD SOCIETY
New Series, Volume 52

COLLECTING THE NEW, RARE AND CURIOUS

*Letters Selected from the Correspondence of the
Cornish Mineralogists Philip Rashleigh, John Hawkins
and William Gregor, 1755–1822*

Edited with an Introduction by

R. J. Cleevely

Exeter
2011

ISBN 978-0-901853-52-3

Devon Libraries

Typeset by Kestrel Data, Exeter, Devon.

Printed and bound in Great Britain by
Short Run Press Ltd, Exeter, Devon.

Contents

Acknowledgements

Firstly, I owe a great debt of gratitude to Andrew Thorpe, the Society's Editor, for his considerable efforts and advice over the past few years and I need to record that without his dedication the publication of this selection of letters would not have been achieved. It follows that this has to be extended to the officers of the Devon and Cornwall Record Society for including this title in their significant series of publication of the South-West's archives.

My thanks have to be given to Professor Hugh Torrens at Keele University for had he not allotted the contribution on Philip Rashleigh required for the *Oxford Dictionary of National Biography* to me, I would never have examined the archives at Truro. I have to record my gratitude to past colleagues at the Natural History Museum, 'Bob' Symes and the late John Thackray (when the Museum's archivist), who encouraged this interest; while I also owe a debt to Dr. C. N. Page, editor of the TRGSC for getting the project underway by publishing my initial results.

Inevitably, both Christine and Colin Edwards have continually provided advice, information, encouragement and assistance, especially by arranging for the examination of letters in the Carew archives at the Cornwall Record Office, Truro.

Other archivists and librarians deserve my appreciation for their help when examining material in their care; particularly all staff in the CRO Search Room; Angela Broome, Librarian of the RIC Courtney Library; Gina Douglas, Librarian at the Linnean Society, London, and other librarians at Bristol University and the Royal Society in London. It is also necessary to record my gratitude to former colleagues at the Natural History Museum, South Kensington for access to material in that institution's libraries; to the Warwick County Record Office for details of the Pennant Papers; and to the Sir Arthur Quiller Couch Memorial Fund for grants towards the cost of photo-copying.

It is equally important to acknowledge the kind and thoughtful actions of Sir Richard Carew, and those of other past and present members of the Rashleigh, Hawkins and Johnstone families, who ensured that these archives were preserved and made available to researchers.

I have also benefited from the knowledge and advice of the Rashleigh collection acquired by the late Roger Penhallurick when Curator at Truro Museum and his successor Sara Chambers – which enabled me to see the material mentioned in all these letters.

My wife has endured my long involvement with the archives of this Cornish trio, the many hours I have spent at the computer, and has patiently accompanied me on visits to Trewithen, Cornelly, Creed, Diptford, Bratton Clovelly and Caerhays.

Introduction

From various sources over the years, the Cornwall Record Office (CRO) has obtained archive material belonging to the Rashleigh and Hawkins families. Several authors have already utilised the rich Hawkins archive. In the 1950s, Sir Arthur Russell acquired a number of letters from the family and used these for his biographical papers on John Hawkins and William Gregor.[1] Subsequently, Francis Steers made various selections related to Sussex (including several to the geologist Gideon Mantell); he also published a catalogue of those then held at the West Sussex Record Office, Chichester and a series of letters relating to the Roman villa at Bignor linked to the work of Samuel and Daniel Lysons and their *Magna Britannica*.[2] More recently, Professor Lack has listed those relevant to Sibthorp and Hawkins' joint expedition to the Levant in his authoritative account *The Flora Graeca Story* (1999).[3] Material from the Rashleigh Archive was used extensively by Russell (1952), Trengove (1972), Embrey and Symes (1987), Jones (1995), Penhallurick (1997) and Cooper (1999, 2001, 2006).[4] And I have described elsewhere the contributions made by all three to the development of mineralogy, especially through their assistance to continental workers.[5]

The extensive archive of Rashleigh's nephew Reginald Pole Carew (1753–1835), now at Antony House, contains letters written between 1772 until 1808, most of them during the period when Carew travelled throughout Europe, but which somehow he preserved and brought back to England.[6] These letters contain information on family matters, especially Philip Rashleigh's role as guardian to his Carew nephews and niece and the role of his brother Charles in managing their estate. Inevitably Pole Carew's accounts of his journeys mention political and historical events in Europe.[7] But more significantly, they contain information on the initial growth of Rashleigh's mineral collection, that was largely due to Carew's efforts in negotiating exchanges and purchases with other European collectors in Hungary, Germany and Scandinavia (for example Baron Heynitz (1778/79), Pallas and Engeström (1780/81)) , or in notifying Rashleigh of potential sales (e.g Scopoli (1777)).[8] Subsequently, Hawkins initiated exchanges with Baron Trebra, Baron Born and others.[9] But that with the Austrian collector Jacquin proposed in February 1789, languished until July 1792 and never materialised. Later, an ageing immobile house-bound Rashleigh had to rely on dealers – Mrs Forster, James Sowerby and Henry Heuland – or auctions for additions.

It was through Carew that Rashleigh was contacted by Thomas Pennant, who was seeking information on the natural history of Cornwall for his publications.[10] Rashleigh provided information and specimens of marine animals (remarking on the difficulties of their preservation) and contributed accounts of the fishery and mining activities in the county (see letters 1786–87, Pennant Papers, Warwickshire County Record Office). A series of letters to Messrs G. C. Fox of Falmouth that mention Government plans reflect Rashleigh's prime concern as a member of parliament to serve the interests of Cornwall. Correspondence between Rashleigh and Sowerby in archives at Truro, Bristol and London, yield Rashleigh's own views on collecting and also reveal the gradual recognition of meteorites. By using these and the Rashleigh, Hawkins and Gregor letters that have been acquired by collectors to augment those in Truro, it is hoped to progress towards the relatively complete record that Francis Steers had envisaged.[11]

Historians are fortunate that the correspondence of many figures of the past has survived. Inevitably, these letters provide an insight into the exact nature of the writer's relationships with contemporaries, whether as friend, relative, collaborator, or fellow researcher. In addition, more personal thoughts and opinions become available to augment any published biographies and obituaries. Often, such letters reveal characteristic traits of style, language and personality that add colour to such accounts and yield a clearer picture of the writer. However, in a recent assessment of the letters of Francis Burney, Crump pointed out that one cannot always expect to find the 'the real' nature and thoughts of the writer, for, as Samuel Johnson, suggested those written to a friend might require 'a more artful self-presentation' in order to please and not cause offence.[12] But it is apparent that such deceptions were never practised either by Rashleigh, or by his friends, for their principal concern was to inform and assist one another with their particular pursuits and interests.

In a discussion of the value of a volume of an individual's personal and professional letters, it has been emphasised that they are all historical documents which can 'deepen our understanding of the historical process of science'.[13] Such letters enable us 'to see the meandering way of discovery' and may 'expose the half-formed thoughts' written to 'test friendly criticism'. Inevitably, they contrast with the subsequent printed record of consciously prepared scientific papers or formalised textbooks, and indicate the personal and human relationship involved in all scientific activity. Several of the letters included here convey this while those of Gregor show the very immediacy and hurried nature of his communications. The letters that inform Rashleigh of his suspicion that coal (10 May 1801), or rubies (17 Mar. 1803) might occur in the county reflect Gregor's excitement and caution: 'I shall therefore . . . keep my own counsel & I sh'd be obliged to you to say nothing'.

A review of trends in historiographical research also emphasised the need to use all available records when assessing the contributions of individual scientists.[14] In addition to the general background of chemical, geological and mineralogical knowledge revealed by this correspondence, Gregor's accounts convey the particular circumstances in which his experiments were conducted. These letters were written at a time when mineralogy was very fashionable and in the process of change, while geology itself was at a significant phase of its development. All three writers seem to be quite well informed about such progress, for example Lavoisier's new approach to chemistry is mentioned by Gregor when writing to Hawkins in August 1791. It is apparent they were well aware of the mineral discoveries made throughout Europe and had access to the relevant literature (often through joint efforts to procure or borrow new publications).

The letters record changes and provide historical evidence of the situation in the United Kingdom. Several contain impressions of their contemporaries, such as Synott's opinion of Kirwan (10 July 1796); Rashleigh's own ideas about Count Bournon (17 Jan. 1804; 15 Apr. 1806), or Raspe (15 Nov. 1790; 30 Nov. 1791), and Hawkins's opinions of Werner, Klaproth and Baron Born.[15] Research by Michael Cooper on an extensive series of letters from the mineral dealer Henry Heuland to Rashleigh that were written during the later phase of his collecting (1807-1809), has provided considerable insight on the wider international influence of such activities, but this awaits publication.[16]

Two other series of letters demonstrate the wide interest in geology and the fashion for tours at the time. After meeting Hawkins during a continental tour, John Wedgwood became very enthusiastic and used the opportunity of several collecting tours around the British Isles to avoid becoming involved in the family business.[17] John Hailstone endeavoured to improve his knowledge by touring the country to collect material, visit mines and meet geologists on succeeding Edward Clarke as Professor of Mineralogy at Cambridge.[18] Although Hawkins was unable to join him on a journey to Europe, and their proposed translation of Werner's theory was not achieved, surviving letters reveal a measure of collaboration.

THE LETTERS

It might be thought surprising that such a wealth of material was kept. Biographers, historians and archivists have benefited from this, but it is highly unlikely that the correspondence was saved for this purpose, unlike that of many distinguished nineteenth-century figures. Why were these letters preserved? Why have these survived and not others?[19] Were they selected for some reason, or is it just fortuitous that they have been saved over the intervening years? Did the relatively high cost of postage make them worth keeping? Was it simply the limited supply of light reading matter during that period implied by Altick?[20] Or more likely their availability as reference material, or as mementos? Undoubtedly, many of these archives were retained for the latter reasons as the letters are marked with brief details of author, date and contents, which indicates a form of indexing. Several, particularly those of Hawkins and Pole Carew, were annotated with the date they were answered as a record; John Hawkins also marked the first page by crossing it through with an obvious 'X' to indicate he had dealt with a letter.[21] Writing to Gregor's daughter (8 Mar. 1822) Hawkins revealed that he had preserved her father's letters out of his great regard for him and their friendship. In fact, it is surprising that many of the letters Hawkins received are preserved despite his frequent change of abode. Similarly, there must have been a conscious effort to incorporate those that Rashleigh received whenever he was in London. Yet, it is evident from the context of these letters that not all have survived. Unfortunately, in Gregor's case, only those he sent are available now, although at one time he did retain them (see comment 18 Jan. 1809).

Nor is there any evidence of when or how either of these series began. The earliest surviving letter from Rashleigh to Hawkins (25 Feb. 1789), and that from Hawkins to Rashleigh (5 Mar. 1789), are undoubtedly part of an already established correspondence. As explained above their mutual interests in mining and mineralogy together with their respective families' involvement in local affairs would have resulted in some general level of social acquaintance and written communication. It is also probable that Hawkins and Gregor would have encountered one another when they were both at Cambridge. Later, during Hawkins' various journeys letters ensured contact was maintained, but had the added benefit of providing information and entertainment.

It is apparent from their opening comments that many of Gregor's letters were written in response to those he had just received, such as when writing to Hawkins (5 February 1807):

> I confess, that appearances are against me: I have received two very friendly letters from you, and I have suffered those letters to lie by me without any acknowledgements, for a considerable Time. – In short I may say '*Habeas confitentim reum*' – And what is worse – I have no just cause to bring forward to account for my apparent inattention & ingratitude. – I have long been intending to take up my Pen – But 'tis tomorrow, & tomorrow' – till one wonders at the interval of Time which has passed away in making good resolutions – I throw myself therefore upon your friendship & good nature.

His earliest 'dated' letter to Hawkins was written around 22 October 1790, and that to Rashleigh on 27 October 1791. The latter was probably in reply to a query from Rashleigh about an unusual hailstorm (see letter to the Royal Society (3 Nov. 1791)). The next is several years later when Hawkins, who till then was Gregor's main correspondent, had gone on his second journey to the Middle East, which suggests Rashleigh had become a replacement.

Minerals and rocks, either for collections, or else their analysis and identification were the principal subjects of their communications. Consequently, there are few references to the life-style of the writers or their households, a characteristic feature of those produced by both Fanny Burney and Jane Austen in which they described life around the turn of the century.[22] The criteria of 'landscape and prospect' that Austen considered to be amongst the most important for judging a house are briefly referred to whenever Hawkins and Gregor were seeking accommodation. The family properties of Menabilly, Trewithen and Trewarthenick would all rate highly in that respect and each of Gregor's livings were in attractive situations. The desire of all three to live in Cornwall is expressed in their letters. It is apparent from his comments and behaviour that Rashleigh was always reluctant to be away, while Gregor manipulated his livings to ensure that he could remain near the family estate. Hawkins through his multiple interests, limited resources and family responsibilities reluctantly had to settle in Sussex (see his letter of 7 Aug. 1806). On deciding to settle at Bignor Park, Hawkins then explained his plans for its refurbishment in order to have a residence of his own and avoid the continuing expense of renting a property while he expected to yield further income from the timber on the estate (c. Nov. 1806): 'Contenting myself with a secure home, however small it may be, in a situation I liked with a domain that will pay me about 3½% interest for its cost' Hawkins acknowledged he was not a practical farmer but hoped to seek professional advice on managing his land. Rashleigh advised that without someone to superintend the farm he would have trouble and vexation, but also added the need for good management of the woodland (29 Dec. 1806). All three mentioned the problems they had met when transforming, or repairing their properties, especially the disturbance caused by 'masons and carpenters'.

Brief references to family and other social events such as visitors, or sickness usually occur as excuses for lapses in their correspondence, or halts in their pursuits, as when Gregor, trying to identify a metal, wrote (17 Oct. 1801) that he had been 'so engaged with company & business' that he had been 'unable to enter fully into the matter'. Problems with the various methods and difficulties of travelling or transport were a major concern, both with regard to the carriage of specimens, as well as the failure to keep appointments, as with Gregor's lack of a suitable chaise and horses (27 Oct. 1791). The 'Austen method' of assessing the status of a household by its servants, is not feasible, although there are hints of the existence of such staff. Rashleigh greatly lamented the loss of his reliable 'hind' (19 Dec. 1803), whose judgement and management of everything on his land, he acknowledged had produced very good returns (29 Dec. 1806). But a study of the Carew-Rashleigh archives would provide a far clearer impression of the situation at Menabilly over the years. That series also contains far more comment on family, social and political matters, including the effect of weather on crops and food supply, although Hawkins too expected both his Cornish correspondents to include comments on such matters.

Inevitably, the prime purpose of these letters limits any mention of their cultural activities – there are few accounts of balls or dances (the only references being those of Rashleigh, Nov. 1790, and Wedgwood Jan., 1790). From biographical accounts, it is known that Gregor was both a musician and an artist; following one of his experiments with titanium he advocated it might produce a suitable green for use in watercolours (10 May 1801). Hawkins, described as 'a many-sided Cornish gentleman' (Stearn), as a 'classicist' (Lack); as archaeologist, geologist, mineralogist & house builder' (Steers), had a wide range of interests and abilities that included horticulture, classical languages and antiquities.[23] Following his return from the Levant, he admitted to Rashleigh that he was preoccupied in arranging the information that he had gleaned in Greece and found difficulty in disengaging from this 'favourite pursuit', especially reading the ancient writers whose facts agreed with his own observations (19 Dec. 1806). Rashleigh apparently did not care for music or any other artistic pursuits, being quite satisfied with his mineral collection for amusement.[24]

Even by incorporating material from several archives, it is apparent that the sequence of letters that have survived is extremely disrupted and unlikely to be a true record of the correspondence between or to members of the trio over the years. Date references and writers' acknowledgements are evidence of missing letters. For example, Hawkins (1 Oct. 1802) refers to two of Rashleigh's letters (24 Sept. and 1 Oct. 1801) which either have not survived, or else been acquired by a private collector. The totals for each year range from a single letter to forty-two in 1804 – this high number the result of Rashleigh's involvement with Sowerby and Gregor's work on the supposed zeolite from Stenna Gwinn. Other annual figures have a similar principal subject or interest. Several of the lower totals can be explained by personal circumstances, the death of Rashleigh's wife, Hawkins travels, and so on, but the real cause of the sudden drops is probably that of preservation and survival. The gradual diminishing number of letters between Rashleigh and Hawkins from the early 1800s reflects the changes in their lives.

Rashleigh's poor health, which he had been bemoaning since

October 1791 ('My time is drawing to a close'), limited his mobility and prevented him collecting anything himself. He was forced to rely on others, particularly London dealers such as Sowerby and Heuland, to add to his collection, and most of the letters from this period concern such transactions. At that time Hawkins had to concentrate on establishing his family in Sussex, this in turn led to involvement with other local activities, especially those linked to the discovery of the Roman Villa at Bignor, and Mantell's attempt to establish the sequence of geological formations in the county.[25] As Sibthorp's executor he also had to fulfil an obligation to publish the numerous volumes needed for the '*Flora Graeca*', a task that, together with its horticultural link, led to his involvement in the formation of the Horticultural Society.[26] Following the lapse in communication caused by these interests, Gregor wrote 'I am sorry that you have abandoned the study of Mineralogy & that your valuable collection has been suffered to be useless. – As you were qualified to be of service to others'.[27] In fact, as he explained it was only 'by means of the Chilcotts we have heard of you & yours and I shd. be exceedingly sorry if I were capable of suffering absence to efface from my recollection the ideas of passed obligations & old friends'. Their communications dwindled after 1804, with nothing in 1805, and only two (24 Jan 1806; 5 Feb. 1807) during the long interval until his last known letter (30 June 1813). There, Gregor stated that he had 'not lately written', but this is unlikely to refer to this gap of more than six years. It is known that Hawkins' descendants did destroy material found at Bignor and it is possible this may account for the lack of any letters from that period. By this time, Gregor had found an alternative outlet for his discoveries, contributing descriptions of his experiments to Sowerby's publications, and then to the journal of the recently established Cornwall Geological Society.[28]

Printed transcriptions cannot reproduce the precise nature of the original, or every idiosyncratic feature of their punctuation, format, hand-writing style or other mannerisms adopted by the writer, although Gregor's use of a ' –', or '—' instead of a full stop, or other punctuation has been retained in several letters.[29] These often convey the circumstances, or mood in which a letter was written, or its purpose. Other features such as the economic use of the paper – sometimes finding extra space by returning to the front, or continuing along the side margins, or allowing for folding, or anticipating the use of a seal by only writing in the centre and gradually widening the margins – cannot be shown. Fortunately, the economical method of first writing horizontally and then vertically on the same sheet in order to make full use of the paper and the cost of postage does not occur. Many have the 'FREE' franks available to Members of Parliament and government officials, which were often given to favoured friends. Yet, correspondents maintained that they never begrudged the expense of such communications (see Gregor – 17 Mar. 1803).[30] It is apparent that some letters Rashleigh sent abroad were never received and in one instance, he assumed that the money paid for their postage had been pocketed by the agent (17 Oct. 1792). Inevitably, communications that were sent abroad were more uncertain unless diplomatic channels were utilised; several of Rashleigh's letters to Trebra either went astray or were considerably delayed.

RELATIONSHIPS WITHIN THE TRIO

All three men belonged to land-owning families that had been established in Cornwall for several centuries, and a member of each family held a seat in Parliament during their lifetime.[31] At the very least, they would have known of one another through these political allegiances for there are occasional references in the letters to support for the candidature of those family members standing for election. However, there is no direct evidence of how the three became acquainted, or that this was primarily through their involvement in mineralogy and mining.

Rashleigh was thirty or so years older than the others; Hawkins was some six months older than Gregor and both were at Cambridge between 1780 until 1787. In this context, it is interesting to note the differing modes of address as Gregor always begins those to Rashleigh with 'My Dear Sir' but when writing to Hawkins he merely uses 'Dear Hawkins'. Presumably the first reflects the difference in age and position whilst the second suggests that they were fellow students. Yet Hawkins would have been the greater geological authority and in some respects also the more influential person, despite Rashleigh's position as an MP. For editorial reasons the repetitive closures of their letters, which reflect their level of affability, have been deleted. However, it is worth recording that Rashleigh inevitably used the signature 'Phil' Rashleigh for all his letters and it would not seem to indicate any familiar relationship.

The correspondence confirms that the Gregor and Rashleigh families stayed with each other on several occasions and that Hawkins visited them both on a tour of the South-West after his marriage. At the time Gregor wrote to Rashleigh (26 Aug. 1802) that 'whilst they [Hawkins and his wife] are with you, I shall avail myself of your ...invitation & mount my Horse'. Before the establishment of scientific societies in the region, such social visits were an opportunity for conveying both political and local news, or discussing joint interests. Rashleigh often complained at the lack of fellow scientists in the South-West and that they had to rely upon one another for scientific information, or for news of the activities of others in their branch of science. On learning of Gregor's proposed appointment to the living at Bratton Clovelly in Devon, Rashleigh wrote to Hawkins (16 June 1792) fearing the loss of their collaborator. Such communications were obviously important to each of them and this may also explain the wealth of letters that have been carefully preserved. At one time, Rashleigh waited for a cheap conveyance to reply to Gregor, who then expressed his regret (17 Mar. 1803) explaining that: 'I prize your correspondence much too highly to think of such things'.

In common with general practice, provincial and rural correspondents frequently requested their London contacts to undertake various errands on their behalf. It was the custom to ask about the availability of recently published books and arrange for their purchase, despatch and carriage. Whenever he was absent from town, Rashleigh liked to be informed of any impending auctions of mineral specimens, or the stock available from dealers. Gregor frequently asked Hawkins to undertake particular errands; writing to Hawkins after experiencing difficulties during his experiments (26 Aug. 1791) he requested the acquisition of a microscope and then apparently aware of his friendship with John Wedgwood, Gregor asked: 'Are any crucibles made from porcelain, such as Klaproth uses, to be procured in London, or does Mr. Wedgwood make any vessels for the same purpose?'. Gregor's reason is apparent from a comment Klaproth made several years later in his *Analytical Essays*, where it was emphasised that 'the choice of vessels requires great care since even the best porcelain is attacked . . . I employ silver' and he advocated that a crucible of pure gold would be preferable.[32] After acquiring these articles Gregor wrote (25 Nov. 1791):

But remember, I do not like to employ persons in executing commissions for me, who do not make a statement of what they expend for me. As this would most certainly hinder my begging them to execute any thing for me again.

He frequently included questions on mineralogical and mining subjects, such as blowing houses and the quantities of iron and tin in alloys.

Having been away on his journeys, Hawkins welcomed Rashleigh's letters: 'You gratify me with some Cornish mineralogical news' (27 Aug. 1791). Much later, on his return to England after his second tour, he admitted (28 Oct. 1798):

My long and desultory ramble thro' the Levant have deprived me of the means of hearing from most of my friends . . . at least as often as I could wish and I have much to learn respecting their health and their occupations. Permit me therefore to renew my claim on your correspondence. . . . My long removal from polished Europe has made my very ignorant of the progress of the Arts & Science and I have to learn from you and others their history for the last five years.

Rashleigh was equally pleased and answered immediately (1 Nov. 1798):

The sight of your handwriting gave me very great pleasure the last Post. I was much rejoiced to hear of your being once more on English Ground and I very heartily congratulate you on escaping the many Dangers & Troubles you have encountered. You must have met with great entertainment in the course of your Travels to have detain'd you so many years from your native Soil, & I have no doubts of your communicating some part of your labours at least, the publick, as they must be interesting to all Classes.

Gregor, by then well settled at Creed, also took up his pen 'to offer a few words of congratulation' (undated – J3/15/1717) on his safe arrival and expressed the hope that 'Now that you are once again with us . . . you will remain so', before adding:

> You have certainly done your part in the way of foreign
> research. . . . All that remains for you to do . . . is to make the
> advantages you have gained by your labours truly your own by
> communicating them . . . to your Countrymen.

Gregor, after briefly mentioning his concern over the 'State of the
World', re-established the nature of their earlier correspondence by
embarking upon an account of his chemical experiments, despite
declaring that he had done little in that way.

After his marriage, Hawkins travelled around England searching
for a suitable property, which caused Rashleigh to write (13 Nov.
1802) that 'it forebodes your banishing yourself from this County,
a circumstance many of your Friends will lament.' Consequently,
communication became spasmodic. It was renewed briefly whilst
Hawkins was temporarily at Dallington in Northamptonshire
(through Sowerby) when Rashleigh wrote to thank him (13 June
1804): 'I am very glad to hear of my friend Hawkins . . . as this
is the first I have heard of him since he got to London; I look
upon him as the best mineralogist in this Country', after which
Hawkins resumed their friendly contact. This was renewed again
during 1806, but the pressure of Hawkins' other responsibilities
and his settling in Sussex, together with Rashleigh's declining
health, led to its cessation (see above). The letters between Gregor
and Rashleigh also dwindled away between 1806 and 1808.

Over the years, they had endeavoured to provide each other
with advice; Rashleigh's letters to Hawkins often contain
suggestions about acquiring or improving property, or on estate
management (e.g. 13 Nov. 1802; 29 Dec. 1806); those of Hawkins
conveyed information on European mining techniques, as well
as the availability of specimens and books, while Gregor used
his chemical knowledge to replicate the medical remedies being
used by members of their families (19 Feb 1796, 30 Oct. 1816).
Throughout there are references to family illnesses: Gregor referred
to the inoculation of his young daughter against smallpox (26
Aug. 1802); in a letter (3 Sept. 1808) he explained the practice of
quarantine he had adopted in his household during an outbreak of
scarlet fever during March 1804; on another occasion he provided
a detailed account of his brother Francis's health (30 June 1813).

It is only through his letters that we learn of Rashleigh's own
health problems (see those of 17 Nov. 1804 & 30 June 1813). As
he grew older, his activities became more restricted; in November
1792, at the age of 63, he exclaimed 'my time is drawing fast to

an end and therefore if my Friends propose to favor me with any new Subjects of Curiosity for my amusement – they should not postpone them!'; brief comments refer to a fall in November 1798. Writing to Sowerby on receiving of some fine specimens, Rashleigh exclaimed (1 June 1804): 'Both my time of Life & Infirmities now prevent my Mineralogical excurtions [sic]' after becoming depressed that 'so many of my Friends have lately died suddenly, makes Life very precarious' he remarked '. . . Sudden Deaths are so frequent, even without infirmities, that we must be prepared for that event, perhaps the easiest way of going out of this World by the course of nature'. Thoughtfully, Sowerby responded (6 June 1804):

> I am glad you liked the few things I sent you and shall hope to send you more that I may help to divert you from thinking of old age and infirmities by rational amusement of exploring the works of the Greatest to whom all naturalists are ever praying and pay the most grateful admiration.

But, unable to supply any of Sowerby's desiderata, Rashleigh explained (12 Dec. 1805) that his 'state of health ha[d] affected [him] so much as to go any where beyond a Dining visit & entirely from working after Minerals'. Later, in letter to Pole Carew (21 Oct. 1806) he admitted: 'my infirmities are more troublesome than painful', but had gratefully exclaimed (22 Sept. 1805): 'yet, thank God they haven't reached the vital parts!'. However, by 8 August 1807 he was forced to declare: 'I am grown so infirm as not to live without the Assistance from Servants and so many have been drawn to serve [in the militia] that I must pay their penalty.' Rashleigh's decline is shown by his handwriting, which had become irregular and scratchy – quite unlike the instantly recognisable, bold, precise, rounded script of his normal letters.

POLITICAL, NATIONAL AND LOCAL EVENTS

References to other topics in the letters were incidental to their main scientific objectives. Rashleigh's service as a Member of Parliament for Fowey from 1765 to 1802 is only hinted at by occasional references to his presence in London that was dependent upon 'what business comes before Parliament'.[33] He was always reluctant to leave Cornwall once he had made Menabilly 'so much to my satisfaction' (29 Nov. 1804). In February 1789, during the Regency debate following the onset of George III's illness, Rashleigh had preferred to remain in the country until the King had recovered.[34] Earlier writing to Carew from London (18 Apr. 1780) he had complained: 'I am quite tired of this Place. Our Midnight Debates in a Place full of Unwholesome Air, is enough to hurt any Constitution!' In his view London affected his health, while 'neither the place, or its amusements' could compare with the pleasure he obtained from the countryside.[35] When in town, he resided at Norfolk House, Northumberland St. – an address often used by his foreign correspondents. It would seem that in July 1793, Rashleigh had returned to Cornwall before the parliamentary session had ended, for he was not depicted in the historic painting of all the members of the House of Commons produced by Karl Hickel that summer.[36] Following retirement in 1802, Rashleigh still took a keen interest in Parliamentary matters, requesting Pole Carew to arrange for reports of proceedings and bills to be sent to 'amuse a solitary man' (23 July 1803).

There is some evidence of the electioneering patronage that was prevalent in campaigns for the local Cornish boroughs from letters that express appreciation for support.[37] Gregor reported to Hawkins in 1793 (J3/2/184): 'The Canvas goes on with its usual success – Every Relation & Friend of My Brother must strongly feel their gratitude towards you for your very kind & warm exertions in his behalf'. Several letters during 1796 between Pole Carew and Rashleigh concern their successful campaign at Fowey, after Lord Edgecumbe had invited the former to stand; several others written in the early 1800s refer to subsequent elections.

Occasionally there are brief references to national policies that affected the South-West. During the last decade of the eighteenth century there were frequent parliamentary debates about the export, price and alleged restrictive monopoly of the Cornish copper trade, on whose behalf Francis Gregor was a frequent spokesman.[38] Gregor, writing to Hawkins (13 March 1800), commented 'I have no doubt but that Copper is in your thoughts at present. I fear Mr Pitt will be too strong for us', while Rashleigh's letters to George Fox (1798–99) reveal his own involvement that culminated with a speech to the House on 18 June 1799 about the difficulties of the copper trade.[39] He also revealed his annoyance at changes in property tax in a letter to Hawkins (19 Dec. 1803) which he believed: 'lays a foundation for other taxes which will soon reduce both Peers and Gentlemen to a level with Plebeians, which I think most of the European nations have been destroyed by'. He then continued by reporting 'the Mines are in a flourishing state' but doubted that they could spare the men to attend to Napoleon should he arrive; and closed by expressing his anxiety at the threat of invasion which he believed gave 'no encouragement to improve our situations or increase our collections'. Later, writing to Hawkins (29 Dec. 1806), Rashleigh deplored the effects this threat had had on Cornwall with 'the price of copper dropping, the mines are closed, ships detained in port and the fishermen wait for purchasers'. In several letters sent to Pole Carew at that time, he mentioned the difficulty in obtaining salt suitable for curing the pilchards as normal French supplies had ceased.

Several of Gregor's letters illustrate his response to the threat (14 May 1804): 'Of Politcks, we may say that we have "Confusion & [are] more confounded"'; he further remarked 'Alas! Alas! if Bonaparte does not come soon and make us more at unity with ourselves, we are making rapid advances towards ruin!' A year or so later (26 Nov. 1805), however, a month after the battle of Trafalgar, he wrote to Rashleigh:

> I heartily congratulate you on the glorious Victory, un-parallel'd I believe in the glorious Annals of our Navy – Dearly, indeed it was bought by the Death of Nelson! It gives us, however, new hopes & prospects and will I trust be one of the means under Providence of setting some bounds to the Ambition & Cruelty of the Emperor Napoleon.

Writing to Pole Carew (20 July 1780), Rashleigh mentions the involvement of various relatives during the five days of the Gordon riots in London. The significance of the weather for successful harvest is revealed by Rashleigh's comment (29 Nov. 1804) on other riots at Fowey and Mevagissey that were caused by poor harvests, or on another occasion through contractors at Plymouth buying corn for the army and navy in the confined S.W. region.[40] But Hawkins (14 Sept. 1789) had attributed similar disturbances in the North to the practice of 'forestalling' which kept prices high. Rashleigh's letters to Pole Carew during April 1794 and 1795 are further evidence of the national concern arising from government policies that affected the harvest and corn prices.[41] Gregor had earlier criticised such practices (20 Oct. 1800), saying that '[i]f the present scarcity and . . . dearness of provisions be the result of avaricious management . . . a good tillage does not afford us the comfortable ideas, which it ought to do. – It is better to fall into the hands of God than the hands of man!' Hawkins was more practical, and aimed to understand, or improve, methods and management. He asked about wheat yields to discover their effect on bread production (19 Dec. 1800), or sought to establish the cause and incidence of rust (25 Nov. 1804). Rashleigh, equally concerned, acknowledged 'I have long understood it was a kind of Fungus, but could never discover it by high Magnifiers to my satisfaction' (29 Nov. 1804); he also mentioned the subject to Carew, and later sought information on different varieties of barley that might be resistant (14 May 1806).

All three correspondents expressed general concern at the time of the French Revolution over the effect of radical thoughts. Prompted by Hawkins' account of European riots, Rashleigh exclaimed (1 Dec. 1792) that it 'astonished me to think people of property can support the ideas of the Mob, whose only aim can be plunder. I have never yet heard two men agree on the standard for Equality; or how they would go to bring Property to a par'. The situation in Europe prior to Hawkins departure prompted Gregor to express his concern (15 Feb. 1793):

> You wd. indeed find the Continent in a flame but we have also put a match to combustibles, & I fear that in a few months it will be difficult for a peaceable man to find a simple nook to put his head in where the din of War does not invade him – O War! War! O that folly & wickedness of Mankind!

Continuing unease at the political situation is also apparent in Gregor's letter to Rashleigh (15 June 1797), with a reference to '[t]imes which minister to thinking minds much anxiety for present evils to aweful anticipations of future ones', and he excused an account of his work on Antimonial Ores that would give 'little or no comfort', as a wish 'to cheat . . . a little by endeavouring to forget one's cares by discussing some favourable amusement, without [the] least alloy of Political ones '.[42]

During the years of 'anxiety and alarm', all three men continued to be concerned about Napoleon's threat of invasion. Their letters discussed the abortive efforts to raise and maintain local militia to protect the region; alluded to the rebuffs and successes experienced at sea; and criticised the ineffectiveness of politicians to achieve the desired peace. Political prospects in 1801 bringing 'a change of air', encouraged Gregor to believe (25 Apr. 1801) that an honourable peace might be agreed, that farm price controls could be removed, and that further riots might be avoided by promptly apprehending the culprits. 'By the Blessing of God, the Sun has broken thro' the gloom of our political horizon', he exclaimed with continued optimism on 10 May 1801. But when writing to Hawkins (12 Oct. 1803) Gregor was more apprehensive:

> I shall say little of public Affairs, which at present engage so much of our thoughts and conversation.- For it is a disagreeable subject. It appears to me, that we possess much physical strength in the Country, but very little talent to wield & direct it – Wavering councils & discordant plans suit not with the present crisis. At all events, much misery & bloodshed will ensue from an Invasion – and if the enemy shd. not attempt it, he will protract our expenses, & continue to hold us in the situation of alarm & apprehension & consequent armament & see wherever in future, it suits his cause – In short *Vicenia damns est.* We are in a bad neighbourhood – We do not seem to be under any great apprehensions in this County. We trust rather to our insignificance than to any military protection, which is by me no means great – a few Thousand of French men would do us infinite mischief – We have Meetings & we talk about it & about it – but I cannot say, that our system of defence is organised as yet – It will be favorable for the whole Nation, if the threatened descent is deferred for a few Months longer.

Examples of more local problems occur: Rashleigh had to seek legal remedies about his land tenure at Fowey, but annoyed at the expense of this, he alluded to the stewardship of the Prince by remarking (30 Nov. 1791): 'it is very hard to contribute to support the luxuries and extravagances of a person who [then] lays it out again to Distress You and Deprive You of what Your Ancestors have enjoy'd for a long series of years'. Other letters in 1804 refer to a dispute over mining rights between the Polgooth adventurers and Lord Arundel. Despite their keen interest in the local mines, it is surprising that neither Rashleigh, nor Gregor ever referred to the circumstances in which the miners, tinners and their families lived and worked. Over the years, visitors to Cornwall always stressed the appalling conditions they had witnessed and the hardship endured by the miners.[43] Rashleigh did report (15 Nov. 1790) the settlement of a new contract between the miners and the copper Companies, observing that this would make a difference whatever the quality of the ores, but remarked 'whether they are so good as they ought to be I cannot Judge!'.

The involvement of the three men in local affairs was generally acknowledged, but hard evidence is rather limited. For many years, Gregor was a magistrate, and he also attended important local meetings as indicated by his account of a 'large copper meeting' in Truro (24 Nov. 1792). When busily engaged in preparing minerals to be sent to Mademoiselle de Raab, in October 1791 Rashleigh complained to Hawkins that it was 'a very busy time of year with us by Mayors Chusing and feasting – not the most Pleasant way of spending a week!'. Hony has recorded that Philip Rashleigh, together with his fellow MP Viscount Valletort 'gave Fowey its Town Hall'.[44] Later, when Christopher Hawkins promoted the establishment of a public library in Truro, Rashleigh (17 Oct. 1792) was less inclined to get involved further afield, for he answered: 'I have no great idea of the utility of it, except to those . . . in or near the town'; Gregor decided not to subscribe to the scheme (24 Nov. 1792):

> because I do not think it . . . to be of such a sort as to answer the ideas of a County Library. A County Library ought to consist of books of Science & [those] of value, which you do not meet with in general in the County.

However, in order to gain Rashleigh's support, Sir Christopher sought an opportunity to dine at Menabilly that November.

London seemed to attract their Cornish acquaintances: Gregor's note to Hawkins (8 Jan. 1791) is rather disconcerting:

> It may not, perhaps be amiss for you to know that poor Captain Carlyon in a very deranged state has left his friends & gone to London. As nothing is too absurd for him to do, it may be proper for you to be advertised of his being in London – lest he might be guilty of any other mad act. – This is entre nous !

Gregor also recounted (17 Nov. 1804) the story of John Whitaker, the Rector at Ruan Langthorne, who, having published a History of Manchester, had intended to investigate London at the age of 69. However, 'he never got further than Snow Hill on his own legs [for] London air so deranged his constitution that he would probably have died had he stayed much longer'.

Comments about particular events have been useful in placing un-dated letters. The report by Gregor to Hawkins that 'I had the honour of destroying Miss Masterman in the Parish Church of Lanlivery last Friday and presenting her to Mr. Glanville' has helped to date that letter and another of Rashleigh's.[45] Other accounts of visits by Professor Hailstone to both Gregor and Rashleigh when on a tour of Cornwall in the summer of 1791, have established the date of others.[46] Letters from abroad provide glimpses of the situation in Europe; Hervey (14 July 1755) while enjoying Leipzig, referred to the disagreement between the Kings of Prussia and Poland in the late 1770s; Heynitz (27 Mar. 1780) explained that he had been prevented from writing by the delay in proclaiming peace between Austria and the King of Prussia; another from Stackhouse visiting Paris (18 Sept. 1802) marked the brief period of peace following the Treaty of Amiens.

COLLECTING MINERALS

Any rationale of collecting would accept that it can have various motivations ranging from mere acquisition to that of meaningful research. The first may be driven by chance, or by curiosity and then the hope of obtaining the rare and unusual. Once begun, it can become competitive, especially if striving for the most complete, the largest, or the finest. Such an achievement could result in some form of social prestige through attaining the dignified position of a 'man of learning'. Alternatively, collecting can have the altruistic scientific objective of improving knowledge by establishing an orderly system of classification, often through accumulating a range of specimens showing the full extent of variation. A memorandum from Charles Greville (undated DDR 5764/6) reflects the more objective purpose of serious collectors to obtain 'good examples of all classes' and even the 'different matrices in which they are found'. It is evident from the manuscripts catalogue and Rashleigh's letters that his collecting had several motives. The expansion of tin and copper mining during his lifetime through the exploitation of the rich upper zones of the Cornish deposits had led to his interest in mineralogy. Over the years he attempted to obtain examples of all the tin and metal ores, but whenever opportunity offered, he was also very pleased to acquire unique, perfect, or beautiful specimens of other minerals.

Following the Enlightenment interest in the various branches of natural history became very fashionable. Apart from discovering the rare and curious species formed by the creator, it was also believed that such research would help to understand God's great Divine Plan. For many, mineralogy was the easiest branch to study and it also offered the chance of economic benefits, if such finds could be worked or utilised in some way. Consequently, scientists, mining adventurers and collectors were keen to explore all available exposures around the United Kingdom. Borlase (1758), Maton (1794–96), and Hatchet (1796) all made such journeys, while references to visits by Reden (23 Nov. 1791), Lindenthal (15 Nov. 1790) and Lippi (21 July 1795) indicate that foreign collectors followed the same course.[47] A link with the fashionable European tours of the more affluent members of society is shown by letters from Rashleigh's friends Hervey and Stackhouse, and the journeys abroad of Hawkins, John Wedgwood and Hailstone. Each of the latter made separate visits to Cornwall in pursuit of their geological interests, while other letters from Hawkins contain accounts of his tours of Derbyshire (14 Sept. 1789) and Flintshire (19 Dec. 1800), and those of Wedgwood mention his various trips around the British Isles in search of specimens.[48]

These tours by mineral collectors, together with those of geological and mining surveys of explorers (often conducted as agricultural surveys), led to the development of geological maps. Rappaport has described how several French naturalists co-operated in resolving the problems of geological cartography by plotting the location of mineral deposits and rock-types on topographical maps during their forays.[49] They then linked these spot symbols and realised they formed regular patterns which they named 'bandes'. This technique was used over a period of forty years to compile the numerous sheets published in the *Atlas et description mineralogiques de la France* (1780). Similar techniques were then adopted to produce localised and regional mineralogical/geological maps of various parts of the British Isles.[50] In fact, the 'Mineralogical map of the Western Counties' published by Maton (1797) in his topographical account of two journeys through the South West in 1794 and 1796 – when he stayed with Rashleigh and enthused over his collection – is considered as the first regional geological map of any part of the country.[51] Maton preferred to use different stipple engraving styles, lines and shading to demarcate his nine divisions.[52] Gradually as geological understanding developed, as the stratigraphical sequences were unravelled, and the formation and occurrence of all the various rock types realised, the method used to distinguish them on these maps became more intricate. The original use of colour tints and shading to depict them now attempted to match that of the rock, graduated symbols and letters were given to each rock-type or stratigraphical age, while keys or tables helped to indicate their supposed sequence.

Embrey and Symes reviewed the history of mineralogy in the South-West and explained that the occurrence of the exotic, fine crystallised minerals which everyone sought, was due to their primary mineralisation taking place in conditions that enabled free crystal growth and that subsequent processes either protected, or else enhanced this.[53] Embrey had earlier pointed out that minerals could not be considered as equivalent to biological specimens for, in general, they did nor possess typical features.[54] He ventured to argue that 'a fine specimen' would be atypical as their size, colour, and form are all variable characters which depend upon formative growth conditions. Both subjective and objective considerations are made when deciding the qualities and aesthetic appeal of a particular mineral specimen. Inevitably, specimens acquired as 'natural curiosities' or as decorative objects were dismissed once they were no longer fashionable, while carelessness in storage or handling could reduce, or completely ruin, both the scientific and commercial value of a specimen.

Wilson has emphasised that private collectors were often responsible for forming many of the significant mineral collections.[55] As a result of the great interest in the subject at that time, Wilson noted that collectors were able to draw upon a greater number of sources including professional mineral dealers, while the nobility realised that it was to their advantage to provide access to their significant collections for study and to establish scientific institutions and mining academies.[56] The more practical mineralogists were principally concerned with the advancement of mining through this branch of geology.[57] This analytical approach was important to miners and assayers, which led to chemical qualitative analysis gradually becoming the basis of mineralogical classification.

In the eighteenth century, many collections were formed by members of the professions, the middle classes, or what Wilson termed the 'middle aristocracy'. The list of donors Rashleigh compiled as a key to his manuscript catalogue contains many who would fall into such a category. Surprisingly, this key does not include the names of Heynitz or Pallas, despite evidence in these archives of exchanges made with them through contacts initiated by Pole Carew.[58] Letters from various European collectors offer exchanges for British material they desired, e.g. Jakob Wyttenbach (Bern), Baron Trebra (Freyberg), others indicate that Lindenthal and Carlo Lippi (Naples) appear to have travelled around Europe in order to gather and exchange specimens. Rashleigh's satisfaction with the material he acquired through these exchanges varied; in a letter to Hawkins (22 Mar. 1789) he complained that the crystallisations he had received from Scopoli 'were very insignificant' but exclaimed that those 'I had from Baron Trebra . . . some very perfect & I believe not common'. In Britain, Rashleigh maintained a lengthy exchange with Sir Walter Synnot (an Irish collector) between 1780 and 1796. Other letters reflect Rashleigh's local links – some from mine-owners such as the Williams family of Scorrier, or collectors such as John Moyle and William Day. Several mention the attitudes of the mine captains, or their proprietors to such visits and the extent of the miners' knowledge of minerals.

Various letters from Christopher Hervey (a university friend) during a European tour, indicate that Rashleigh had started to collect soon after leaving Oxford University: 'I shall I believe on my way make a visit to some of the German mines, and if I find any thing of that sort that I think worth your acceptance, I shall attempt to find a method of conveying it to you' (14th July 1755). Two other letters (26th Oct. 1755 & 1st July 1756) mention specimens of iron obtained for him from the mines on Elba. Writing to Pole Carew (11 Dec. 1780), Rashleigh explained his enthusiasm: 'I am one who takes as much Pleasure in observing the Productions of Nature as others do in Cards & Dice, or Race Horses'. Later, he stated his objectives in collecting (23 Feb. 1781):

> I am not desirous of the variety of Stones which turn to no Use, unless their Elegance in Colour or Crystallization make them Valuable; my chief desire is to procure Specimens of the different appearances of the Mettals & Semi-Mettals with their Crystallizations & all the very Beautiful formations of Metals, Spars, Crystals & Fluors; I do not run to Earths, Clays & Sands. – I find it very difficult to confine these objects of Amusement within reasonable bounds.[59]

In a hand-written catalogue he outlined his purpose 'to obtain knowledge of the substances produced in a Mining County'. Ideally, he believed that such a collection should contain a wide range of all the available varieties and also duplicates of these; his Mss catalogue indicates that initially he endeavoured to achieve a full range of the tin ores. In later letters to Sowerby, Rashleigh revealed that he had realised that some examples gathered in his early days were of little value for these had suffered from being kept with specimens of Mundick (iron pyrites). He remarked (3 Mar. 1804) that 'crystals of this kind are very beautiful but exceedingly prejudicial in destroying every thing near them by decomposing', and declared (13 June 1804) that this was 'the worst weed that can get into a cabinet'.

Eyles explained that, in the eighteenth century, the earth sciences were not easily sub-divided, and that the study of rocks (petrology) had not developed, with the result that a clear distinction between minerals and rocks was not clear-cut.[60] Often, both mineral and rock specimens were referred to as 'fossils', for at that time this term was applied to anything dug up out of the ground and was not just applied to life-forms from the past. Writing to Sowerby, Rashleigh commented (21 Apr. 1804) that '[s]ome Gentlemen collect rocks and similar stones, which I think encumber a House too much. Unless they have something useful, or ornamental belonging to them, they seem to me not worth a place in the Barn!'. It is also interesting to note the change over the years in Rashleigh's attitude to the branch of crystallography; or at least in acquiring specimens with crystal faces. Initially, he was not concerned, and, indeed, was rather critical, for he considered it 'to be a labourious study – more tedious than amusing' and 'certainly not very entertaining to the generality of people' (27 July 1804). However, as this became important for classification, he began to seek examples with good crystal development (31 Oct. and ?Dec. 1789).

With the application of the increase in chemical knowledge to Mineralogy that subject was 'raised from a frivolous amusement to a sublime science'.[61] But the remarks Rashleigh made in his own publication still summarised the attitude of the majority of collectors:

> The Editor . . . does not profess to be well enough acquainted with the science and nomenclature of Chemistry, or to be sufficiently practised in chemical experiments to give complete Analyses . . . But accurate representation of curious specimens of the Mineral Kingdom may contribute to the Amusement of those who delight in such studies. . . .

In fact, Thomas Allan expressed the hope in his *Mineralogical Nomenclature* (1819) that Mineralogy might still be treated as an 'amusement' rather than a study, despite its increasing complexity, which had led to the need for his reference work.

Unusually, for the period, Rashleigh diligently recorded the source and localities of the specimens. In an undated note (5757/1/79) to Scaddan at Penzance, he listed four specimens for which he requested that their localities should be added. During 1804, in several letters to Sowerby he apologised for false information on minerals he had sent and explained that these arose from errors made by the mine adventurers who had provided them. Gregor too, had occasion to write about the incorrect provenance of minerals he had supplied. In his discussion of the rare and unusual minerals found in the South-West, Kingsbury explained that one reason for this was the reluctance of the finders to reveal the precise localities at which these scarce specimens occurred. He referred to the significance of Rashleigh's 'unusual care' in recording details that had enabled those minerals that had not been described at the time of his publications to be 're-discovered' through such information.[62]

Eventually, Rashleigh's poor health prevented visits to the mines: as he put it, 'as I am nearly confined to my own House and neighbourhood, I have few opportunities of seeing any new Minerals' (26 May 1805). As mentioned above, he became entirely dependent upon London dealers for any significant additions to his collection (see letters from the Forsters (1799–1806) and the extensive sequence (1807-1809) with their nephew Henry Heuland). In fact, as he explained to Sowerby (17 Jan. 1804), the quantity of minerals then available in London meant that they had become cheaper than those in Cornwall.

Surviving lists of Rashleigh's purchases reveal that, due to the extravagant prices that prevailed for the rare, or fine specimens, he spent a considerable amount of money. Writing to Hawkins, Rashleigh acknowledged (25th March 1805) that '[b]y your visit to Mrs Forster I have added a few rare specimens . . . to my Collection, but at Extravagant Prices'; however, he excused this since 'it is the only thing I am Extravagant in, and there is some indulgence to be allowed; as these neither Eat, Drink, or Pay Taxes: and I consider that it would cost me more to Travel for them either by myself or any other person'.

Rashleigh's remarks in other letters demonstrate the increasing cost of collecting. On 15 November 1790 he wrote of 'Strangers who come into this County . . . seeing a Specimen which appears beautiful, give a great price for it, and the Dealers then think every thing they can procure is inestimable'; and on 3 September 1801 that good minerals were 'now sold at such extravagant Prices as to prevent those of moderate fortune from engaging in Mineralogical pursuits'. By 13 November 1802 he was declaring that 'the Expence of procureing Specimens has increased to such extravegance, that if my Collection was not considerable at present, I should not have begun'. Commenting on its growing popularity (29 Dec. 1806), he stated that he 'ha[d] scarce seen any collection where the minerals of this County are not superior to those of any other, but they are got to Enormous price by an increase of Collectors'. These high prices were caused by the fashion to participate in the search for knowledge and thereby improve one's social status through acquiring the finest pieces and specimens of 'new' minerals.[63]

Rashleigh published two volumes describing and illustrating his collection (1797, 1802) to facilitate study, but he acknowledged the deficiency of their illustrations. He had mentioned this concern to Hawkins (? Oct. 1791): 'I wish I could find a good clever man to Draw & Colour some of my Minerals'. However, he had realised that, at the time, few artists had the necessary experience to accomplish this. The figures he published were amongst the earliest attempts to provide accurate coloured representations of minerals.[64] In his dealings with Sowerby, he asked him (13 June 1804) to undertake drawing three highly valued 'curious' specimens which he believed would 'require much more skill and judgment in drawing' than usual.

As one of the few specialist collectors in Britain, Rashleigh was asked to serve on small committees assessing the value of the collections of Charles Hatchett and Charles Greville when these were offered to the British Museum.[65] Then, together with Greville and William Babington, he was asked to comment on the state of the museum's own collection, which they concluded was far poorer than a visitor might expect, particularly in its representation of examples from British localities (Hatchett, too, had considered it a 'disgrace to both the museum and the nation'). Of the three correspondents represented here, only Rashleigh's mineral collection can be considered to have had a significant position either in his own time, or subsequently. William Borlase was one of the first to recognise this, and by 1797, it was claimed to contain every mineralogical rarity found in Cornwall: 'the inspection of which its truly worthy and liberal possessor has been on all occasions ready to gratify those who study science'.[66] Such publicity led to a spate of visitors ranging from scientists such as Hatchett, Hailstone, Count Reden and Dr Herschel to curious travellers such as the Dean of Christchurch and Walter Scott, who it is alleged after being rebuffed named the villain in the novel Rob Roy after him.[67]

Hawkins acquired mineral specimens throughout his life, especially those from Cornwall, and had various reasons for doing so.[68] He was particularly interested in the practical and economical aspects of mining, liked to encourage the classification and chemical analysis of minerals, and was also prompted by a desire to assist his friends and acquaintances. Yet he was never averse to improving his own collection when opportunity offered, as the letters dealing with Rashleigh's contribution to Mademoiselle de Raab's collection during 1791-92 reveal. But some months after his marriage, Hawkins visited his friends whilst touring Cornwall and explained that, as a married man, he could no longer afford to add to his collection (1 Oct. 1802). A little later, he became fully occupied in coping with the antiquities acquired during his travels. This caused Rashleigh to deplore that he had turned to 'Foreign objects' rather than Mineralogy, and comment that, as Hawkins was now 'better informed' on Mines and their production than most Englishmen', this information would have been of great benefit to those concerned with the mines of Cornwall (13 Nov. 1802). Subsequently, Hawkins maintained (25 Nov. 1804) that 'without a Cabinet of well arranged specimens' it was impossible to study Mineralogy. Rashleigh had once believed (20 July 1792) that Hawkins' collection was 'the most perfect and best arranged in this part of the World' and had always hoped for the chance to see it. But this was never realised, for, when finally settled in Sussex, Hawkins (31 Nov. 1806) explained to Rashleigh that he feared there would be 'room for very few of my minerals until I build a room for that purpose. My finances when I form'd this collection did not permit me any great expenditure of this sort & I found the prices of fine specimens every where extravagantly high. My Cornish specimens are by far the most valuable part & I owe the best of them to your goodness.' On learning of this, Gregor wrote, perhaps selfishly (30 June 1813): 'I am sorry that you have abandoned the study of mineralogy . . . as you were qualified to be a service to others'.

In subsequent letters, Hawkins frequently mentioned his hopes, plans and difficulties in accommodating the various collections he had accumulated, but these were never fulfilled or solved, even when restoring the house at Bignor. 'My new house, large as it is, will not, I fear, contain room enough, for even a part of my Collection of Minerals and rocks. But I shall be obliged to erect a separate building for the purpose' (letter to Mantell on 3 Mar. 1817).[69] A decade later after visiting Cornwall, Hawkins revealed to Mantell that he still intended to do this (21 Jan. 1830):

> I find by experience that common habitable rooms are very ill adapted to this purpose and it is my intention after my removal to Bignor to build a detached room, or two, for the very extensive collection I have of the earlier formations formed in Greece, Italy and Germany, Hungary and England, of which perhaps the most interesting portion is the volcanic. A museum of this sort cannot well have too much glass-light in a climate which has so little sunshine. Mr Murchison has recommended a very expert maker of cabinets which I shall employ. My long stay in Cornwall has enabled me to prosecute my geological researches in that county, and to add very considerably to my collection of simple minerals.

Ultimately, as his other interests and duties took over, Hawkins abandoned these ideas. A German dealer purchased most of his collection when it was eventually sold in 1905.[70]

Gregor, the other member of the trio, when explaining his own activities to Rashleigh, declared (15 Feb. 1808) that, as Rashleigh knew, he had 'no collection', his 'object being only, when I have the leisure . . . to discover new substances or varieties'. Gregor always endeavoured to ensure Rashleigh had examples, for he believed (17 Mar. 1804) that 'your valuable Cabinet shd. contain specimens of every curious Mineral that is found in Cornwall'. Subsequently (30 June 1813), he told Hawkins that '[w]ith respect to the Amusements which I suffer to fill up the intervals of my Leisure from my business & my Duties: I draw occasionally and subject minerals to analysis, if I ever meet with such as appear worthy of it'. Rashleigh, writing to Sowerby (7 Mar. 1808), after accepting a rare specimen from Gregor, explained that 'where a Gentlemen does not collect, My Conscience is not hurt by accepting Specimens I do not possess; for it very often happens that the rarest Minerals are obtained to exhibit on a Chimney piece or some other exposed situation'. This reflected that 'collecting' had initially followed the fashionable practice of securing the rare, new, or 'curious', specimens as they

were discovered; and the more perfect they were, the better.[71]
High praise for any minerals obtained or received tended to be in
the form of 'exceedingly curious', or 'exceedingly pretty' (15 Nov.
1777) and these appraisals occur throughout letters discussing
mineral finds.

Storage was always an important factor and apart from the
problems of suitable cabinets, or methods of classification and
arrangement, the letters from collectors often stress a desirable
specimen size. Hawkins himself specified that as 'the general size of
my specimens is about four inches square' (5 Mar. 1789) he preferred
donations to his collection to match; Wedgwood, on sending
some blocks of Bath Stone to him (1 Jan. 1790), overcame this by
remarking that 'you will be able to make your pieces to your own
size'. When seeking examples of Cornish minerals for the Austrian
collector Eleanor Raab, Hawkins not only asked Rashleigh that
these should be 2½ inches by 1½ inches in size, but drew a template
on his letter (12 Sept. 1791). Lists and letters in the archive indicate
that suitable 'small specimens' were found but Rashleigh feared
(20 July 1792) that such examples might be regarded as a 'box of
straw' and not 'things sufficient . . . which would be acceptable to
a Lady'. A few were rejected by Hawkins, but others he kept for
himself, leaving Rashleigh to provide replacements. Earlier, when
Pole Carew had reported that a collection of Harz minerals was for
sale, Rashleigh enquired as to the size of its specimens, but was told
'I know not how to answer . . . as they are so continually varied,
tho' I think from 2 to 6 inches long and 2 to 4 inches broad – this
is a very vague definition, and yet it is more . . . than the Subject
is capable of'.[72] Hatchett was forced to sell his collection once the
family home had to be sold, as he no longer had 'room to arrange'
it (10 Dec. 1798).

The carriage and transport of the specimens acquired by
purchase, or despatched on exchange, was another major concern
of collectors at that period. When time was not important, it is
evident that the Cornish collectors used sea transport to convey
goods and provided the name of either the captain, or his ship
for the recipient to contact. Generally, the wagons of the regular
carrier services across the country were used as they were thought
to be safer and more reliable even though things were 'a long time
travelling between London and Cornwall and back again' (13 June
1804).[73] However, although it was recognised that ' the coach is
certainly the most expeditious conveyance', many considered it to
be 'the most hazardous and much the most expensive' (15 Apr.

1804), and Rashleigh maintained that he seldom received things safe. Walter Synnot realised that despite the handling instructions marked on boxes they were inevitably thrown around by handlers on coaches and ships. On one occasion transporting a rare delicate specimen for Rashleigh from Yorkshire to London, he kept it by him on the seat of his coach and then carefully carried it out himself at each overnight stop (5 Sept. 1792). At times it was possible to arrange for specimens and books to be incorporated into supplies of household materials ordered from London. For example, in May 1805 Rashleigh informed Sowerby that Twinings were sending him a box of tea, which might be utilised. Reference has been made to Gregor's requests for Hawkins to obtain laboratory equipment. But rather more surprising were Trebra's commissions asking Rashleigh to arrange for a quantity of mahogany wood to be sent to him in Germany (1 Feb. 1789) and then a request for an extensive collection of kitchen and table-ware (20 Dec. 1789) – and finally a quantity of seeds (Oct. 1799) – all of which were apparently managed satisfactorily.

SYSTEMATIC ARRANGEMENT OF MINERAL COLLECTIONS

In his *Dictionnaire de Chymie* (1766; trans. 1777), the French Academician Macquer emphasised that chemistry was scarcely entitled to the name of science, since it was little more than a collection of facts, the causes and relationships of which were imperfectly understood. This reflected the interest during the Enlightenment in discovery rather than in theory, as chemistry became one of the principal tools of the natural philosophers in their investigation of the systems of 'Nature'. A reviewer in the *Gentleman's Magazine* in 1789 explained that many learned and curious gentlemen had applied their attention to the branch of Mineralogy as this was one of the most advantageous inquiries towards the uses and concerns of society.[74] This general interest can be seen in Goethe's use of chemical metaphors in his novel *Die Wahlverwandschaften* (1809) in which he used the theory of chemical affinity as a basis for describing the changing relationships of two married couples.[75]

Brock (1992: 128) stated that most 18th century chemistry was qualitative and that at that time it was not possible to calculate how much of each ingredient was needed to produce a successful reaction.[76] But towards the end of that century, by refining the technique of methodical examination, Margraf had reduced the quantities needed for such experiments. James Watt described Priestley's experimental method of following up odd leads in no particular order – 'his usual way of groping about' – as just wondering what might turn up.[77] Yet, as Michael Faraday pointed out (1827), 'method is one thing; accuracy in applying a method 'depends entirely upon manipulation and . . . skill is always a requirement!'.[78] Gregor's detailed accounts of his own experiments reveal that he, too, operated in a rather haphazard and unskilled way when endeavouring to measure the quantities he used.

Numerous authors have described the historical development of mineralogy from a social amusement to a multi-disciplined branch of geology. Some, like Porter, have concentrated on the gradually growing importance of chemistry; others, like Burke, on the recognition of the significance of crystallography, or on the changing systematic methods of classification and arrangement; and others still, like Eyles, on the growth and dispersal of knowledge.[79] A few have widened their attention of collectors and collecting.[80] Gmelin noted that 27 different systems of mineral classification were produced between 1647 and 1771.[81] Robert Jameson reviewed this sequence of gradual improvements in mineral classification in a Preface to his *System of Mineralogy* (1804).

The aim of the scientists, collectors and naturalists to discovery the underlying relationships of the natural systems resulted in numerous speculative explanatory classifications. Eighteenth century mineralogists had two basic problems: firstly to identify individual minerals and then to establish a system of classifying them.[82] The Abbé Haüy (1743-1822; see below) separated these early methods according to the criteria that had been used, either chemical or visually apparent characters. Later, Berzelius used the term 'artificial' for methods that utilised several chemical properties, distinguishing these from the early 'natural' methods that relied upon the external and other physical properties of form, colour, hardness, lustre and cleavage which could be readily observed, together with the more general characters of use, value and occurrence.[83] White Watson adopted these physical criteria when cataloguing and arranging the Duchess of Devonshire's mineral collections in 1798.[84] The Introduction to Rashleigh's manuscripts catalogue indicates that he also followed the natural method: 'in order to form a Judgement ... of a Stone, the first idea of it is from Inspection, therefore all the different appearances should be collected'. To maintain his collection, he felt it was necessary to obtain a wide range of varieties and duplicates before undertaking any experiments on any particular mineral.

Cronstedt, who pioneered the use of the blowpipe in mineral analysis, is generally acknowledged to have made the first serious attempt to categorise minerals by their chemical nature and only used their external physical properties to augment this.[85] The initial 'artificial' classifications were based on rough qualitative chemical tests relating to the action of fire, water and oil on mineral specimens. Wallerius also adopted characters based on chemistry in his *Systema Mineralogicum* (1772) but continued to use easily visible external characters despite dismissing their general use. Yet sufficient accuracy to determine the substance and substances from which a mineral was formed by chemical analysis was not achieved until after 1800. Ultimately it was realised that such compounds were a union of simple substances, whose own properties bore no determinate relation to those of their compound. In fact, neither method was entirely satisfactory; and a combination of both, as advocated by Werner, was often adopted. He recognised that the characters everyone used were undefined and subjective, which led to confusion. By providing precise terminology to determine these features in his *Von den Kenzeichen der Fossilien* (1774), Werner remedied this and produced the first work to arrange minerals in a systematic order.

Roman d'Lisle improved on Werner's system in 1783 by incorporating the crystal forms of minerals. Soon afterwards, in 1784, Kirwan produced the first systematic treatise on mineralogy in the English language.[86] Then Karsten published a more ordered system in his description of the Leske collection (1789) that enabled collectors to organise their cabinets in a scientific manner. Ten years later, when writing to Rashleigh, Hawkins commented (24 Jan. 1799) that 'Karsten was a very young man when he drew up the catalogue of the Leskean Cabinet and there are many inaccuracies in the description and in the arrangement. With regard to the triple arrangement adopted . . . I own I think it just because it is founded on the different doctrines of Mineralogy and the division of Science.' In 1790, Born published the 'Catalogue méthodique' of Mlle Raab's collection that contained the most recent chemical analyses, adopted the latest nomenclature and gave crystallographic descriptions of every mineral then known. The following year Werner published another orderly tabular system in a catalogue listing the extensive collection of Pabst

Ohain (1791), upon which his pupils elaborated before dispersing it throughout Europe.[87] Writing to Rashleigh about these new arrangements Hawkins considered (27 Aug. 1791) that Born's '*Catalogue méthodique*' was still unsatisfactory to 'the naturalist since it ignored external characters and had no precise method of arrangement'. In contrast, he regarded Werner's catalogue as 'the model of good arrangement and description'. Subsequently, (13 Aug. 1792) Hawkins contested Rashleigh's disapproval of Werner's suggestion that separate cabinets should be used for particular collections, as that would permit each to be arranged by the best method.[88] Wilson (1994:100) recorded that Werner had six different collections: 1) systematic; 2) showing distinguishing features; 3) gem specimens; 4) large or aesthetic specimens; 5) topographic according to locality; and 6) petrology.[89]

In Britain, William Babington had followed the trait by producing his own system when organising the Earl of Bute's mineral collection (1795), but eventually adopted Born's system for another catalogue (1799). Haüy produced the *Traite de Minéralogie* (1810) – a lengthy work in 5 volumes – that used categories based on chemical reaction and supposed origin. The Irish-born French chemist Chenevix (mentioned in letters of both Rashleigh and Gregor) published his *Reflexions* (1808) on these methods and systems for determining and classifying minerals that was translated into English in 1811.

After five years in the Levant and Greece, Hawkins returned through Germany, visiting Klaproth in Berlin and acquiring his recently published chemical analyses. Writing to Rashleigh immediately on his return (9 Jan. 1799) he declared: 'Every classification of mineral bodies published before . . . this work, was premature. It is this work which has laid the basis of all natural arrangement of Minerals.' In fact, Klaproth had dedicated this publication to 'his friend John Hawkins as a small memorial of the sincere esteem, love and gratitude that he had received from him' over the years, which, as we know from comments in this correspondence, included financial support as well as arranging to supply him with specimens from Cornwall.[90]

The major advances in chemistry that led to the chemical revolution in mineralogy occurred during Gregor's lifetime and influenced his approach.[91] Despite living in the South-West, Gregor appears to have been well informed of these developments and willing to adopt new techniques if practicable for him. There are several references to the French philosopher Lavoisier: 'I have sent for Lavoisier's <u>Elements</u> and shall read them with particular pleasure and prejudice in his favour' (25 Oct 1790) and giving the opinion (26 Aug. 1791) that these 'works are truly scientific'. Lavoisier and his collaborators had produced a new rational nomenclature for chemistry that gave each substance a name and described its chemical composition. This was explained in his *Traité élémentaire de Chimie* (1789) as a linear process (that is, from the simple to the complex) but adding 'an underlying encyclopaedic logic'.[92] At that time, the science was thought to be involved with analysis and the concept of establishing a table of chemical composition of 'simple substances' which were defined in a purely negative manner that caused problems throughout the following centuries.[93]

Gregor would have been well aware of the analytical techniques used by assayers in mineral extraction used to determine the proportion of a metal that could be commercially extracted from a given ore, where the reactants and products could be carefully weighed. Many of Gregor's letters deal with his analytical experiments to determine the composition of known minerals and new substances, including those which involve his work on menachanite (titanium). These must have been rather boring to the recipients.[94] Unfortunately, the earliest of these was written (c. Oct. 1790) after its discovery and cannot help in establishing just where the initial experiments were carried out. In the early 1790s, after his marriage, Gregor's opportunities for continuing such experiments were limited, interruptions were frequent (see 22 Mar. 1793), but conducted whenever facilities and time allowed; it was only after moving to Creed in November 1794 that he could pursue such work.[95] Inevitably, the terminology used in his accounts is unfamiliar to us, and the occurrence of words such as 'regulus', 'earths' and 'phlogiston' reflects the understanding of the period.[96] When writing to Hawkins, Gregor liked to utilise their knowledge of classical languages – for example, using the Greek empyrean/ empurios when referring to the use of fire in an experiment (11 May 1793). Hawkins was often asked to purchase suitable laboratory equipment for this work; at other times Gregor overcame this himself (24 Nov. 1792): 'I have constructed a pair of bellows for bending glass tubes & wh. I find very convenient as it saves your lungs the trouble of puffing and blowing'. On a later occasion (16 Nov. 1798), the practical innovative use of a piece of charcoal provided a suitable sealed container in which to heat a very small quantity of crystals and thus ensure nothing was lost. In other letters (4 Nov. 1791; 4 May 1793), his carelessness produced unsatisfactory results revealing that it was not always possible in his laboratory to ensure the exactitude and precision necessary for reliable results. Gregor achieved considerable fame as an analytical chemist by determining the nature of minerals found in Cornish mines. He published data on wavellite, fluellite, corundum, topaz, autunite, tobernite, stannite, niccolite, gersdorffite and mimetite.[97] Several of these accounts were submitted to Sowerby for publication together with his illustrations of Gregor's specimens (see above and note 28). Unfortunately, apart from those Gregor is thought to have donated to Rashleigh, the fate of only two others is known, and that of Scorodite merely by chance.[98] When establishing the chemical nature of wavellite (initially named hydrargillte and widely referred to as the 'Barnstaple Zeolite'), Gregor realised that it was identical to other mineral specimens found at Stenna Gwinn in Cornwall.[99]

Rashleigh also attempted to experiment, but seldom reached any satisfactory conclusion.[100] He excused this through his 'not being much used to the Liquid process' (15 May 1789), and admitted to Hawkins (29 Nov. 1804) that 'all my knowledge of Chimestry is so antiquated'. Writing to Sowerby (15 Apr. 1806) he acknowledged that his own collection could not match the well-arranged minerals of William Day, for his own was 'made at various times, in many years' and that 'my Chimical Masters were all of the Old School'; and that, since then, ideas had changed. Shortly before that (17 Mar. 1803), Gregor had commented on the rapid growth of the science: 'there are so many Mushroom names that spring up in a short time, that it is almost impossible to keep pace with them!'.

In 1801, Haüy – known as the 'father of modern crystallography – had introduced a crystallographic approach to determine minerals, which was promoted in Britain through the arrival of the Count de Bournon, a French royalist refugee, who became involved in curating the collections of St. Aubyn and Greville.[101] Writing to Sowerby (17 Jan. 1804), Rashleigh acknowledged:

> Perhaps you have Count de Bournon to assist you in drawing your Crystals; he is the first Man in this Country who understands it. This is a part of knowledge I do not begin with, & am now too far advanced in Life to undertake such a laborious study. All parts of Mineralogy has been so much improved within these few years, that the Old Books & Old Masters neither Teach or learn any thing worth knowing, on this subject. The little

variation which modern Chymists find on critical examination, & give new names to makes a new Edition of a Nomenclature frequently wanted.

William Day's letter (5 Nov. 1799) conveys the earlier uncertainties about the process of crystallisation and 'its place in the Allmighty's creative processes'. Later (27 July 1804), when referring to Bournon again, Rashleigh expressed his opinion that 'Crystalliography' was 'more tedious than amusing, for it is a laborious study & not very entertaining'. From a letter to Sowerby (15 Apr. 1806) it would appear that Rashleigh had tried to adapt to the Count's methods: but despite considering him as 'an excellent Cristalliographer' had concluded that he was 'so deliberate and particular in his descriptions that he fatigues his readers'. Gregor too had complained (14 May 1804) that there was 'too much excursion into the Region of Theory in the Count's paper to please me entirely. What he asserts . . . may be plausible till it be pushed aside by some more captivating speculation.'

In his review of early nineteenth century classifications, Burke indicated that not all the systems used at that time were based solely on chemistry for Frederick Mohs, who had succeeded Werner at Freiberg, still continued to use his predecessor's method based on a variety of mineral characters (1822).[102] Elsewhere in Germany, Gustav Rose used a system based on both crystallographic and chemical criteria.[103] Although often based on theory, such differing classification systems were an essential contribution to research and led to the advance of knowledge. Yet, the difficulty of matching the hierarchy of the zoological classification prevailed, especially in determining the nature of mineral 'species'. Subsequently, Whewell realised that this was due to the lack of a viable theory and the imprecise state of chemical knowledge 'to assert relations between their intimate constitution and their external attributes'.[104] Today, more intricate technology is used in chemistry to recognise, analyse and classify minerals, then establish their structure or the reactions that had been involved in their formation.

HISTORY OF THE EARTH

'Theories of the earth' were a feature of eighteenth century geology and although speculation on the nature and origin of the rocks was at times imaginary, in others, especially those based on field observations, they approached modern understanding.[105] Many, however, were concerned with reconciling geological phenomena with theological beliefs. Amongst the more significant were several first published towards the end of the previous century, but which were reprinted, revised and translated for eighteenth century editions. These included Burnett's *Sacred Theory of the Earth*, (1681), John Woodward's *An Essay Toward a Natural History of the Earth* (1695), Whiston's *A New Theory of the Earth* (1696) and works by John Ray (1691, 1692),[106] which were all linked to biblical teaching. They all emphasised the well-designed nature of the Creator's systems that brought order out of chaos, or else had limited the effect of natural terrestrial forces. But other works by Leibnitz (1749) and Buffon (1749, 1779) either avoided referring to the deluge, or denounced the idea.[107]

In 1785, Werner published his *Kurze Klassification* indicating the neptunian origin of the earth's crust based on his observations of the essentially sedimentary formations found in Germany.[108] This had a far greater impact amongst geologists than other, earlier, theories. Ospovat has given two reasons for this: first, it was the only classification of the rocks that provided a universally applicable system and established that they were deposited in a definite order; and, secondly, it used suitable nomenclature for the rocks and the manner of their formation.[109] He emphasised that Werner's theory was flexible, accounted for all the phenomena observed in his day and allowed for both the simultaneous formation of different rocks as well as the formation of similar rocks at different periods.[110] However, Werner did not recognise that igneous rocks had been formed from a molten core.

Although an unorthodox deist, James Hutton's observations and subsequent deliberations led to his publishing a concept of a dynamic earth with a continuing ordered system of rejuvenation and decay as part of a natural geological cycle.[111] This established the doctrine of uniformitarianism which allowed the length of time and continuity for such processes to operate in varying kind and degree from place to place and from time to time, which became the accepted model for understanding the structure and history of the earth.[112]

The subsequent acceptance, interpretation and criticism of Hutton's theories has become a significant topic in historiographical research, but it is interesting to note one of the reasons suggested for the initial lack of response after their publication in 1788 and 1795 was Britain's predicament with regard to France.[113] Dean postulated that at that time 'Gallic science was un-utterably repulsive to the majority of Englishmen'.[114] After the French Revolution, its Reign of Terror, the presence of refugees and later the threat of invasion, meant that, for many, anything linked to France was unacceptable and Hutton's theory strongly reflected French geological thought. Such concern over the implications of the revolution on English society and the probability of invasion were frequent subjects in letters at this time, even to the extent of considering whether it was still worth adding to a collection as it might well be ransacked, or lost.[115]

The two principal controversies that occupied geologists during the period were those of 'Neptunism versus Plutonism' and 'Uniformitarianism versus Catastrophism'. In the case of the latter, Hutton's theory, expanded during the nineteenth century by Lyell, ensured that uniformity eventually prevailed, although it is now recognised that the broader concept has more limitations than Hutton's actualistic understanding.[116] The instances of catastrophes were accepted as episodes in this natural cycle, but the 'progressionists' of the nineteenth century invoked such episodes to explain drastic changes in geological faunas.[117] A predisposed geological public selected aspects of the work of Werner and Hutton – accepting the former as the protagonist of Neptunism, and the latter as the supreme Vulcanist. Unfortunately, this obscured the real contributions of these concepts to the science. Hutton had attacked the issue of neptunism, before the subject became a major geological debate. His concern then was solely over its use in interpreting the structure of the earth rather than as a process responsible for forming igneous rocks. Tomkeieff summarised the major argument of these two opposing theories: 'The Neptunists attributed the origin of all rocks, including basalt and granite, to aqueous precipitation, whereas the Vulcanists regarded certain rocks, including basalt and granites as the products of consolidation of igneous melts, now called magmas, that existed or were formed within the earth.'[118] Dott clarified the major argument between these two beliefs: 'The underlying implication of neptunism is for a structurally static solid earth' whereas in contrast, the plutonists believed that 'the entire earth was dynamic and in a constant state of change'.[119] He also explained that Werner's observation of some coal seams in Bohemia that had caught fire and then altered the nature of adjacent rocks had led to his belief that 'volcanoes were simply the result of superficial combustion of material occurring in the upper strata'. Inevitably, these controversies feature amongst the major studies in the history of geology producing a wealth of literature on the individuals concerned and their theories. The confusing occurrence of igneous rocks such as basalt and granite, or the metamorphosed – apparently stratified – gneissic rocks, caused difficulties which led some to suppose that these too were deposited as sediments. Eventually, the evidence of intrusive granites, good examples of angular unconformities between adjacent rock formations and the adoption of the principle of superposition, enabled the nature of such relationships to be established.

REFERENCES TO THESE SUBJECTS IN THE CORRESPONDENCE

Several letters between Rashleigh and Hawkins, who both agreed with Werner as to the marine origin of basalt, provide insight into the general level of this debate in Britain, and some of the reasoning involved. Hawkins wrote to Rashleigh (18 Mar. 1789) that '[m]y freind [sic] Werner has lately been involved in a violent dispute with some of the fire-spouting mineralogists of Germany for having asserted that basalt has been formed in the humid way'. Rashleigh responded (22 Mar. 1789):

> I am very much inclined to think with Mr. Werner that basalt is formed by moisture, which being withdrawn leaves the substantial matter in the form we hear of. . . . Were these forms occasion'd by Fire, the angles in general would not have been so sharp as represented, especially in such large bodies, which could never have been formed by Fire without some cinerous marks. One should have been at Staffa to have argued on this subject, & I have seen the top and bottom of the Pillars as well as the Country around them.

A few months later (10 May 1789), Hawkins seemed to be less positive: 'I will not assert that basalt has been formed in the humid way ideas but nothing can be weaker and inconclusive than the arguments advanced in proof of its fiery origin'. But on various field excursions, he had again proudly become an advocate of the neptunists, writing (14 Sept. 1789): 'You would have been much amused . . . to hear me and Dr. Hope disputing two whole days on the Huttonian Theory, myself a Neptunist, the Dr. a Plutonist'.

The various protagonists were generally influenced by the nature of the rocks with which they were most familiar. Many British geologists, who had studied igneous deposits, adhered to the plutonist arguments. Others, such as Robert Jameson, in Edinburgh, who had studied at Freiburg under Werner, favoured the neptunist theory.[120] However, as other letters report, not all of Werner's students were so adamant in their conviction. John Wedgwood, writing to Hawkins (12 Aug. 1791), referred to the fact that Gregory Watt, 'tho' a pupil of Werner's', had become 'a convert to the igneous formation system of basalt':

> He tells me he means ... to give a statement of the two doctrines extracted from the works of the two different supporters of each system . He will . . . leave everyone to form their own opinion on the subject.[121] . . . If this is executed with judgement & impartiality it will be a very acceptable present to all lovers of mineralogy for such a thing has long been wanted.

Hawkins referred to this when reporting another field debate to Rashleigh (27 Aug. 1791):

> Prof. Hailstone who sides with me in referring the general strata of the earth to an aquatic formation, met with the fire-spouting Dr. Beddoes. . . . a witticism of ... one of the party, 'That they had Hailstones and Coals of Fire.'[122] . . . A pupil of Werner's, young Watt of Birmingham, intends to publish . . . an impartial statement of the two doctrines of the formation of basalt. Although I know he has become a convert to the Igneous Theory we may expect something much more satisfactory . . . than what is contained in Dr. Beddoes paper.[123]

Gregor also mentioned this visit (26 Aug. 1791) declaring that Beddoes was 'a great stickler for the cause of Fire in the formation of Loads, Basalt &c. – he is certainly a very ingenious man'. But a decade later, describing the general puzzlement over the presence of iron nodules in the Veryan limestone, which had been attributed to the Civil War, Gregor realised this was a natural geological process, and he declared 'I leave the Neptunists & Vulcanists to settle the point' (1 June 1800). Recognising the importance of Werner's *Kurze Klassification*, Hawkins, Hailstone, Wedgwood and Beddoes considered embarking on an English translation (as their letters in the summer of 1792 show). Werner's students continued to improve it, and their final version was published in 1817 (under his name but after his death) as the *Letzes Mineral-System*. Believing Werner's new theory on the origin of lodes' had great relevance to mining in Cornwall, Hawkins provided a summary (11 June 1792) and concluded that 'the same humid precipitation which created the strata and the montane masses, formed too, the contents of the lodes'. Subsequent letters from Rashleigh (16 June 1792) and Hawkins (10 July 1792) supported this and clarified their own ideas.

'STONES FALLEN FROM CLOUDS' – EARLY RECORDS OF METEORITES

The letters also reflect interest in another scientific topic that occurred around the turn of the century concerning the exact nature of 'The Stones that fall from the Sky'. The gradual realisation that accounts of such phenomena were true was made in the early 1800s. At first they were explained as belated falls of volcanic extrusions, or else derived from lunar volcanoes. Modern technology has since established that meteorites may be derived from asteroids, the moon, Mars, or comets. They are distinguished on their chemical composition into stony, iron and stony-iron types, then further divided on their texture into chondrites, chondrules and achondrites. Almost all chondrites contain some iron-nickel metal, whereas metal is rare or absent in achondrites.[124]

Several collectors mentioned in these archives were peripherally linked to the Royal Society's investigation in 1802 that began to resolve the question of their origin. Born's collection, which contained several European examples, had been purchased by Greville; Hatchet had obtained a Siberian specimen in 1790 from Pallas and had later acquired the Sitarik specimen that had fallen in Senegal.[125] These, together with the Yorkshire 'Wold Cottage' meteorite of 1795 (the oldest recorded fall on the British mainland), were used to establish their chemical composition. Analysis revealed the significant nickelliferous iron content which together with the sworn statements concerning the fall of the Wold meteorite in Yorkshire in December 1795 led to their acceptance as extra-terrestrial objects.[126] Greville and Hailstone were also closely associated with those involved in the British and Italian sightings; while Count Bournon conducted the mineral observations for the inquiry.[127]

Sir Joseph Banks had not been convinced that rocks extruded by Vesuvius would take eighteen hours to fall, and, recognising that specimens of the Sienna and Wold meteorites were similar, he realised that the latter could not have been derived from the same eruption. Together with Sir Charles Blagden, then Secretary, Banks, as President, instigated an investigation by Edward Howard. A letter from Hawkins informed Rashleigh (19 Dec. 1800):

> A paper is now preparing for the Royal Society on a very curious subject that of stones which have fallen out of the air, & the fact is sufficiently well attended, and the substances are now analyzing. There is reason to suspect that the famous mass of native Iron discovered in Siberia has been generated in this way. I have been lately drawing up, an historical account of the like accidents which I suppose will now no longer be disbelieved.

Following his chemical analysis Edward Howard, reported that he had 'separated the metal and stone, discovered the presence of nickel in all the iron fractions of the chondrites and the so-called 'native iron masses'.[128] These key factors established the link between the different fallen objects examined and his results were presented at three successive meetings held at the Royal Society during 1802.[129] Both Rashleigh and St. Aubyn attended one of the 1802 sessions. From the context of Rashleigh's letter to James Sowerby (7 Aug. 1804), it has been inferred that no examples of meteorites had been on display at these sessions, as Rashleigh still sought to see one:

> I have many times been disappointed in seeing any piece of Stones that are said to have fallen from the Clouds in many Kingdoms, & I regret it the more, as I believe a similar thing happened in this County last Winter, from a very small piece I had given me a few Weeks since; by which I endeavoured to make further enquiries by a very good man, but he is such an unbeliever of these matters & laughs so much at those who credit this extraordinary circumstance, that I got only a vauge [sic] account of it.

He was fortunate for Sowerby had succeeded in obtaining the Wold Cottage meteorite from Edward Topham and in the hope of being able to examine the small piece mentioned by Rashleigh, he responded (29 Oct. 1804):

I have got the Sky fallen stone from Yorkshire at my home, and anxiously wish to compare yours with it, and it would be doing me a great favor to send it at any expence by the first coach or other carriage you find convenient it were well perhaps to make it more of a parcell by adding any thing to it of any sort if only paper or wax. Pray do you know of the rest of the stone yours was broken from ? If so I shall be glad of the information. Do not mind <u>Laughers</u> or <u>Quizers</u> it was well for them the Yorkshire Stone of 56 lb weight did not interrupt their belief by breaking their pates.

Further letters were exchanged between November 1804 and May 1805 concerning the despatch and receipt of a fragment Sowerby sent to Rashleigh.[130] Uncertainty still prevailed; as can be seen in Sowerby's statement that '[w]hen the Phænomen of their production will be understood I do not know'. Having had time to study the fragment, a delighted Rashleigh expressed his own thoughts (16 June 1805):

The piece of the Yorkshire Stone that fell from the Atmosphere is so totally different from every Mineral or Fossil that has come to my view that it is a great Acquisition; & very extraordinary for those which have fallen in various places & in different Kingdoms should be so similar in their appearance & contents. Some various Ideas of Attraction & Cohesion will one time or other give more Philosophical accounts of these — Stones, & by that introduce a variety of reasoning for other Mineral subjects. For I must consider this substance as a Fossil generated in the Air, though all other known Rocks & Stones are formed in the Earth. Such a novelty will set many Philosophers to study the cause of such a substance in the Atmosphere, & apply similar reasoning to many things under the earth.

This idea of Rashleigh's had also been suggested in a work published in France by Izarn (1803).[131] It had also been anticipated by E. D. Clarke, Professor of Mineralogy at Cambridge, who for a time thought that meteorites were somehow formed in the air by a process involving cohesion and attraction. Between the years 1811 and 1815, Clarke had been very keen to examine the 'Yorkshire Stone' and had repeatedly written to Sowerby requesting this.[132]

Rashleigh continued (16 June 1805) by endeavouring to explain the associated explosive noises, forces and smell that had been described by the observers of such falls:

> There are some Ores which when in Melting will be very refractory on Water falling on them when in a Liquid State, & make it very dangerous to be within reach of the fragments that are sent about it like Shot. May not these Meteors when heated by Lightning [sic] or any Atmospherical influence, fall through a moist vapour, and hiss & crack about like those of copper &c. ?

The widespread interest in such specimens was referred to by Gregor in a letter to Rashleigh (June 1805), following a visit to London during which he had visited dealers where Mrs. Forster had wanted 12 guineas for a 1½ inch fragment:

> Amongst the dear rarities in Mineralogy, nothing seems now to be more earnestly called for, than specimens of Stones fallen from the Clouds – They sell for very high prices – and the demand for these has risen. The price of the Siberian Iron wh. is supposed to have some sort of relationship to the former – I saw a thin piece of this last at Mrs. Forster's, about an Inch and half in breadth for wh. she asked twelve guineas ! – Really, if we exclude loss of life & limb and conflagrations, it wd. be a very profitable windfall, for any person to have a shower of these stones in his neighbourhood, during a Thunder Storm.

Eventually, it seems, Banks supplied Rashleigh with an example: 'I hear Sir Joseph has been kind enough to send me, I believe by Dr. Wynne, a piece of one of the Stones that fell from the Clouds, which I shall much esteem' (14 May 1806). Several later letters from Sowerby refer briefly to 'meteor stones' in one of which he reports the death of Edward King who had published the first account of such stones in 1796 and the sale of his collection (29 May 1805).[133] In that work King had referred to the hailstorm that had occurred at Menabilly on 20 October 1791 and figured models of the hailstones Rashleigh had measured.[134] Rashleigh described this storm in a letter he sent to the Royal Society (3 Nov. 1791).

CONCLUSIONS

This selection of correspondence clarifies the close relationship and co-operation between scientists needed to make progress during the eighteenth and nineteenth centuries. Personal comments and opinions by the writers colour our knowledge of developments in geology and other contemporaneous political events. The letters contain useful information on the activities and motivations of private collectors at that time, especially those of the Cornish trio. Their joint contribution to the progress of mineralogy through providing and exchanging specimens with others throughout Europe was significant, especially the assistance given to Martin Klaproth.[135] The letters reveal that the contacts that Pole Carew and Hawkins had made with European mineral collectors, mining directors and other geologists during their travels were the channels through which this was accomplished. Hawkins' own diverse interests and affable nature had established links with such differing personalities as Baron Born, Martin Klaproth, Abraham Werner, John Wedgwood, and John Hailstone.[136] It is also apparent that Hawkins assisted in introducing new theories and classification systems into Britain, while the articles he published in the early volumes of the *Transactions of the Royal Geological Society of Cornwall* demonstrated his interest in the geology of South-West England and his influence in the improvement of mining.

From the letters it is possible to gauge the growth of Rashleigh's own mineral collection and confirm that its fame was also an important factor, for this encouraged visitors and prompted him to seek and exchange material. His publication of the first illustrated reference to British minerals (1797 & 1801) led to foreign collectors seeking Cornish specimens, while Sowerby's subsequent use of Rashleigh's material encouraged others to collect and contribute to his own new work. Rashleigh's collection has become an extremely valuable record of its time, owing to his endeavours to accumulate many different examples of each Cornish mineral. Over the years, by collecting from Cornish mines, or through agents, or by encouraging the miners and their captains, he ensured the acquisition of a wide range of specimens. As a result of his recording details of the provenance of these specimens with unusual care, Rashleigh is recognised as one of the most notable early Cornish mineralogists. This data has since allowed modern researchers to establish the existence of scarce minerals in his collection, or locate new specimens.[137]

The Rev. William Gregor must be considered as a special example of the English parson-naturalist owing to his restricted pre-occupation of analysing new finds in the hope of discovering new substances.[138] His contribution to science was recognised in his own lifetime by Allan, who attributed five analyses to him (Wavellite; Sp. Arseniate; Sp. Carbonate; Uranium (Uran Mica); Titanium (Menacanite)).[139] His meticulous accounts of experiments help historians to understand the techniques used at that time and illustrate Gruber's assertion that such letters are historical documents. However, Gregor's principal claim to fame has to be as the discoverer of titanium.

Their individual contributions to geology were recognised quite early, for all three were made honorary members of the newly formed Geological Society of London within its first twelve months: Gregor was the 14th on the list, Rashleigh the 31st (in 1807) and Hawkins the 60th (in 1808). Almost a decade earlier, in May 1788, Rashleigh had been elected a Fellow of the Royal Society as 'a gentleman well skilled in several branches of Science, and particularly the Mineralogy of his native county' supported among others by Henry Cavendish and Charles Greville. Hawkins was elected as a Fellow of the Royal Society in May 1791; the notice described him 'as a gentleman well versed in Mineralogy and metallurgy as well as other branches of useful knowledge'.[140] After visiting Rashleigh in the 1790s, Maton had praised such 'men of large fortune [who] with wide connections' had cultivated a branch of useful knowledge. On having perused these letters, readers might consider that his conclusion that '[s]uch men are ornaments of their country; and they are the best benefactors to science, for whilst they find amusement for their own leisure, they promote its popularity, and encourage its votaries'[141] should also apply to the other members of this Cornish trio.

Notes

1 Sir A. Russell, (1954) 'John Hawkins, FGS, FRHS, FRS, 1761–1841: a distinguished Cornishman and early mining geologist', *Journal of the Royal Institution of Cornwall*, New Series, 2, 2 (1954), pp. 97-106; idem., 'The Rev. William Gregor (1761–1817), discoverer of titanium', *The Mineralogical Magazine*, 30, 229 (1955), pp. 617-624.

2 F. Steers, *I Am, My Dear Sir . . . A Selection of Letters Written*

Mainly to and by John Hawkins FRS, GS 1761–1841 (Chichester: West Sussex Record Office, 1959); idem., *The Hawkins Papers: A Catalogue* (Chichester, West Sussex Record Office, 1962); *The Letters of John Hawkins and Samuel and Daniel Lysons, 1812–1830* (Chichester: West Sussex Record Office, 1966). Hawkins contributed an account of the Natural History & Mineralogy of Devon to Vol. 6 of *Magna Britannica* (1822).

3 H. W. Lack, *The Flora Graeca Story: Sibthorp, Bauer and Hawkins in the Levant* (Oxford: Oxford University Press, 1999); idem., *The Flora Graeca Story: Oxford's Finest Botanical Treasure. Sibthorp, Bauer and Hawkins in the Levant: An Exhibition at the Bodleian Library, Oxford 19 July 1999–25 September 1999* (Oxford: Bodleian Library, 1999).

4 Sir A. Russell, 'Philip Rashleigh of Menabilly, Cornwall and his mineral collection', *Journal of the Royal Institution of Cornwall*, New Series, 1, 2 (1952), pp. 96-118; L. Trengove, 'William Gregor (1761–1817) discoverer of titanium', *Annals of Science*, 29, 4 (1972), pp. 361-95; P. G. Embrey, and R. F. Symes, *Minerals of Cornwall and Devon* (London: British Museum (Natural History), 1987); R. W. Jones, 'Philip Rashleigh and his specimens of British minerals (1797 & 1802)', *Mineralogical Record*, 26, 4 (1995), pp. 77-84; R. D. Penhallurick, 'The mineral collection of the Royal Institution of Cornwall', *U.K. Journal of Mines & Minerals*, 18 (1997), pp. 17-32; M. P. Cooper, 'Letters from Henry Heuland (1778–1856) to Philip Rashleigh (19764-1811) in the Cornwall Record Office', unpublished transcription of 60 letters 1 April 1807 to 30 May 1809 (1999); 'Keeping it in the family: the Humphreys, Forsters and Heulands', *Matrix*, 9 (2001), pp. 3-31; *Robbing the Sparry Garniture: A 200-Year History of British Mineral Dealers* (Tucson, 2006).

5 R. J. Cleevely, 'The contributions of a trio of Cornish geologists to the development of 18th century mineralogy' *Transactions of the Royal Geological Society of Cornwall*, 22, 3 (2000), p. 90; R. J. Cleevely, 'Carew and Rashleigh – a Cornish link during the "Age of the Curiosity Collector"; their association with Peter Pallas, the "Russian" German traveller-naturalist (1741–1811)', *Royal Institution of Cornwall Journal*, 2002, pp. 9-29; R. J. Cleevely and C. M. Bristow, 'Rev. William Gregor (1761–1817): the contributions of a Cornish cleric and analytical chemist', *Journal of the Royal Institution of Cornwall*, 2003, pp. 85-108, Appendices 1 and 2, pp. 106-7.

6 However, from the contents of the letters it is evident that not all have survived, for letters from both Carew and Rashleigh are missing; It would also appear that the letters Carew sent to Rashleigh must have been returned to him, or else acquired for the Carew archive at a subsequent time.

7   Other letters, not included here, contain discussion of European whaling fleets, cattle disease in France; patriotic enthusiasm at George III's Spithead review of the Fleet, proposals to build a fort on land at Torpoint, and Eastern European property valuation.

8   For full details concerning Pallas, see Cleevely, 'Carew and Rashleigh', pp. 9-29; for reference to Engeström see letters in Carew archive: CC/J/11/38 and 39, 13 and 27 Apr. 1781; and regarding Scopoli, see CRO: DDR/5302/1/150, 3 Aug. 1777.

9   See full chronological list for these letters.

10 Because of the hazards of travelling off the beaten track, Pennant resorted to correspondence and circulating a printed list of queries prior to his tours in order to obtain information for his publications (see Rees and Walters, *The Library* (5th Series) 25 (2), 1970, pp. 136, 139). References in letters indicate that he visited Cornwall in 1787. Perhaps the absence of any Pennant letters at Truro can be explained by the fashion to collect autographs, for at the end of the eighteenth century, and then again in the 1820s, autograph collecting became a fashionable pursuit (see A. N. L. Mumby *The Cult of the Autograph Letter in England*, (London: Athlone Press, 1962), pp. 5 and 8. Evidence for this practice is provided by the autograph volumes of the Rogers family of Penrose now in the archive at CRO, Truro 'RP' containing letters from Gregor and Rashleigh amongst those from more famous names.

11 Steers, *I Am, My Dear Sir*, p. xxii.

12 Justin Crump (ed), *A Known Scribbler: Francis Burney on Literary Life* (London: Broadview Press, 2002), p. 32; Samuel Johnson, *Lives of the English Poets: Pope* (vol. 4), p. 153.

13 J. W. Gruber, 'The Richard Owen Correspondence: An Introductory Essay', in J. W. Gruber and J. C. Thackray (eds), *Richard Owen Commemoration: Three Studies* (London: Natural History Museum Publications, 1992), pp. 1-24. Gruber suggests (p.19) that arranging such ephemeral letters might be construed as equivalent to a pleasant pastime such as stamp collecting, but with a degree of voyeuristic excitement.

14 N. Reingold, 'On not doing the papers of great scientists', *British Journal for the History of Science*, 20 (1987), pp. 29-38.

15 See letters for Hawkins views on Klaproth (31 Dec. 1789) and Born (12 Sept. 1791); on Werner, see J. Hawkins, *Transactions of the Royal Geological Society of Cornwall*, 2 (1822), p. 147.

16 A copy of Michael Cooper's Mss of Heuland's letters (1807 -1809) is available at CRO, Truro. This contains full transcriptions of 49 Heuland letters and 8 mineral lists; there are references to 54 Rashleigh communications.

17 On John Wedgwood , see B. and H. Wedgwood, *The Wedgwood Circle 1730–1897* (London: Studio Vista, 1980), pp. 95-96, 102, 12-113.

18 John Hailstone toured Cornwall in summer of 1791 when he visited Rashleigh and Gregor.

19 Gruber, 'The Richard Owen Correspondence', p.20, where he refers to the various reasons that led to its attrition and preservation.

20 R. D. Altick, *The English Common Reader: A Social History of the Mass Reading Public 1800–1900* (Chicago: University of Chicago Press, 1963), pp. 30-66.

21 See the example cited by R. Cleevely in *Journal of the Royal Institution of Cornwall* (2003), p. 91.

22 See reference to Burney's conversational letters to her godfather Samuel Crisp in C. Harman, *Fanny Burney: A Biography* (London: HarperCollins, 2000), p. 83) and N. Nicholson, *The World of Jane Austen* (London: Weidenfeld and Nicholson, 1991), pp. 11-12.

23 See W. T. Stearn, 'The background and origin of the Flora Graeca', *Biological Journal of the Linnean Society*, 8, 4 (1976), p. 285; Steers, *I Am, My Dear Sir*; Lack, *The Flora Graeca Story*, p. 16.

24 See his letters to Pole Carew 11 Dec. 1780 and 23 Feb. 1781, and to Sowerby 21 Apr. 1804 and 5 May 1804.

25 Hawkins letters to Mantell are in the Mantell Papers at the Alexander Turnbull Library, Wellington, New Zealand – Steers, *The Letters of John Hawkins and Samuel and Daniel Lysons*, ii, xxii.

26 'Hawkins proved to be a conscientious and faithful executor': Stearn, 'Background and origin', p. 295; R. J. Cleevely, letter to editor, *The Linnean*, 21, 1 (2005), p. 12.

27 See Gregor's letter to Hawkins (30 June 1813).

28 For lists of Gregor's contributions to Sowerby's *British Mineralogy*. see Cleevely and Bristow, 'Rev. William Gregor', Appendices 1 and 2, pp. 106-7.

29 At this period, many people had a highly personal approach to writing and spelling, often with a fine disregard for the use of punctuation and capital letters: see P. O'Brian, *Joseph Banks* (London: Collins Harvill, 1987), p. 11, in reference to Warren Dawson's editorial criticism of the modern practice of correcting such 'characteristic mannerisms' in Dawson (ed), *The Banks Letters* (London: British Museum, 1958). Steers, *The Letters of John Hawkins and Samuel and Daniel Lysons*, p. vii comments on Hawkins' spelling peculiarities and the editorial difficulties presented by his punctuation, paragraphing, lack of conventional capitals and often dates.

30 Postage was expensive in the mid-eighteenth century and could range from 6d to 2s.6d., which had to be paid by the recipient, not the sender. Members of Parliament and government officials had

the privilege of free postage and were allowed to use addressed envelopes – called 'covers' and generally known as 'free franks'. Walter Synnot (23 Apr. 1781) acknowledged a supply of franks sent for his use by P.R. There are examples of at least three types of these franks amongst letters from RPC to PR =6; PR to RPC = 12; JH to PR = 10; W.G to P.R. = 5; as well as those from other collectors.

31 For references see Cleevely, 'The contributions of a trio of Cornish geologists', p. 90.

32 M. H. Klaproth, *Beiträge zur Chemischen Kenntniss der Mineralkörper* (Posen & Berlin: 1795), translated as *Analytical Essays towards promoting the Chemical Knowledge of Mineral Substances* (London: T. Cadell and W. Davies, 1801), pp. 499-509.

33 See letter June 1796. Between 1768–74, Rashleigh's name only occurs twice in the 14 Divisional lists: see L. B. Namier and J. Brooke *The House of Commons 1754–1790* (London: HMSO for the History of Parliament Trust, 1964), vol. 3, p. 348.

34 See his letter to Hawkins (25 Feb 1789).

35 Carew wrote to Rashleigh on 18 June 1775 with reference to parliament that 'I sincerely rejoice that you have at length escaped from a Place you have so little affection for'. Rashleigh's liking for country pleasures was revealed (11 Sept 1776) when he reported: 'unlucky in fishing and fowling, but both seasons are not yet in their Prime', and also (16 Oct. 1777): when 'shooting pheasants' in Dorset .

36 Rashleigh is not shown among the many MPs at *The House of Commons* in the painting by Karl Hickel (dated 1793–4), which is now in the National Portrait Gallery.

37 E. Jaggard, *Cornwall Politics in the Age of Reform 1790–1885* (London: Royal Historical Society, 1999); E. Jaggard (ed.), *Liberalism in West Cornwall: The 1868 Election Papers of A. Pendarves Vivian, M.P.* (Exeter: Devon and Cornwall Record Society, N.S. 42, 2000).

38 R. G. Thorne, *The House of Commons 1790–1820* (London: Secker and Warburg for the History of Parliament Trust, 1986), vol. 4, p. 83.

39 Ibid., vol. 5, p.9. The increase in copper coinage by the Board of Trade in 1807 briefly improved the situation for county's mines.

40 See CRO, Truro, Croft Andrew/B42/62 for Rashleigh's hand-written copy of a resolution concerned with the suppression of rioters dated 18 Feb. 1773. For references to food riots at Poldice in 1795 and at Redruth in 1796, see F.E. Halliday, *A History of Cornwall* (London: Duckworth, 1959), p. 283.

41 M. Daunton, 'The Wealth of the Nation', in P. Langford (ed), *The Eighteenth Century, 1688-1815* (Oxford: Oxford University

Press, 2002), 159-160; R. Porter, *English Society in the Eighteenth Century* (London: Penguin Books, 1982), pp. 220 and 334.

42 In England, arising from fears of revolution, the campaign and movements for Reform were repressed and public meetings prohibited; the Foxite Whigs were generally absent from Parliament; the Irish problem was also manifest; Britain had abandoned the Gold standard; Bonaparte had been successful in Italy; and the Channel and North Sea fleets had successively mutinied at Spithead and Nore in April and May 1797.

43 Other accounts of Cornish mining are reproduced in Halliday, *History of Cornwall*, pp. 273-306. The dismal scene at the Consolidated Mines at Gwennap in March 1787 was described in the travel diaries of William Beckford: see A. L. Rowse, *A Cornish Anthology* (London: Macmillan, 1968). In a discussion of accommodation, S. Gerrard, *The Early British Tin Industry* (Stroud: Tempus, 2000), pp. 50-53, points out that, owing to the frequent change in the focus of the tin-workings prior to the nineteenth century, settlements were not established, but could be located near to a source of foodstuffs. The character of these homes varied according to the permanence of employment and how many workers were itinerant.

44 T. L. Hony, 'The Rashleigh family', *Royal Cornwall Polytechnic Society, 106th Annual Report*, New Series IX, Part III (1939).

45 This reference (J3/12/1354 – ?25 Oct.1790) to the marriage of Mr. Francis Glanville and Miss Loveday Sarah Masterman at Lanlivery Church which occurred on Friday 22nd Oct. 1790 was alluded to by Rashleigh (J3/12/1372): 'On Thursday Mr. Glanville & Miss Masterman enter'd into partnership with a very large Capital.' The associated statement – that 'Next Friday there is to be a Grand ball at Tregethnan, many Cards of Invitation are dispersed and many Excuses return'd' might be construed to refer to the celebrations.

46 The year of letters NHM R.Beq. No. 24 (24 July 1791) and J3/2/138 (26 Aug. 1791) are confirmed by their contents, which mention Hailstone's tour of Cornwall and the recent publication of Gilpin's book on 'Forest Scenery'.

47 W. Borlase, (1758) *The Natural History of Cornwall* (Oxford: privately printed, 1758); W. G. Maton, *Observations relative chiefly to the natural History, Picturesque Scenery & Antiquities of the Western Counties of England* (Salisbury: J. Eaton, 1797); for Hatchet see A. Raistrick (ed), *The Hatchett Diary: A Tour through the Counties of England and Scotland in 1796 visiting their Mines and Manufactories* (Truro: Bradford Barton, 1967).

48 See letters from Hailstone to Hawkins re his European tour in CRO, Truro (14 Sept. 1792 and 20 Dec. 1792); re his Cornish

tour (18 Sept. 1791). Letters from Wedgwood in Hawkins archive CRO, Truro and others in the Wedgwood Museum, Barlaston, Staffordshire mention his various trips around the U.K. Later, both E. D. Clarke (1791) and Charles Hatchett (1796) made similar collecting tours of the U.K.

49 R. Rappaport, 'The geological atlas of Guettard, Lavoisier and Monnet', in C. J. Schneer (ed), *Towards a History of Geology* (MIT Press, 1969), pp. 272-87, at 272.

50 G. L. H. Davies, *Sheets of Many Colours: The Mapping of Ireland's Rocks, 1750–1890* (Dublin: Royal Dublin Society, 1983); D. A. Bassett, 'Wales and the geological map', *Amgueddfa: Bulletin of the National Museum of Wales*, 3 (winter 1969), 10-25.

51 J. Challinor, *The History of British Geology: A Bibliographical Study* (Newton Abbot: David & Charles, 1971), p. 79. The designation 'first' is entirely dependent upon the category used; it is generally acknowledged that William Smith's map published in 1815 is the first significant map of the country.

52 Maton, *Observations*, p. 204 in his 'Explanation of the map'.

53 See Embrey and Symes, *Minerals of Cornwall and Devon*, p. 8, fig. 11 for a generalised table of the magmatic origin of various minerals; and p. 13, fig. 19 for the hydrothermal sequence of mineralisation that can occur in an ore body.

54 P. G. Embrey, 'Minerals', in J. M. Chalmers-Hunt, *Natural History Auctions 1700-1972* (London, Sotheby Parke Burnett, 1976), pp. 39-44.

55 W. E. Wilson, 'The history of mineral collecting 1530–1799', *Mineralogical Record*, 25, 6 (1994), p. 46.

56 Ibid., p. 152.

57 T. Porter, 'The promotion of mining and the advancement of science: the chemical revolution of mineralogy', *Annals of Science*, 38 (1981), p. 544.

58 In the Rashleigh Papers (RIC, RASH/1) there are some 40 lists of minerals sent to British and European collectors during the 1780s and 1790s. A cursory assessment of these reveals that some 2,000 specimens were despatched in that period. Several of these were part of the exchanges organised through his nephew R. Pole Carew, when he travelled around Europe with an un-specified investigative role as a Foreign ambassador.

59 For further comments on this, see letters to Sowerby, 21 Apr. 1804; 25 Mar. 1805; 7 Mar. 1808; and for letters that contain comments about the mines and miners, see 3 Mar. 1804; 6 Apr 1804; 13 June 1804.

60 V. A. Eyles, 'The extent of geological knowledge in the eighteenth century, and the methods by which it was diffused', in Schneer (ed), *Towards a History of Geology*, pp. 159-183.

61 R. Townson *Philosophy of Mineralogy* (London: 1798), p. 114.
62 A. W. G. Kingsbury, 'Some minerals of special interest in south-west England', in K. F. G. Hoskins and G. J. Shrimpton, (eds), *Present Views of Some Aspects of the Geology of Cornwall and Devon* (Truro: Royal Geological Society of Cornwall, 1965), pp.251, 252.
63 See reference to Greenough's complaint recorded in his diary for 1805: 'The supply of Strontian is by no means equal to the demand . . . the finest pieces were purchased immediately' – see P. Weindling, 'The British Mineralogical Society: a case study in science and social improvement', in I. Inkster and J. Morrell (eds), *Metropolis and Province: Science in British Culture, 1780–1850* (University of Pennsylvania Press, 1983), p. 127.
64 Russell, 'Philip Rashleigh', p. 113. Gregory Watt echoed this opinion in his critical review of Rashleigh's two volumes (*Edinburgh Review*, 4 (1804), pp. 117-20), arguing that the delineation of a mineral's external features was an inadequate indication of its characteristics. He also considered that the local mining terms Rashleigh had used were unintelligible to many British inhabitants and that other more interesting beautiful Cornish minerals should have been included.
65 See Hatchett letters of Dec. 1798.
66 Maton, *Observations*, pp. 149-50.
67 In his last novel *Rob Roy*, Scott named the villain Rashleigh Osbaldistone – this character was variously described as a thoroughly nasty and selfish hypocrite, a malignant Jacobite plotter, or as the ugliest, bandy-legged, bull-necked, limping scoundrel – a Richard the Third in all but his humpback, or as a most conceited coxcomb, he was finally killed by Rob Roy. Daphne Du Maurier used Philip Rashleigh's name in her novel *Frenchman's Creek* set in Cornwall at the time of Charles II; he was the unfortunate victim of piracy and the deceit of the heroine.
68 Further study of the series of letters from the Cornish collector-dealer John Tregoning, now at the Natural History Museum (Russell Bequest), would clarify Hawkins' own interest in collecting and mining.
69 Hawkins' letters are in the Mantell Papers at the Alexander Turnbull Library, Wellington, New Zealand.
70 His collection was eventually sold at auction by J. C. Stevens on 14 April and most lots were purchased by the dealer F. Krantz of Bonn: see *Nature*, 224, April 1905; Russell, 'John Hawkins', p. 103.
71 This follows the practice advocated by Francis Bacon: 'We have to make a collection or particular natural history . . . of everything in short that is in nature new, rare, and unusual'; see J. Spedding,

R. L. Ellis and D. D. Heath (eds), *The Works of Francis Bacon* (London: Longmans Green, 1868-90), vol 4, p. 169.

72 See Pole Carew's letter (4 Nov. 1777).

73 Rashleigh favoured 'Russell's Waggons' and this service is mentioned in many of his letters; see also D. Gerhold, *Road Transport before Railways: Russell's London Flying Wagons* (Cambridge: Cambridge University Press, 1993).

74 Review of A.F. Cronstedt, *An Essay towards a System of Mineralogy* (2nd edn., London: Charles Dilly, 1788; first published as '*Versuch einer Mineralogie*', 1758, 1775, 1780), in *Gentleman's Magazine,* 1789, p. 59.

75 A general interest in Chemistry can be seen in Goethe's use of chemical metaphors in his novel *Die Wahlverwandschaften* (1809) in which he used the theory of chemical affinity as a basis for describing the changing relationships of two couples – see D. Knight, 'Romanticism and the sciences' and J. Adler, 'Goethe's use of chemical theory in his elective affinities', in A. Cunningham and N. Jardine (eds), *Romanticism and the Sciences* (Cambridge: Cambridge University Press, 1990), pp. 13-24, 263-279.

76 W. N. Brock, *The Fontana History of Chemistry* (Glasgow: Fontana Press, 1992), p. 128.

77 See J. Uglow, *The Lunar Men: The Friends who made the Future, 1730-1810* (London: Faber and Faber, 2002), p. 237.

78 M. Faraday, *Chemical Manipulation: Being Instructions to Students in Chemistry* (1827).

79 T. M. Porter, 'The promotion of mining and the advancement of science'; J. G. Burke, 'Mineral classification in the early nineteenth century', in Schneer, *Toward a History of Geology*, pp. 62-77; Eyles, 'The extent of geological knowledge in the eighteenth century', ibid., pp. 159-83.

80 Wilson, 'The history of mineral collecting 1530–1799'.

81 J. F. Gmelin, translation of Linnaeus *Natursystem des Mineralreichs.* (Nürnberg: 1771), p. 84. Much later, in 1824, mineralogists were still devising new systems. Mitscherlich, a friend of Berzelius, who had first established a system based on chemistry, wrote: 'As for the chemical system of mineralogy, no one thinks any longer in any other terms' but he qualified this by adding 'everyone . . . is developing a system . . . of his own, according to his own method'. H. G. Söderbaum (ed), *Jac. Berzelius Lettres: Correspondance entre Berzelius et Eilhard Mitscherlich (1818–1847)* (Uppsala: Almgvist, 1932), p.40

82 See W. E. Wilson, 'Mineral books: five centuries of mineralogical literature', *Mineralogical Record*, 25, 4 (1995), pp. 49-60, and 'Addendum 1800–1962', pp. 60-64. Other reviews of these historic attempts at classification include F. A. Adams, *The*

Birth and Development of the Geological Sciences (New York, Dover Publications, 1938 and 1954), chapter 6; Burke, 'Mineral classification in the early nineteenth century'; and, concentrating on British instances, W. Campbell Smith, 'A history of the first hundred years of the mineral collection in the British Museum', *Bulletin of the British Museum (Natural History)*, (Historical Series), 3, 8 (1978), pp. 137-159.

83 J. Berzelius, *An Attempt to Establish a Pure Scientific System of Mineralogy* (London: Black, 1814); idem., 'Des changemens dans le système de minéralogie chimique', *Annales de chimie et de physique*, 31 (1826), pp. 34-5.

84 See M. P. Cooper, 'The Devonshire mineral collection in Chatsworth House', *The Mineralogical Record*, 36, 3 (2005), p. 251-2, 254. for evidence of how they were displayed in specially-built cabinets.

85 Cronstedt, *Essay towards a System of Mineralogy*, with categories of Erdarten; Erdharze; Salts, Metals. Blowpipe analysis utilised two types of flame – a blue oxidising flame in which combustion occurs, and a bright yellow, luminous, ragged and noisy reducing flame. Depending on the reagents used and the substance tested, the chemical and colour changes that occur help to identify the material being tested. Ideally a steady and continuous blast of air needs to be maintained for several minutes. Users had difficulty in achieving this. A modified technique used by E. Daniel Clarke, a later experimenter, could cause explosions (see his *The Gas Blowpipe, or Art of Fusion by Burning* (London: T. Cadell and W. Davies, 1819).

86 R. Kirwan *Elements of Mineralogy* (London: 1784): with Earths; Stones; Salts; Inflammables.

87 A. G. Werner, *Ausführliches und systematisches Verzeichnis des Mineralien-kabinets des weiland kurfürstlich Sächsischen Berghauptmans Herrn Karl Eugen Pabst von Ohain.* (2 vols., Freiberg: 1791).

88 It would appear that Rashleigh's letter has not survived.

89 Wilson, 'The history of mineral collecting 1530–1799', p. 100.

90 Klaproth, *Analytical Essays*. For further information on Klaproth, see Cleevely, 'The contributions of a trio of Cornish geologists', pp. 108, 112.

91 T. M. Porter, 'The promotion of mining and the advancement of science', pp. 543-570.

92 B. B. Vincent, 'A view of the chemical revolution through contemporary textbooks: Lavoisier, Fourcroy and Chaptal', *British Journal for the History of Science*, 23, 4 (1990), p. 440.

93 B. B. Vincent, 'Mendeleev's periodic system of chemical

elements', *British Journal for the History of Science*, 19, 1 (1986), pp. 4-5.

94 At least 29 of Gregor's letters contain detailed descriptions of his experiments. It is possible that he used the letters as an additional method of recording his numerous analyses; the account of hydrargillite sent to Sowerby and published in *British Mineralogy* is in the style of a letter. However, it would be expected that Gregor maintained a record of his activities, although doubts about the provenance of particular minerals expressed in his letters suggest he may not have kept a journal, but relied entirely on his memory.

95 Letters between 29 Oct. 1790 to 7 May 1793; for an explanation of the name 'menachanite' see Cleevely and Bristow, 'Rev. William Gregor', p. 104, note 30.

96 Fortunately, there are several good published glossaries of classical chemical terms that provide clarification when needed – see for example J. Eklund, 'The incompleat chymist: being an essay on the eighteenthcentury chemist in his laboratory, with a dictionary of obsolete chemical terms of the period', *Smithsonian Studies in History and Technology*, 33 (1975); M. Crosland, *Historical Studies in the Language of Chemistry* (London: Constable, 1978); W. E. Flood, *The Dictionary of Chemical Names* (New York: Philosophical Library, 1963); J. Grant, *Hackh's Chemical Dictionary*, (3rd edn, Philadelphia: Blakiston, 1944). Using the term 'phlogisticated' (15 Feb. 1793), Gregor pointedly noted '*I use that word with no reference to Theory*'. During the 18th century, Phlogiston was a hypothetical substance thought to account for inflammability, then later it was thought to have many more properties. Major advances were only made after this theory had been overthrown.

97 W. Gregor, 'Experiments on a mineral substance formerly supposed to be a Zeolite', *philosophical Transactions of the Royal Society of London*, 95 (1805), pp. 331-48.

98 N. Carruth, R. Cleevely and D. I. Green, 'A Scorodite specimen figured by James Sowerby and analysed by William Gregor', *U.K. Journal of Mines and Minerals*, 28 (2007), pp. 4-6.

99 D. I. Green, T. E. Cottrell, I. Jones, D. Cox and R. Cleevely, 'Wavellite: its discovery and occurrences in the British Isles', *U.K. Journal of Mines and Minerals*, 28 (2007), pp. 11-30; R. Cleevely, 'Discovery of the 'Barnstaple Zeolite' – a minor geological controversy of the early 1800s', *Transactions of the Devonshire Association*, 2007 [2008], pp. 133-67.

100 Letters 15 May 1789, 15 Nov. 1790, 16 June 1792: 'I have . . . two or three bits . . . which I have been dissolving but not being much used to the Liquid process, I have not yet determin'd the contents.'

For Mss notes made by Rashleigh of published analyses by others see RIC/RASH/1/90/49.

101 *The Catalogue de la Collection Minéralogique de Comte de Bournon* was published in London in 1812 and contained a memoir on the structure of crystals by L'Abbé Haüy.

102 Burke, 'Mineral classification in the early nineteenth century', pp. 62-3.

103 G. Rose, Das krystallo-chemische Mineralsystem, (Leipzig: 1852).

104 W. Whewell, *History of the Inductive Sciences* (New York: Appleton, 1884), vol. 2, p. 349.

105 Eyles, 'The extent of geological knowledge in the eighteenth century', p. 162.

106 J. Ray, *The Wisdom of God Manifested in the Works of Creation* (London: 1691); idem, *Miscellaneous Discourses Concerning the Dissolution and Changes in the World* (London: 1692).

107 G. W. Leibnitz, *Protogaea* (Göttingen: 1749); G. L. L. Buffon, *Histoire naturelle* (Paris: 1749, 1779); see also J. Roger, 'Les epoques de la nature: histoire naturelle', *Mémoire du Museum National d'Histoire Naturelle (Science de la Terre)*, 10 (1962).

108 For comment on A. G. Werner, *Kurze Klassification* (Dresden: 1785), see A. M. Ospovat, 'Reflections on A. G. Werner's "Kurze Klassification"', in Schneer, *Toward a History of Geology*, pp. 242-256.

109 Ibid.

110 Ibid., p. 249. Ospovat clarified (p. 250-1) that Werner's terminology and interpretation of rock formation was based on a very general and broad recognition of their occurrence, texture and structure.

111 J. Hutton, *Theory of the Earth; or an Investigation of the Laws Observable in the Composition, Dissolution, and Restoration of Land upon the Globe* (Edinburgh: J. Dickson, 1788); idem., *Theory of the Earth with Proofs and Illustrations.* (Edinburgh: William Creech, 1795).

112 See Challinor, *The History of British Geology*, p. 69.

113 Adams, *Birth and Development of the Geological Sciences*, esp. Chapter 7; M. A. Macgregor, *et al*, 'James Hutton 1726–1797', *Proceedings of the Royal Society of Edinburgh*, Sect B (Biology) LXIII (iv) (1950), pp. 351-402; G. Y. Craig and J. H. Hull (eds), *James Hutton – Present and Future* (London: Geological Society Special Publication No. 150, 2002); R. Porter, *The Making of Geology: Earth Science in Britain 1660–1815* (Cambridge: Cambridge University Press, 1977).

114 D. R. Dean, 'James Hutton and his public, 1785–1802', *Annals of Science*, 30, 1 (1973), pp. 89-105.

115 Using a comment by James Watt (19 Aug. 1795) – 'These cursed

French have murdered Philosophy and continue to torment Europe' – Uglow (*Lunar Men*, p. 477) suggests that the British reaction to French chemistry and the French wars blighted the work of British scientists, for apart from weakening practical scientific cooperation it *'began to look politically dubious'*.

116 R. H. Dott, 'James Hutton and the concept of a dynamic Earth', in Schneer, *Toward a History of Geology*, pp.122-141.

117 D. A. Bassett, 'James Hutton, the founder of modern geology: an anthology', *Geology*, 2 (1970), pp. 5-76.

118 S. I. Tomkeieff, 'James Hutton and the philosophy of geology', *Proceedings of the Royal Society of Edinburgh*, Sect B (Biology) LXIII (iv) (1950), pp. 387-400.

119 Dott, 'James Hutton', p. 129. The basic divisions of each theory were: by Hutton – Primary/ Secondary; Igneous/Sedimentary; and by Werner – Primitive/Transitional; Floetz/Alluvial/Volcanic.

120 For modern comment on Werner's theories see Ospovat, 'Reflections'. See note 101.

121 Gregory Watt (1777–1804), the second son of James Watt, published his *Observations on Basalt* in 1804 in which he proved that crystalline rocks may develop when molten rocks cool down very slowly. He died from consumption soon after, but his evidence influenced von Buch's work on volcanoes.

122 This phrase occurs in Psalm 18 'The Highest gave his thunder Hail stones and Coals of Fire' and was first quoted in this context in his account of meteorites by E. King, *Remarks Concerning Stones said to have Fallen from the Clouds, Both in these Days and in Ancient Times* (London: George Nicol, 1796).

123 'Thomas Beddoes MD (1760-1808) was a major figure in the social and intellectual ferment of the closing decades of the eighteenth century and championed pneumatic chemistry. He tried to do too much, too fast . . . in an already overcrowded life running a medical practice in Bristol' and 'suffered from the lack of close critical colleagues' (R. Porter, review of D. Stanfield, *Thomas Beddoes MD 1760–1808* (1984) in *British Journal for the History of Science*, 19, 1 (1986), p. 122; see also Uglow, *Lunar Men*, p. 461).

124 See R. Hutchison and A. Graham (1994) *Meteorites: The Key to our Existence* (London: Natural History Museum, 1994), for a general illustrated account. In 1879, Townshend Hall (*Mineralogical Magazine*, 3, 13, pp. 1-17), after referring to several previous authoritative lists, compiled his own list of British meteoric falls between 1360 and 1876. He recognised four types of record: 1) established observations (which included the Wold Meteorite); 2) mistakes; 3) historic errors; and 4) hoaxes. Several of the earliest falls he listed occurred in the South West.

125 Raistrick, *Hatchett Diary*; C. Greville, 'An Account of some stones said to have fallen on the earth in France; and of a lump of native iron said to have fallen in India', *Philosophical Transactions of the Royal Society*, 93, 1 (1823), pp. 200-204.

126 C. T. Pillinger and J. M. Pillinger, 'The Wold Cottage meteorite: not an ordinary chondrite', *Meteoritics and Planetary Science*, 31, 5 (1996), pp. 589-605; this also gives a full account of the life of Edward Topham.

127 Greville was the favourite nephew of Sir William Hamilton, who obtained information on the Siena shower; his uncle cleared Greville's debts in return for the affections of his mistress, who became Lady Emma Hamilton – (see ibid., note 16) – this enabled Greville to purchase Born's collection. Hailstone was a friend of Hervey, who saw the Sienna fall and also associated with Edward Topham the original owner and publicist of the Wold meteorite (ibid., notes 6 and 9).

128 E. C. Howard et al., 'Experiments and observations on certain stony and metallic substances which at different times are said to have fallen on the Earth; also on various kinds of native iron', *Philosophical Transactions of the Royal Society*, 92 (1802), pp. 168-212. The presence of iron was fortunate, for more recently (A. Graham, *Catalogue of Meteorites* (Tucson, 1985), it has been realised that there is a 10% chance that a fall would have no free metal. In fact, the falls at Alais (France) in 1806 and that at Stannern (Czechoslovakia) in 1810 lacked such evidence. See Pillinger and Pillinger, 'The Wold Cottage meteorite'.

129 Ibid., p. 589.

130 Letters from Sowerby: 18 Nov. 1804; 7 May 1805; 29 May 1805; and from Rashleigh 26 May 1805.

131 J. Izarn, *Des pierres tombées du ciel ou Lithologie Atmospherique* (Paris: 1803), which contains references to many earlier accounts including that at Ensisheim on 7 Nov. 1492, that had been engraved with a cryptic comment in Latin stating: 'Concerning this stone many have said much, everyone something, no one enough'. Other theories are briefly mentioned in Pillinger and Pillinger, 'The Wold Cottage meteorite', pp. 597-8.

132 R. J. Cleevely, 'The Sowerbys and their publications in the light of the manuscript material in the British Museum (Natural History)', *Journal of the Society for the Bibliography of Natural History*, 7, 4 (1975), p. 345.

133 See Sowerby's letters (17 Mar 1807 and 2 Sept. 1807).

134 King, *Remarks concerning Stones*; Rashleigh's copy in CRO DDR/1/5761. For the reference to Rashleigh's hailstones see pp. 18-19.

135 For the assistance given to Klaproth, see Cleevely, 'The contributions of a trio of Cornish geologists', pp. 108-12.

136 The addition of the names John Sibthorp, Franz Bauer and Gideon Mantell would serve to emphasize this point. Among these was Count Alexis de Golowkyn of Moscow who sought specimens of all the figured Cornish minerals – see Heuland's letter to Rashleigh (11 June 1807).

137 Kingsbury, 'Some minerals of special interest in south-west England', pp. 252-3.

138 It also led to foreign collectors: see P. H. Armstrong, *The English Parson-Naturalist: A Companionship between Science and Religion* (Leominster: Gracewing, 2000). For further comment see Cleevely and Bristow, 'Rev. William Gregor', pp. 86-87.

139 Table of Classes in T. Allan, *Mineralogical Nomenclature* (3rd edn., Edinburgh: A. Constable and Co., 1819).

140 R. J. Cleevely, 'A note on John Hawkins (1761–1841) and the Hawkins archive', *Archives of Natural History*, 27, 2 (2000), p. 261.

141 Maton, *Observations*, p. 150.

Editor's note

My original intention was to provide transcriptions of all the letters in the archives of Philip Rashleigh, John Hawkins and William Gregor relating to their interest in collecting, identifying and analysing minerals. Unfortunately it was not possible to publish all of these in a single volume, for apart from its impractical size, the cost would have been prohibitive.

The following chronological table provides a complete list of all the relevant letters in the various archives. This reference list illustrates the variation in the frequency of the letters and the wide range of correspondents. Undated letters have been placed according to their content by using references to events, or to the specimens and experiments discussed; occasionally post marks and the annotations of the recipient have also been helpful. The letters marked in **bold** have been selected for inclusion in this volume (in cases where only an extract has been used, this is denoted by an **E** after the date). Many of the selected letters relate to the mineralogical activities of the writers, but others that deal with political, family and social matters occurring during the period have been included in order to provide additional interest.

Only some of the letters referred to in the Introduction have been selected for publication. However, it is hoped that transcriptions of all the letters listed will be made available in Truro for reference at the RIC Courtney Library and the County Record Office.

A note on the published transcriptions

All 'openings' and most 'closures' have been omitted.

Abbreviations completed by superscript letters are printed here at normal size.

In many instances the contents of letters that are virtually continuous (to make the best use of the paper) have been broken into paragraphs according to subject for ease of reference.

[page torn with loss] Damage to this area of letter either along edge, or as holes, or other disintegration.

[... ......] Indicates that Word / or letters have been interpreted.

− − / −— These symbols were frequently used to indicate the end of a sentence, or a subject, but in most cases these have been replaced by conventional punctuation, although others have been left to illustrate the style.

List of references used in this volume for the institutions holding the material

General Rashleigh Correspondence

RASH/	Rashleigh Letters, Courtney Library, RIC, Truro
5757/and other numbers	
	DDR, Rashleigh papers, CRO, Truro
LinnPULT	Richard Pulteney Archive, Linnean Society, London
TP/12	Pennant Papers, Warwick, CRO/2017/TP11
RS/1/910	Rashleigh of Stoketon, Saltash, CRO, Truro
RP/17	Rogers of Penrose – Autograph Album, CRO, Truro

Gregor letters to Hawkins

Gregor letters to Rashleigh & Sowerby

Rashleigh letters to James Sowerby

Hawkins – Rashleigh correspondence

NHM Sow	Sowerby Archive, General Library, Natural History Museum, London
NHM R Beq	Russell Bequest, Mineral Library, Natural History Museum, London
DM1186	Eyles Collection, Special Collections, University Library, Bristol
J3/2; J3/3; J3/4	Hawkins Papers, CRO Truro
RSocMS	Sowerby family, Royal Society Library, London
RASH/	Rashleigh Letters, Courtney Library, RIC, Truro

Rashleigh – Pole Carew Correspondence

CC/J; CC/K; CC/L; CC/O	Antony House Archives
5302, 5304, 5305	DDR, Rashleigh papers, CRO, Truro

Reference	Date	Author	Place	Recipient	Comments
5300/31	**14 July 1755**	C. Hervey	Leipzig	Rashleigh	
RS/1/910	**28 Dec. 1764**	Ld. Edgecumbe	Bath	Rashleigh	
CC/O/66/1	27 June 1772	Pole Carew		Rashleigh	to Garlick Hill, London
CC/O/66/3	2 July 1772	Pole Carew		Rashleigh	to Garlick Hill, London
CC/O/66/2	20 Jan. 1773	Pole Carew		Rashleigh	to Menabilly
CC/O/66/4	5 Apr. 1773	Pole Carew		Rashleigh	to Beaufort Buildings
CC/O/66/7	30 May 1773	Pole Carew		Rashleigh	to Menabilly
CC/O/66/5	1 June 1773	Pole Carew		Rashleigh	to Beaufort Buildings
CC/O/66/6	[June] 1773	Pole Carew		Rashleigh	
CC/O/66/8	6 June 1773	Pole Carew	Bristol	Rashleigh	to Menabilly
CC/O/66/9	15 June 1773	Pole Carew		Rashleigh	to Menabilly
CC/O/66/10	20 June 1773	Pole Carew		Rashleigh	to Menabilly
CC/O/66/11	29 June 1773	Pole Carew		Rashleigh	to Menabilly
CC/O/66/12	12 Dec. 1773	Pole Carew		Rashleigh	to Menabilly
CC/O/66/13	16 Jan. 1774	Pole Carew	Bristol	Rashleigh	to Menabilly
CC/J/8	27 Jan. 1774	Rashleigh	Northumb'ld St	Pole Carew	
CC/O/66/14	28 Jan. 1774	Pole Carew	Oxford	Rashleigh	to Northumberland St
CC/J/8	31 Jan. 1774	Rashleigh	Northumbl'd St.	Pole Carew	
CC/J/8	22 Feb. 1774	Rashleigh	Northumbla' St.	Pole Carew	
CC/O/66/15	25 Apr. 1774	Pole Carew		Rashleigh	to Northumberland St.
CC/J/8	29 Apr. 1774	Rashleigh	London	Pole Carew	
CC/O/66/16	11 May 1774	Pole Carew		Rashleigh	
CC/O/66/17	21 June 1774	Pole Carew		Rashleigh	
CC/J/8- Jul	7 July 1774	Rashleigh	Menabilly	Pole Carew	
CC/O/66/18	12 July 1774	Pole Carew		Rashleigh	
5302/155	5 Nov. 1774	Pole Carew	Oxford	Rashleigh	to Menabilly
CC/J/8	10 Nov. 1774	Rashleigh	Menabilly	Pole Carew	
CC/J/8	18 Dec. 1774	Rashleigh	Menabilly	?Charles Rashleigh	
Missing	*11 Mar. 1775*	*Rashleigh*		*Pole Carew*	
CC/O/66/19	14 Apr. 1775	Pole Carew		Rashleigh	to Garlick Hill
CC/O/66/20	25 Apr. 1775	Pole Carew		Rashleigh	
5302/105	7 May 1775	Pole Carew	Oxford	Rashleigh	to Garlick Hill
CC/J/8	6 June 1775	Rashleigh		Pole Carew	
CC/O/66/21	**18 June 1775**	**Pole Carew**	Oxford	Rashleigh	
5302/106	2 July 1775	Pole Carew	Oxford	Rashleigh	
CC/J/9/4	**20 July 1775**	**Rashleigh**	Menabilly	Pole Carew	
CC/O/66/22	8 Aug. 1775	Pole Carew		Rashleigh	
5302/110	13 Aug. 1775	Pole Carew	London	Rashleigh	to Menabilly
5302/115	31 Dec. 1775	Pole Carew	Angouleme	Rashleigh	to Menabilly
5302/123	27 Apr. 1776	Pole Carew	Angouleme	Rashleigh	to Strand
CC/J/9/5	11 Sept. 1776	Rashleigh	Menabilly	Pole Carew	
5302/133	**1/26 Jan. 1777**	**Pole Carew**	Vienna	Rashleigh	to Garlick Hill
CC/J/8	21 Feb. 1777	Rashleigh	Beaufor Blds	Pole Carew	

Reference	Date	Author	Place	Recipient	Comments
5302/136	23 Feb. 1777	Pole Carew	Vienna	Rashleigh	to Garlick Hill
5302/143	**19 Apr. 1777**	**Pole Carew**	Vienna	Rashleigh	to Menabilly
5302/146	27 Apr. 1777	Pole Carew	Vienna	Rashleigh	to Garlick Hill
5302/149	**2 June 1777**	**Pole Carew**	Vienna	Rashleigh	to Menabilly
CC/J/8	6 June 1777	Rashleigh	Garlick Hill	Pole Carew	
5302/148	**12 June 1777**	**Pole Carew**	Vienna	Rashleigh	to Menabilly
CC/J/8	26 June 1777	Rashleigh	Menabilly	Pole Carew	
Missing	*3 July. 1777*	*Rashleigh*		Pole Carew	[*see 7 Aug. 1777*]
5302/150	**3/9 Aug. 1777**	**Pole Carew**	Dresden/Berlin	Rashleigh	
5302/154	**28 Sept. 1777**	**Pole Carew**	Hague	Rashleigh	to Handford/Blandford
CC/J/9/6	**16 Oct. 1777**	**Rashleigh**	Menabilly	Pole Carew	
5302/156	4 Nov. 1777	Pole Carew	Hague	Rashleigh	
CC/J/9/7	15 Nov. 1777	Rashleigh		Pole Carew	
5302/168	? Dec. 1777	Pole Carew	Hague	Rashleigh	
5757/1/4	6 Jan. 1778	J. Mudge	Plymouth	Rashleigh	
RASH/4/40	6 Jan. 1778	Baron Heynitz	Freyburg	Rashleigh	in French
5302/160	n.d [Feb. 1778]	Pole Carew	Hague	Rashleigh	
5302/159	13 Feb. 1778	Pole Carew	Hague	Rashleigh	to Garlick Hill
5302/162	**24 Mar. 1778**	**Pole Carew**	Hague	Rashleigh	to Garlick Hill
5302/166	21 Apr. 1778	Pole Carew	Hague	Rashleigh	to Garlick Hill
5757/1/5	3 Aug. 1778	Baron Heynitz	Freyburg	Rashleigh	in French
5302/175	15 Sept. 1778	Pole Carew	Hague	Rashleigh	to Menabilly
CC/O/66/23	29 Sept. 1778	Pole Carew	Hague	Rashleigh	to Menabilly
5302/177	30 Oct. 1778	Pole Carew	Hague	Rashleigh	to Menabilly
Missing	*10 Dec. 1778*	*Rashleigh*		Pole Carew	[*see 5 Jan. 1779*]
CC/O/66/24	5 Jan. 1779	Pole Carew	Hague	Rashleigh	to Menabilly
CC/J/10/88	25 Jan. 1779	Rashleigh	London	Pole Carew	
CC/O/66/25	23 Feb. 1779	Pole Carew	Hague	Rashleigh	
CC/O/66/26	19 Mar. 1779	Pole Carew		Rashleigh	
CC/O/66/27	21 Apr. 1779	Pole Carew.		Rashleigh	
Missing	*18 May 1779*	*Pole Carew*		Pole Carew	[*see 24 July 1779*]
CC/O/66/28	15 June 1779	Pole Carew		Rashleigh	
CC/J/10/90	24 July 1779	Rashleigh	Menabilly	Pole Carew	a la Hay
CC/O/66/29	5 Aug. 1779	Pole Carew		Rashleigh	
CC/J/10/91	**2 Sept. 1779**	**Rashleigh**	Menabilly	Pole Carew	a la Hay
Missing	*14 Sept. 1779*	*Rashleigh*		Pole Carew	[*see 12 Oct. 1779*]
CC/O/66/30	**12 Oct. 1779**	**Pole Carew**	Hague	Rashleigh	to Menabilly
CC/J/10/39	**28 Oct. 1779**	**Rashleigh**	Menabilly	Pole Carew	
CC/O/66/31	8 Nov. 1779	Pole Carew	Hague	Rashleigh	
CC/O/66/33	8 Feb. 1780	Pole Carew	Hague	Rashleigh	
CC/O/66/34	18 Feb. 1780	Pole Carew	Hague	Rashleigh	
CC/O/66/35	29 Feb. 1780	Pole Carew	Hague	Rashleigh	
Missing	*6 Mar. 1780*	*Rashleigh*		Pole Carew	[*see 19 Mar. 1780*]
CC/O/66/36	19 Mar. 1780	Pole Carew	Hague	Rashleigh	
5757/1/103	27 Mar.? 1780	Baron Heynitz	Freyberg	Rashleigh	in French
CC/O/66/37	28 Mar. 1780	Pole Carew	Hague	Rashleigh	
CC/O/66/38	**11 Apr. 1780**	**Pole Carew**	Hague	Rashleigh	
CC/J/10/40	18 Apr. 1780	Rashleigh	London	Pole Carew	a la Hay
CC/O/66/39	2 May 1780	Pole Carew	Hague	Rashleigh	

Reference	Date	Author	Place	Recipient	Comments
5757/1/9	16 May 1780	W. Synnot	Derby	Rashleigh	
5757/1/6	27 May 1780	G. Keate	Bloomsbury	Rashleigh	
CC/0/66/40	**4 July 1780**	**Pole Carew**	Copenhagen	Rashleigh	
CC/J/11/32	**20 July 1780**	**Rashleigh**	Menabilly	Pole Carew	to Stockholm
5757/1/7	**13 Oct. 1780 E**	**Pole Carew**	Stockholm	Rashleigh	
CC/J/11/33	**18 Nov. 1780 E**	**Rashleigh**	Menabilly	Pole Carew	to St. Petersburg
CC/J/11/34	11 Dec. 1780	Rashleigh	Menabilly	Pole Carew	to St. Petersburg
Missing	*25 Dec. 1780*	*Pole Carew*			
CC/J/11/35	15 Feb 1781	Rashleigh	London	Pole Carew	to St. Petersburg
CC/J/11/36	**23 Feb. 1781**	**Rashleigh**	London	Pole Carew	to St. Petersburg
CC/J/11/37	27 Feb. 1781	Rashleigh	London	Pole Carew	to St. Petersburg
5757/1/8	12/23 Mar. 1781	P. Pallas	St. Petersburg	Rashleigh	
CC/J/11/38	**13 Apr. 1781 E**	**Rashleigh**	London	Pole Carew	to St. Petersburg
5303/14	23 Apr. 1781	W. Synnot	Matlock	Rashleigh	
CC/J/11/39	**27 Apr. 1781**	**Rashleigh**	London	Pole Carew	to St. Petersburg
Missing	*7/18 May 1781*	*Pole Carew*		*Rashleigh*	*[see 25 June 1781]*
5757/6/9	24 June. 1781	P. Pallas	St. Petersburg	Rashleigh	
CC/J/11/40	**25 June 1781**	**Rashleigh**	Menabilly	Pole Carew	to St. Petersburg
5757/1/10	17 Sept. 1781	Pole Carew	Cherson	Rashleigh	
CC/J/11/41	13 Dec. 1781	Rashleigh	Menabilly	Pole Carew	
5757/1/11	29 Dec. 1781	Charpentier	Freyberg	Rashleigh	in French
DDR/S/1/1045	15 Jan. 1782	Pole Carew	Warsaw	Rashleigh	
5757/1/13	30 Jan. 1782	W. Synnot	Derby	Rashleigh	
5757/2/65	30 Jan 1782	W. Synnott			Cover of 5757/1/13
RASH/1/43	2 Feb. 1782	W. Synnot	Derby	Rashleigh	
5757/1/14	4 Feb. 1782	W. Synnot	Derby	Rashleigh	
5303/11	30 Mar. 1782	W. Synnot	Derry	Rashleigh	
5757/1/15	9 Apr. 1782	P. Pallas	St. Petersburg	Rashleigh	
CC/J/12/29	12 Apr. 1782	Rashleigh	Menabilly	Pole Carew	
5757/1/16	15 May 1782	W. Synnot	Derby	Rashleigh	
CC/J/12/30	16 May 1782	Rashleigh	Menabilly	Pole Carew	
CC/J/12/31	20 May 1782	Rashleigh	Menabilly	Pole Carew	
5757/1/17	27 May 1782	W. Synnot	Derby	Rashleigh	
5303/16	**28 May 1782**	**Pole Carew**	New Bond St.	Rashleigh	
CC/J/12/32	1 June 1782	Rashleigh	Menabilly	Pole Carew	
5757/1/18	27 June 1782	W. Synnot		Rashleigh	
CC/J/12/33	29 June 1782	Rashleigh	Menabilly	Pole Carew	
5757/1/19	29 Sept. 1782	W. Synnot	Derby	Rashleigh	
CC/J/12/34	30 Nov. 1782	Rashleigh	Menabilly	Pole Carew	
CC/J/12/35	8 Dec. 1782	Rashleigh	Menabilly	Pole Carew	
CC/J/12/36	15 Dec.1782	Rashleigh	Menabilly	Pole Carew	
RASH/3/51	22 Mar. 1783	Wm. Borlase	Roscady	Rashleigh	
5757/1/20	23 Apr. 1783	R. Phillips	St. Agnes	Rashleigh	is fragile
5757/1/21	18 Aug. 1783	R. Raspe	Redruth	Rashleigh	is fragile
5757/1/22	17 Oct. 1783	R. Raspe	Redruth	Rashleigh	is fragile
5757/1/23	**23 Dec. 1783**	**R. Pulteney**	Blandford	Rashleigh	
RASH/1/44	4 Jan. 1784	H. Seymer	Handford	Rashleigh	
Missing	*21 Feb. 1784*	*Rashleigh*		*Pulteney*	

Reference	Date	Author	Place	Recipient	Comments
5757/1/24	**7 May 1784**	**W. Synnot**	Ireland	Rashleigh	
5757/1/25	**8 May 1784**	**R. Pulteney**	Blandford	Rashleigh	
5757/1/27	6 July 1784	R. Phillips	St Agnes	Rashleigh	
5757/1/29	24 July 1784	J.L de Unger	Bronswic	Rashleigh	
5757/1/28	25 July 1784	W. Synnot	Ballymoyer Lodge	Rashleigh	
RS/1/1046	**28 July 1784**	**J. Rashleigh**	Ballinado	Rashleigh	
Unavailable	*2 Aug. 1784*	*Rashleigh*		*Trebra*	*[see 22 Nov. 1784]*
Unavailable	*25 Oct. 1784*	*Rashleigh*		*Trebra*	*[see 22 Nov. 1784]*
Missing	*17 Nov. 1784*	*Rashleigh*		*Pulteney*	
5757/1/32	22 Nov. 1784	R. Carne	Falmouth	Rashleigh	
5757/1/31	22 Nov. 1784	von Trebra	Zellerfeld	Rashleigh	
5757/1/30	**27 Nov. 1784**	**R. Pulteney**	Blandford	Rashleigh	
5303/26	27 Dec. 1784	W. Synnot	Ballymoyer	Rashleigh	
5305/27	Feb. 1785	Rashleigh	Fowey	Pallas	draft
Unavailable	*15 Mar. 1785*	*Rashleigh*		*Trebra*	*[see 31/5/85]*
Unavailable	*22 Apr. 1785*	*Rashleigh*		*Trebra*	*[see 31 May 1785]*
Unavailable	*6 May 1785*	*Rashleigh*		*Trebra*	*[see 21 Aug. 1785]*
5757/1/34	31 May 1785	von Trebra	Zellerfeld	Rashleigh	
5757/1/33	C	C	C		translation
LinnPULT.	18 June 1785	Rashleigh	Menabilly	Pulteney	
Unavailable	*2 July 1785*	*Rashleigh*		*Trebra*	*[see 3 Sept. 1785 and 27 Oct. 1785]*
5757/1/35	16 July 1785	W. Synnot	Ballymoyer Lodge	Rashleigh	
5757/1/104	21 Aug. 1785	von Trebra	Zellerfeld	Rashleigh	
5757/1/35	3 Sept. 1785	von Trebra	Zellerfeld	Rashleigh	
5757/1/37A	27 Oct. 1785	von Trebra	Zellerfeld	Rashleigh	
5757/1/37	27 Oct. 1785	von Trebra	Zellerfeld	Rashleigh	translation
Unavailable	*1 Nov. 1785*	*Rashleigh*		*Trebra*	*[see 16 Dec. 1785]*
RASH/1/47	8 Nov. 1785	W. Synnot	Ballymoyer Lodge	Rashleigh	
5757/1/38	12 Dec. 1785	W. Synnot	Ireland	Rashleigh	
5757/1/39	16 Dec. 1785	von Trebra	Zellerfeld	Rashleigh	
5757/1/40	6 Mar. 1786	L C de Claviere	Lisbon	Rashleigh	
5757/1/45	26 Mar. 1786	von Trebra	Zellerfeld	Rashleigh	
Unavailable	*12 May 1786*	*Rashleigh*		*Trebra*	*[see 11 Dec. 1786]*
5757/1/46	18 May 1786	von Trebra	Zellerfeld	Rashleigh	
5757/1/42	C	C	C		translation
TP/12/21	20 May 1786	Rashleigh	London	Pennant	
5757/1/41	23 May 1786	Ignace de Asso	Amsterdam	Rashleigh	
TP/12/23	13 June 1786	Rashleigh	Menabilly	Pennant	
5757/1/43	18 June 1786	W. Synnot	Newry	Rashleigh	
TP/12/24	7 Aug. 1786	Rashleigh	Menabilly	Pennant	
Unavailable	*25 Aug. 1786*	*Rashleigh*		*Trebra*	*[see 11 Dec. 1786]*
5757/1/44	14 Sept. 1786	Ignace de Asso	Amsterdam	Rashleigh	
5757/1/47	10 Nov. 1786	L.C. de Claviere	Lisbon	Rashleigh	is fragile
TP/12/25	19 Nov.1786	Rashleigh	Menabilly	Pennant	
5757/1/49	11 Dec. 1786	von Trebra	Zellerfeld	Rashleigh	
5757/1/48	C	C			translation
Unavailable	*2 Jan. 1787*	*Rashleigh*		*Trebra*	*[see 9 Feb. 1787]*
Unavailable	*18 Jan. 1787*	*Rashleigh*		*Trebra*	*[see 20 Dec. 1787]*

Reference	Date	Author	Place	Recipient	Comments
5757/1/50	9 Feb. 1787	von Trebra	Zellerfeld	Rashleigh	
5757/1/51	7 June 1787	W. Synnot	Dublin	Rashleigh	
TP/12/26	23 June 1787	Rashleigh	Menabilly	Pennant	
Unavailable	*7 July 1787*	*Rashleigh*		*Trebra*	*[see 20 Dec. 1787]*
Missing	*12 July 1787*	*Pennant*		*Rashleigh*	*[see 28 July 1787]*
Missing	*21 July 1787*	*Pennant*		*Rashleigh*	
TP/12/27	28 July 1787	Rashleigh	Menabilly	Pennant	
5757/1/52	20 Dec. 1787	von Trebra	Zellerfeld	Rashleigh	
5757/1/53	C	C	C		translation
Unavailable	*28 Jan. 1788*	*Rashleigh*		*Trebra*	
5757/1/54	23 Feb. 1788	von Trebra	Zellerfeld	Rashleigh	
J3/2/17	11 Feb. 1789	J. Wedgwood	Etruria	Hawkins	
NHM RBeq.13	**25 Feb. 1789**	**Rashleigh**	Menabilly	Hawkins	
5757/1/56	5 Mar. 1789	Hawkins	Sunbury	Rashleigh	
J3/ 1371	6-17 Mar.1789	Rashleigh	Hawkins		
5757/1/55	18 Mar. 1789	Hawkins	Upper Brook St.	Rashleigh	
NHM R Beq. 14/15	**22 Mar. 1789**	**Rashleigh**	Menabilly	Hawkins	
J3/2/18	25 Mar. 1789	J. Wedgwood	Etruria	Hawkins	
J3/2/19	1 Apr. 1789	J. Wedgwood	Etruria	Hawkins	
J3/2/131	1 May 1789	Rashleigh	Menabilly	Hawkins	
5757/1/58	**10 May 1789**	**Hawkins**	Upper Brook St	Rashleigh	
NHM R Beq. 16	15 May 1789	Rashleigh	Menabilly	Hawkins	
J3/2/21	27 May 1789	J. Wedgwood	Conway	Hawkins	
5757/1/59	11 June 1789	J. Rogers	Penrose	Rashleigh	
5757/1/57	1 Sept. 1789	von Trebra	Zellerfeld	Rashleigh	
5757/1/109	**14 Sept. [1789]**	**Hawkins**	Buxton	Rashleigh	
NHM R Beq. 17	31 Oct. 1789	Rashleigh	Menabilly	Hawkins	
5757/1/60	**31 Dec. 1789**	**Hawkins**	5 Chandos St.,	Rashleigh	
NHM RBeq. 41	n.d. [? Jan. 1790]	Rashleigh		Hawkins	
NHM RBeq. 42/43	**n.d. [? Jan. 1790]**	**Rashleigh**		Hawkins	
NHM RBeq 54	**1 Jan. [1790]**	**J. Wedgwood**	Bath	Hawkins	
J3/2/36	9 Jan. 1790	J. Wedgwood	Etruria	Hawkins	
J3/2/37	**16 Jan. 1790**	**J. Wedgwood**	Etruria	Hawkins	
J3/2/151	**17 Feb. 1790**	**J.W. Hawkins**	Batworthy	Hawkins	
J3/2/40	23 Feb. 1790	J. Wedgwood	Etruria	Hawkins	
J3/2/42	1 Mar. 1790	J. Wedgwood	Etruria	Hawkins	
J3/2/1553	6 Mar. 1790	Rashleigh	Norfolk St.	Hawkins	
J3/2/44	20 Mar. 1790	J. Wedgwood	Etruria	Hawkins	
5757/1/61	**23 Mar. 1790**	**Baron Lindenthal**		Rashleigh	
J3/2/49 (fragment)	26 Apr. 1790	J. Wedgwood	Etruria	Hawkins	
J3/2/163	7 June 1790	J. Wedgwood		Hawkins	
NHM RBeq 52-53	**22 July 1790**	**J. Wedgwood**	Etruria	Hawkins	

Reference	Date	Author	Place	Recipient	Comments
J3/12/ 1372	pre 22 Oct. 1790	**Rashleigh**	? Menabilly	Hawkins	
J3/12/ 1354	**25 Oct. 1790**	Gregor		Hawkins	
J3/12/ 1353	n.d. [c. Oct. 1790]	Gregor		Hawkins	
5757/1/62	**4 Nov. 1790**	**Hawkins**	Sunbury	Rashleigh	
NHM R Beq. 18/19	**15 Nov. 1790**	**Rashleigh**	Menabilly	Hawkins	
J3/2/170	17 Nov. [1790 ?]	Hailstone	Cambridge	Hawkins	
J3/12/1397 [incomplete]	**? Jan. 1791**	Gregor		Hawkins	
J3/12/ 1355	**n.d. Jan. 1791**	Gregor		Hawkins	
J3/2/186	**8 Jan.** [? 1791]	Gregor	Cairhaise, nr. Tregony	Hawkins	
J3/2/172	31 Mar. 1791	Hailstone	Cambridge	Hawkins	
NHM R Beq. 23	22 May 1791	Rashleigh	London	Hawkins	
NHM R Beq. 24	**n.d. [24 July 1791]**	**Rashleigh**		Hawkins	
J3/.2/177	**12 Aug. 1791**	**J. Wedgwood**	Etruria	Hawkins	
J3/2/138	**26 Aug. [1791]**	**Gregor**	Killiow	Hawkins	
5757/1/64	**27 Aug. 1791**	**Hawkins**	Sunbury	Rashleigh	
NHM R Beq. 25	31 Aug. 1791	Rashleigh	Menabilly	Hawkins	
5757/1/65	**12 Sept. 1791**	**Hawkins**		Rashleigh	
NHM R Beq. 156	**18 Sept. 1791**	**Hailstone**	Cambridge	Hawkins	
NHM R Beq. 26	**? Oct. 1791**	**Rashleigh**		Hawkins	
J3/2/183	n.d. ? Oct.[1791]	Gregor		Hawkins	
5757/1/66	**27 Oct. 1791**	**Gregor**	Caerhayes	Rashleigh	
J3/2/214	**Nov.? 1791**	**Hailstone**	Cowes	Hawkins	
RSoc-L&P-9	**3 Nov. 1791**	**Rashleigh**	Menabilly	President of Royal Society	
J3/2/215	4 Nov. [?1791]	Gregor		Hawkins	
5757/1/67	**23 Nov. 1791**	**Hawkins**		Rashleigh	
J3/2/220	**25 Nov. [1791]**	**Gregor**	Caerhayes	Hawkins	
NHM R Beq. 27/28	**30 Nov. 1791**	**Rashleigh**	Menabilly	Hawkins	
NHM R Beq. 29/30	Catalogue of Minerals for Miss Raab sent by Rashleigh				
RASH/1/24/2	Catalogue of Minerals sent to Miss Raab – Altered & Exchanged by Hawkins				
J3/2/185	**? Jan. 1792**	**Gregor**		Hawkins	
J3/2/188	15 Jan. 1792	Hailstone	Cambridge	Hawkins	
Unavailable	24 Feb. 1792	Rashleigh		Treba	[see Nov/Dec 1792]
J3/2/190	**12 Mar. 1792**	**Hailstone**	Cambridge	Hawkins	
J3/2/195	30 May? 1792	Hailstone	Cambridge	Hawkins	
5757/1/68	**10 June 1792**	**Hawkins**		Rashleigh	
J3/2/ 196	**16 June 1792**	**Rashleigh**	Menabilly	Hawkins	
5757/1/69	20 June 1792	J. Wyttenbach	Bern	Rashleigh	in French
J3/2/197	1 July 1792	Hailstone	Cambridge	Hawkins	
5757/1/71	10 July 1792	Hawkins		Rashleigh	
J3/2/198	14 July 1792	Hailstone	York	Hawkins	
NHM R Beq. 31/32	20 July 1792	Rashleigh	Menabilly.	Hawkins	

Reference	Date	Author	Place	Recipient	Comments
Missing	*1792*	*Rashleigh*		*Hawkins*	*[2nd letter]*
J3/2/199	10 Aug.1792	Hailstone	Hamburg	Hawkins	
RASH/1/48	13 Aug. 1792	Hawkins		Rashleigh	
RASH/1/49	19 Aug. 1792	R. Phillips	St. Agnes	Rashleigh	
J3/2/86	26 Aug. [1792]	Gregor	Caerhayes	Hawkins	
RASH/1/50	5 Sept. 1792	W. Synnot	Malton, Yorkshire	Rashleigh	
J3/2/203	**14 Sept. 1792**	**Hailstone**	Hamburg	Hawkins	
J3/2/90	16 Sept. 1792	T. Beddoes	Shifnal	Hawkins	
J3/2/206	30 Sept. 1792	Gregor	Caerhayes	Hawkins	
J3/2/93	2 Oct. 1792	J. Wedgwood	Etruria	Hawkins	
Missing	*1792*	*Rashleigh*		*Hawkins*	*re alluvial strata*
5757/1/70	3 Oct. 1792	Hawkins	Chandos St.	Rashleigh	
J3/2/ 209	**17 Oct. 1792**	**Rashleigh**	Menabilly	Hawkins	
5757/1/72	23 Oct. 1792	J. Moyle	Chacewater	Rashleigh	
5757/1/107	?Nov./Dec. 1792	von Trebra	Zellerfeld	Rashleigh	translation
5757/1/73	5 Nov. 1792	Hawkins		Rashleigh	
J3/2/ 213	4-27 Nov. 1792	Rashleigh		Hawkins	
J3/2/219	**24 Nov. 1792**	**Gregor**	Coldrinnick	Hawkins	
5757/1/74	**28 Nov. 1792**	**Hawkins**		Rashleigh	
NHM R Beq. 33/34	**1 Dec. 1792**	**Rashleigh**	Menabilly	Hawkins	
Missing	*10 Dec. 1792*	*Hawkins*		*Rashleigh*	
J3/2/224	**20 Dec. 1792**	**Hailstone**	Freyberg	Hawkins	
J3/2/226	15 Feb. 1793	Gregor	Caerhayes	Hawkins	
5757/1/63	21 Feb. 1793	R Crawshay		Rashleigh	
J3/2/191	22 Mar. [1793]	Gregor		Hawkins	
J3/2/184	[?1792/93]	Gregor		Hawkins	
NHM R Beq 7/8	**4 May 1793**	**Gregor**		Hawkins	
5757/1/73	6 May 1793	Brook Watson	Tournai	Rashleigh	
J3/2/194	11 May [?1793]	Gregor		Hawkins	
5757/1/76	7 June 1793	W. Synnot	London	Rashleigh	
J3/2/231	**4 July 1793**	**Hailstone**	Cambridge	Hawkins	
J3/2/232	5 July 1793	Rashleigh	Menabilly	Hawkins	
NHM R Beq. 35/36	12 July 1793	Rashleigh	Menabilly	Hawkins	
5757/1/78	14 Oct. 1793	von Trebra	Zellerfeld	Rashleigh	
RASH/4/42	24 Mar. 1794	J. Moyle	Chacewater	Rashleigh	
RASH/1/52	17 June 1794	W. Day	York St.	Rashleigh	
RASH1/66	**27 June 1794**	**Gregor**	Caerhaise	Rashleigh	
RASH/1/53	**5 July 1794**	**W. Day**	York St.	Rashleigh	
5764/9	**21 July 1794**	**Wm. Day**	York St.	Rashleigh	
RASH/1/54	18 Aug. 1794	Gregor	Caerhayes	Rashleigh	
RASH/1/55	30 Aug. 1794	Gregor		Rashleigh	
RASH/1/56	10 Nov. 1794	Gregor	Creed	Rashleigh	
RASH/1/57	**13 Dec. 1794**	**C. Hatchett**		Rashleigh	
CC/K/25	**12 Apr. 1795**	**Rashleigh**	Menabilly	Pole Carew	
Missing	*21 Apr. 1795*	*Pole Carew*		*Rashleigh*	*[see 24 Apr. 1795]*
CC/K/25	**24 Apr. 1795**	**Rashleigh**	Menabilly	Pole Carew	
5757/1/80	**21 July 1795**	**C. Lippi**		Rashleigh	

Reference	Date	Author	Place	Recipient	Comments
CC/K/25	27 Nov. 1795	Rashleigh	Menabilly	Pole Carew	
CC/K/25	9 Dec. 1795	Rashleigh	Menabilly	Pole Carew	
CC/K/26	11 Dec. 1795	Rashleigh		Pole Carew	
5757/1/81	20 Jan. 1796	E. King		Rashleigh	
J3/2/134	? Feb. 1796	Wenman	Oxford	Hawkins	
RASH/1/58	19 Feb. 1796	Gregor	Creed	Rashleigh	
CC/K/26	[? Mar.] 1796	Rashleigh		Pole Carew	
C/K/26	12 May 1796	Rashleigh	Lake	Pole Carew	
Missing	*19 May 1796*	*Pole Carew*		*Rashleigh*	*[see 22 May 1796]*
CC/K/26	22 May 1796	Rashleigh	Menabilly	Pole Carew	
5303/23	**26 May 1796**	**W.Synnot**	Mountjoy Sq.	Rashleigh	
CC/K/26	n.d. [?June 1796]	**Rashleigh**		Pole Carew	
5757/1/82	**10 July 1796**	**W. Synnot**	Ballymoyer	Rashleigh	
CC/K/26	4 Aug. 1796	Rashleigh	Mt. Edgecumbe	Pole Carew	
Missing	*two letters*	*Pole Carew*		*Rashleigh*	*[see 26 Aug. 1796]*
CC/K/26	26 Aug. 1796	Rashleigh	Menabilly	Pole Carew	
5304/27	**12 Nov. 1796**	**C. Lippi**	Naples	Rashleigh	
5757/1/83	27 Jan. 1797	J.S. Tobin	Bristol	Rashleigh	
5757/1/84	22 Feb. 1797	J.S. Tobin	Bristol	Rashleigh	
5757/1/85	**15 June 1797 E**	**Gregor**	Creed	Rashleigh	
RASH/1/61	**8 Sept. 1797 E**	**Gregor**	Tregony	Rashleigh	
5757/1/86	19 Oct. 1797	J. Jagd	Milton Abott	Rashleigh	
RASH/1/63	**Sept. 1798**	**R. Hoblyn**		Rashleigh	
RASH/1/62	29 Sept. 1798	Gregor	Liskeard	Rashleigh	
DDR/5304/37	**28 Oct. 1798**	**Hawkins**	Sunbury	Rashleigh	
J3/15/1717	n.d. [?Nov. 1798]	**Gregor**		Hawkins	
J3/15/1678	**1 Nov. 1798**	**Rashleigh**		Hawkins	
RASH/1/64	16 Nov. 1798	Gregor	Creed	Rashleigh	
5757/1/88	**20 Nov. 1798**	**J.S. Tobin**	Bristol	Rashleigh	
RS/12/1	2 Dec. 1798	Rashleigh	London	G.C. Fox	
5757/1/89	**10 Dec. 1798**	**C. Hatchett**	Hammersmith	Rashleigh	
5757/1/91	**17 Dec. 1798**	**C. Hatchett**	Hammersmith	Rashleigh	
5757/1/90	28 Dec. 1798	Wm. Day	Leicester Place	Rashleigh	
5757/1/92	**9 Jan. 1799**	**Hawkins**	Sunbury	Rashleigh	
5757/1/94	**24 Jan. 1799**	**Hawkins**	Sunbury	Rashleigh	
5304/41	**4 Feb.1799**	**Hawkins**	Sunbury	Rashleigh	
RS/12/10	4 Mar. 1799	Rashleigh	London	G.C. Fox	
Unavailable	19 Mar. 1799	Rashleigh		Trebra	*[see 24 Oct. 1799]*
RS/12/8	**26 Mar. 1799**	**Rashleigh**	London	G.C. Fox +	
RS/12/2	**11 June 1799**	**Rashleigh**	London	G.C. Fox	
RASH/4/43	**3 July 1799**	**W. Day**	London	Rashleigh	
5304/45	1 Aug. 1799	Pole Carew	Berkeley Sq.	Menabilly	
5304/46	9 Aug. 1799	Pole Carew	Sonning Hill	Menabilly	
5757/1/95	9 Aug. 1799	Mrs. Forster	Soho	Rashleigh	
5304/47	16 Aug. 1799	Pole Carew	Berkeley Sq.	Menabilly	
5757/1/96	16 Sept. 1799	J.Williams Jnr	Scorrier	Rashleigh	

Reference	Date	Author	Place	Recipient	Comments
5757/1/97	**20 Sept. 1799**	**J. Tobin**	Bristol	Rashleigh	
5757/1/98	24 Oct. 1799	von Trebra	Bretleben	Rashleigh	in German
5757/2/1/1	24 Oct. 1799	von Trebra	Bretleben		translation
5301/1/152	24 Oct. 1799	von Trebra	Bretleben		translation
5757/1/93	**5 Nov. 1799**	**W. Day**		Rashleigh	

+ Part of a series of eleven letters that Rashleigh sent to Messrs. G.C. Fox between Dec 1798 & June 1799

Reference	Date	Author	Place	Recipient	Comments
5757/2/4	13 Mar. 1800	Gregor	Creed	Rashleigh	
5757/2/5	21 Mar. 1800	Gregor	Creed	Rashleigh	
5305/1	26 Apr. 1800	Pole Carew	Berkeley Sq.	Norfolk St.	
5305/2	*10 May 1800*	*Pole Carew*	*Berkeley Sq.*	*Norfolk St.*	
Missing	*24 May 1800*	*Rashleigh*		*Pole Carew*	*[see 28 May 1800]*
5305/3	28 May 1800	Pole Carew	Berkeley Sq.	Menabilly	
5757/2/6	1 June 1800	Gregor	Creed	Rashleigh	
RASH/1/67	7 Aug. 1800	Gregor	Creed	Rashleigh	
5757/1/1	20 Oct. 1800	Gregor	Creed	Rashleigh	
5305/7	**19 Dec. 1800**	**Hawkins**	Sunbury	Rashleigh	

Reference	Date	Author	Place	Recipient	Comments
5305/10	2 Jan. 1801	Rashleigh	Menabilly	Jonathan Rashleigh	
5757/2/7	25/26 Apr. 1801	Gregor	Creed	Rashleigh	
5757/2/8	**10 May 1801**	**Gregor**	Creed	Rashleigh	
5757/2/9	30 June 1801	Gregor	Creed	Rashleigh	
Missing		*Rashleigh*		*Phillips*	
5757/2/11	15 July 1801	R. Phillips	Flushing	Rashleigh	
5757/2/10	19 July 1801	R. Phillips	Flushing	Rashleigh	
Missing	*23 July*		*Rashleigh*	*Phillips*	
5757/2/12	27 July 1801	R. Phillips	Flushing	Rashleigh	
J3/3/264	20 Aug. 1801	Gregor	Trewarthenick	Hawkins	
J3/3/267	**3 Sept. 1801**	**Gregor**	Creed	Hawkins	
J3/3/268	**3 Sept. 1801**	**Rashleigh**	Menabilly	Hawkins	
5757/2/13	15 Sept. 1801	Gregor	Creed	Rashleigh	
5757/2/14	? Sept. 1801	R. Phillips	Flushing	Rashleigh	
5757/2/15	2 Oct. 1801	? no signature	London		re Dartmoor circles
5757/2/3	**15 Oct. 1801**	**Gregor**	**Creed**	Rashleigh	
5757/2/16	17 Oct. 1801	Gregor	Creed	Rashleigh	
5757/2/18-19	17 Dec. 1801	Gregor	Creed	Rashleigh	
5757/2/17	28 Dec. 1801	R. Phillips	Flushing	Rashleigh	

Reference	Date	Author	Place	Recipient	Comments
Missing	*16 June 1802*	*Rashleigh*		*Taylor Combe*	
Missing	*27 June 1802*	*Rashleigh*		*Taylor Combe*	
5757/2/20	30 June 1802	Taylor Combe	Bloomsbury	Rashleigh	
5757/2/21	26 Aug. 1802	Gregor	Creed	Rashleigh	
5305/16	**18 Sept. 1802**	**J. Stackhouse**	Paris	Rashleigh	
Missing	*24 Sept. 1802*	*Rashleigh*		*Hawkins*	
Missing	*1 Oct. 1802*	*Rashleigh*		*Hawking*	*[see 1 Oct. 1802]*
5757/1/102	? 1 Oct .1802	Hawkins	Trewithen	Rashleigh	
Missing	*12 Nov. 1802*	*Hawkins*		*Rashleigh*	
NHM RBeq 37/38	**13 Nov. 1802**	**Rashleigh**	Menabilly	Hawkins	
5757/2/25	**17 Nov. 1802**	**Gregor**	Creed	Rashleigh	
5757/2/22	22 Feb. 1803	Gregor	Creed	Rashleigh	

Reference	Date	Author	Place	Recipient	Comments
5757/2/26	17 Mar. 1803	Gregor	Creed	Rashleigh	
Missing 2 letters	Apr. 1803	Pole Carew		Rashleigh	[see 9 Apr. 1803]
CC/L/36	9 Apr. 1803	Rashleigh	Menabilly	Pole Carew	
CC/L/36	16 May 1803	Rashleigh	Menabilly	Pole Carew	
CC/L/36	27 May 1803	Rashleigh	Menabilly	Pole Carew	
Missing	June 1803	Pole Carew		Rashleigh	[see 6 June 1803]
CC/L/36	6 June 1803	Rashleigh	Menabilly	Pole Carew	
CC/L/36	12 June 1803	Rashleigh	Menabilly	Pole Carew	
Missing	18 June 1803	Pole Carew		Rashleigh	[see 21 June 1803]
CC/L/36	21 June 1803	Rashleigh	Menabilly	Pole Carew	
CC/L/36	26 June 1803	Rashleigh	Menabilly	Pole Carew	
Missing 2 letters	July 1803	Pole Carew		Rashleigh	[see 7 July 1803]
CC/L/36	7 July 1803	Rashleigh	Trehane	Pole Carew	
CC/L/36	13 July 1803	Rashleigh	Menabilly	Pole Carew	
NMM Sow 47/2	13 July 1803	Rashleigh	Fowey	Sowerby	
Missing	14 July 1803	Pole Carew		Rashleigh	[see 15 July 1803]
CC/L/36	15 July 1803	Rashleigh	Menabilly	Pole Carew	
CC/L/36	17 July 1803	Rashleigh	Menabilly	Pole Carew	
Missing	19 July 1803	Pole Carew		Rashleigh	[see 23 July 1803]
CC/L/36	23 July 1803	Rashleigh	Menabilly	Pole Carew	
Missing 2 letters	Aug. 1803	Pole Carew		Rashleigh	[see 9 Aug. 1803]
CC/L/36	9 Aug. 1803	Rashleigh	Menabilly	Pole Carew	
Missing	13 Aug. 1803	Pole Carew		Rashleigh	[see 17 Aug. 1803]
CC/L/36	17 Aug. 1803	Rashleigh	Trewarthennick	Pole Carew	
Missing	25 Aug. 1803	Pole Carew		Rashleigh	[see 29 Aug. 1803]
CC/L/36	28 Aug. 1803	Rashleigh	Menabilly	Pole Carew	
Missing	24 Sept. 1803	Rashleigh		Hawkins	[see 1 Oct. 1803]
CC/L/36	4 Oct. 1803	Rashleigh	Menabilly	Pole Carew	
RASH/1/68	6 Oct. 1803	Gregor	Creed	Rashleigh	
J3/2/290	12 Oct. 1803	Gregor	Creed	Hawkins	
5757/2/27	12 Nov. 1803	Gregor	Creed	Rashleigh	
Missing	Dec. 1803	Hawkins	Dawlish	Rashleigh	
NHM R Beq. 39/40	19 Dec. 1803	Rashleigh	Menabilly	Hawkins	
5305/25	5 Jan. 1804	J. Williams	Scorrier	Rashleigh	
DM1186-Eyles	17 Jan.1804	Rashleigh	Menabilly	Sowerby	
5757/2/28	14 Feb. 1804	Gregor	Creed	Rashleigh	
NHM R Beq. 1/2	14 Feb. 1804 E	Gregor	Creed	Hawkins	
DM1186-Eyles	3 Mar.1804 E	Rashleigh	Menabilly	Sowerby	
RASH/1/69	8 Mar. 1804	J. Sowerby	Lambeth	Rashleigh	
NHM Sow-47/3	13 Mar. 1804	Rashleigh	Menabilly	Sowerby	
5757/2/29	17 Mar. 1804	Gregor	Creed	Rashleigh	
5757/1/106	26 Mar. 1804	J. Sowerby	Lambeth	Rashleigh	
NHM Sow-47/4	28 Mar. 1804	Rashleigh	Menabilly	Sowerby	
NHM Sow-47/5	30 Mar. 1804	Rashleigh	Menabilly	Sowerby	
5757/2/23	2 Apr. 1804	J. Sowerby	Lambeth	Rashleigh	
NHM Sow-47/6	6 Apr. 1804	Rashleigh	Menabilly	Sowerby	
RASH/1/70	7 Apr. 1804	J. Sowerby	Lambeth	Rashleigh	
NHM Sow-47/7	15 Apr. 1804	Rashleigh	Menabilly	Sowerby	

Reference	Date	Author	Place	Recipient	Comments
NHM Sow-47/8	21 Apr. 1804	Rashleigh	Menabilly	Sowerby	
5757/2/24	24 Apr. 1804	J. Sowerby	Lambeth	Rashleigh	
NHM Sow-47/9	27 Apr. 1804	Rashleigh	Menabilly	Sowerby	
NHM Sow-47/10	**5 May 1804 E**	**Rashleigh**	Menabilly	Sowerby	
5757/2/31	8 May 1804	J. Sowerby	Lambeth	Rashleigh	
5757/2/30	**14 May 1804 E**	**Gregor**	Creed	Rashleigh	
NHM R Beq. 3/4	**20 May 1804 E**	**Gregor**	Creed	Hawkins	
DM1186-Eyles	1 June 1804	Rashleigh	Menabilly	Sowerby	
5757/2/32	6 June 1804	J. Sowerby		Rashleigh	
DM1186-Eyles	**13 June1804**	**Rashleigh**	Menabilly	Sowerby	
NHM Sow-47/11	15 June 1804	Rashleigh	Menabilly	Sowerby	
NHM Sow-47/12	6 July 1804	Rashleigh	Menabilly	Sowerby	
Missing	*17 July 1804*	*J. Sowerby*	*Lambeth*	*Rashleigh*	*[see 7 Aug. 1804]*
J3/3/296	**27 July 1804**	**Rashleigh**	Menabilly	Hawkins	
5757/2/34	28 July 1804	John Gould			re Pyrites
DM1186-Eyles	**7 Aug. 1804**	**Rashleigh**	Menabilly	Sowerby	
5757/2/35	23 Aug. 1804	Gregor	Creed	Rashleigh	re thunderstones
5757/1/101	**26 Aug. 1804 E**	**Gregor**	Creed	Rashleigh	
Missing	*26 Sept. 1804*	*Rashleigh*		*Gregor*	
5757/2/36	3 Oct. 1804	Gregor	Creed	Rashleigh	is fragile
Missing	*?*	*Rasheigh*		*Hatchett*	
5757/2/76	22 Oct. 1804	Hatchett	Hammersmith		
5757/2/37	**29 Oct. 1804**	**J. Sowerby**	Lambeth		re meteorites
5757/1/108	**? Nov. 1804**	**Gregor**	Creed	Rashleigh	
J3/3/298	**17 Nov. 1804**	**Gregor**	Creed	Hawkins	
5757/2/38	18 Nov. 1804	J. Sowerby		Rashleigh	note
5757/2/75	19 Nov. 1804	Hatchett	Hammersmith		
5757/2/39	**25 Nov. 1804**	**Hawkins**	Dallington	Rashleigh	
5305/ 20	**28 Nov. 1804 E**	**Gregor**	Creed	Rashleigh	
J3/3/299	**29 Nov. 1804**	**Rashleigh**		Hawkins	to Dallington
Missing	*?*	*Rashleigh*		*Gregor*	
5757/2/69	13 Dec. 1804	Gregor		Rashleigh	
Missing	*2 Jan. 1805*	*Pole Carew*		*Rashleigh*	*[see 3 Jan. 1805]*
CC/L/38	3 Jan. 1805	Rashleigh	Menabilly	Pole Carew	
5757/2/40	**5 Jan. 1805**	**J. Sowerby**	Lambeth	Rashleigh	
NHM Sow-47/28	21 Feb. 1805	Rashleigh	Menabilly	Sowerby	note
RASH/4/44	4 Mar. 1805	Mrs. Forster	Soho	Rashleigh	
NHM Sow-47/13	**25 Mar. 1805 E**	**Rashleigh**		Sowerby	
Missing	*?*	*Rashleigh*		*Gregor*	
5757/2/70	**26 Mar. 1805**	**Gregor**	Creed		
5305/29	**8 Apr. 1805**	**Mrs. Forster**	Soho	Rashleigh	
Missing	*?*	*Rashleigh*		*Gregor*	
5757/2/71	**25 Apr. 1805**	**Gregor**	Creed		
RSoc MS409	2 May 1805	Rashleigh		Sowerby	
5757/1/105	7 May 1805	J. Sowerby		Rashleigh	
NHM Sow-47/14	**26 May 1805 E**	**Rashleigh**	Menabilly	Sowerby	
5757/2/41	**29 May 1805**	**J.Sowerby**	Lambeth	Rashleigh	
5757/2/42	4 June 1805	H. Warburton	Cambridge	Rashleigh	
Missing	*10 June 1805*	*J. Sowerby*		*Rashleigh*	*[see 16 June 1805]*
DM1186-Eyles	**16 June 1805**	**Rashleigh**	Menabilly	Sowerby	
NHM Sow-47/15	20 June 1805	Rashleigh	Menabilly	Sowerby	
Missing	*24 JUne 1805*	*Sowerby*		*Rashleigh*	*[see June 1805]*

Collecting the New, Rare and Curious

Reference	Date	Author	Place	Recipient	Comments
5757/2/44	25 June 1805	Mrs Forster			re 15 Specimens costing £22-10-6d
NHM Sow-47/16	28 June 1805	Rashleigh	Menabilly	Sowerby	
Missing	*29 June 1805*	*Rashleigh*		*Mrs Forster*	
Missing	*6 July 1805*	*Rashleigh*		*Mrs Forster*	*draft re £22-10-6*
5757/2/43	11 July 1805	Mrs Forster		Rashleigh	
5757/2/72	**25 July 1805**	**Gregor**	Creed	Rashleigh	
5757/2/45	n.d. [July 1805]	C.V. Penrife		Rashleigh	re pieces of wood
CC/L/38	1 Aug. 1805	Rashleigh	Menabilly	Pole Carew	
Missing	*? Aug. 1805*	*Pole Carew*		*Rashleigh*	*[see 28 Aug. 1805]*
CC/L/38	28 Aug. 1805	Rashleigh	Menabilly	Pole Carew	
Missing	*4 Sept. 1805*	*Pole Carew*		*Rashleigh*	*[see 10 Sep. 1805]*
CC/L/38	10 Sept. 1805	Rashleigh	Menabilly	Pole Carew	
Missing	*20 Sept. 1805*	*Pole Carew*		*Rashleigh*	*[see 22 Sep. 1805]*
CC/L/38	22 Sept. 1805	Rashleigh	Menabilly	Pole Carew	
RASH/1/71	**22 Sept.1805**	**Gregor**	Creed	Rashleigh	
Missing	*?*		*Rashleigh*	*Gregor*	
Missing	*?*		*Rashleigh*	*Gregor*	
5757/2/46	30 Sept. 1805	Gregor		Rashleigh	
Missing	*8 Oct. 1805*	*Pole Carew*		*Rashleigh*	*[see 10 Oct. 1805]*
CC/L/38	10 Oct. 1805	Rashleigh	Menabilly	Pole Carew	
Missing	*17 Oct. 1805*	*Pole Carew*		*Rashleigh*	*[see 19 Oct. 1805]*
CC/L/38	19 Oct. 1805	Rashleigh	Menabilly	Pole Carew	
CC/L/38	27 Oct. 1805	Rashleigh	Menabilly	Pole Carew	
RASH/1/72	**26 Nov. 1805 E**	**Gregor**	Creed	Rashleigh	
NHM Sow-47/17	5 Dec. 1805	Rashleigh	Minabilly	Sowerby	
Missing	*9 Dec. 1805*	*J. Sowerby*	*Lambeth*	*Rashleigh*	*[see 18 Dec. 1805]*
NHM Sow-47/18	**12 Dec. 1805 E**	**Rashleigh**		Sowerby	
5757/2/73	**19 Dec. 1805**	**Gregor**	Creed	Rashleigh	
NHM R Beq 11/12	24 Jan. 1806	Gregor	Creed	Hawkins	
Missing	*25 Jan. 1806*	*Pole Carew*		*Rashleigh*	*[see 27 Jan. 1806]*
CC/L/39	27 Jan. 1806	Rashleigh	Menabilly	Pole Carew	
RASH/1/73	? Feb. 1806	Gregor		Rashleigh	
CC/L/39	28 Feb. 1806	Rashleigh	Menabilly	Pole Carew	
Missing	*15 Mar. 1806*	*Pole Carew*		*Rashleigh*	*[see 28 Mar. 1806]*
CC/L/39	28 Mar. 1806	Rashleigh	Menabilly	Pole Carew	
NHM Sow-47-19	**3 Apr. 1806 E**	**Rashleigh**	Menabilly	Sowerby	
5757/2/48	8 Apr. 1806	J. Sowerby	Lambeth	Rashleigh	
5757/2/47	11 Apr. 1806	J.Tobin			re strontian sulphate
5757/2/74	**14 April 1806**	**Gregor**	Creed		
DM1186-Eyles	**15 Apr. 1806**	**Rashleigh**	Menabilly	Sowerby	
Missing	*17 Apr. 1806*	*Pole Carew*		*Rashleigh*	*[see 20 Apr. 1806]*
CC/L/39	20 Apr. 1806	Rashleigh	Menabilly	Pole Carew	
5757/2/50	6 May 1806	J. Sowerby	Lambeth	Rashleigh	
5757/2/49	10 May 1806	J. Sowerby	Lambeth	Rashleigh	
Missing	*10 May 1806*	*Pole Carew*		*Rashleigh*	*[see 14 May 1806]*
CC/L/39	14 May 1806	Rashleigh	Menabilly	Pole Carew	
Missing	*9 June 1806*	*Pole Carew*		*Rashleigh*	*[see 16 June 1806]*
CC/L/39	**16 June 1806**	**Rashleigh**	Menabilly	Pole Carew	

Reference	Date	Author	Place	Recipient	Comments
5757/2/51	**17 June 1806**	**Fichtel**	Strand	Rashleigh	
RASH/1/74	24 June 1806	J. Sowerby	Menabilly	Rashleigh	
Missing	*4 July 1806*	*Rashleigh*		*Fichtel*	
5757/2/55	7 July 1806	Fichtel			re Leverian sale purchases
Missing	*8 July 1806*	*Rashleigh*		*Fichtel*	
Missing	*12 July 1806*	*Rashleigh*		*Fichtel*	
5557/2/53	15 July 1806	Fichtel	London		
5757/2/54	18 July 1806	Sheffield			re Forster minerals
Missing	*19 July 1806*	*Rashleigh*		*Fichtel*	
5757/2/52	post 19 July 1806	Fichtel			
Missing	*24 July 1806*	*Pole Carew*		*Rashleigh*	*[see 27 July 1806]*
CC/L/39	27 July 1806	Rashleigh	Menabilly	Pole Carew	
5305/34	7 Aug. 1806	Hawkins	Bognor	Rashleigh	
RASH/1/75	**8 Aug. 1806**	**John Gould**	Penryn	Rashleigh	
5757/2/58	13 Aug. 1806	Woolston		Rashleigh	re Saxon coins
5757/2/56	17 Aug. 1806	Gregor	Creed		
5757/2/57	17 Aug. 1806	J. Gould			Specimens from Godolphin [+ Note from sister P. Gould]
J3/3/315	**21 Aug. 1806**	**Rashleigh**	Menabilly	Hawkins	
5305/35	**8 Sept. 1806**	**Mrs. Forster**	Soho	Rashleigh	
Missing	*15 Oct. 1806*	*J. Sowerby*	*Lambeth*	*Rashleigh*	*[see 24 Nov. 1806]*
Missing	*17 Oct. 1806*	*Pole Carew*		*Rashleigh*	*[see 17 Oct. 1806]*
CC/L/39	17 Oct. 1806	Rashleigh	Menabilly	Pole Carew	
Missing	*19 Oct. 1806*	*Pole Carew*		*Rashleigh*	*[see 21 Oct. 1806]*
CC/L/39	21 Oct. 1806	Rashleigh	Menabilly	Pole Carew	
5757/2/59	30 Oct. 1806	J.G. Children			re The Little Jew; Red Cornelian
5757/2/60	n.d. 1806	Forster	Madrid		re problems re museum collections
5757/2/61	n.d. 1806	Forster	Madrid		
5757/1/100	**Nov. 1806**	**Hawkins**	Bognor	Rashleigh	
Missing	*n.d. 1806*	*Pole Carew*		*Rashleigh*	*[see 15 Nov. 1806]*
CC/L/39	15 Nov. 1806	Rashleigh	Menabilly	Pole Carew	
NHM Sow-47/20	24 Nov.1806	Rashleigh	Menabilly	Sowerby	
5757/2/63	18 Dec. 1806	J. Sowerby	Lambeth	Rashleigh	
J3/2/323	**29 Dec. 1806**	**Rashleigh**	Menabilly	Hawkins	
5757/2/62	31 Dec. 1806	J. Sowerby	Lambeth	Rashleigh	
5757/2/64	n.d. 1806	Fichtel			re box with specimens of indigo
NHM Sow-47/21	Jan. 1807	Rashleigh	Menabilly	Sowerby	
CC/L/40	1 Jan. 1807	Rashleigh	Menabilly	Pole Carew	
5757/2/67	8 Jan. 1807	Gregor		Creed	
5757/2/149	10 Jan. 1807	R. Hewett	Fowey		re lives on Fowey property
Missing	*14 Jan. 1807*	*Pole Carew*		*Rashleigh*	*[see 17 Jan. 1807]*
CC/L/40	17 Jan. 1807	Rashleigh	Menabilly	Pole Carew	
5305/37	**19 Jan. 1807 E**	**Gregor**	Creed	Rashleigh	
5758/2/52	22 Jan. 1807	Rashleigh	Menabilly	Sowerby	re list of minerals sent

Reference	Date	Author	Place	Recipient	Comments
NHM R Beq 5/6	**5 Feb. 1807**	**Gregor**	Creed	Hawkins	
Missing	*n.d. 1807*	*Rashleigh*		*Gregor*	*[see 19 Jan. 1807]*
5757/2/66	11 Feb. 1807	Gregor	Trewarthennick	Rashleigh	
CC/L/40	15 Feb. 1807	Rashleigh	Menabilly	Pole Carew	
CC/L/40	17 Feb. 1807	Rashleigh	Menabilly	Pole Carew	
Missing	*nd 1807*	*Pole Carew*		*Rashleigh*	*[see 17 Feb. 1807]*
CC/L/40	18 Feb. 1807	Rashleigh	Menabilly	Pole Carew	
Missing	*27 Feb. 1807*	*Pole Carew*		*Rashleigh*	*[see 1 Mar. 1807]*
Missing	*27 Feb. 1807*	*Pole Carew*		*Rashleigh*	*[see 1 Mar. 1807]*
CC/L/40	1 Mar. 1807	Rashleigh	Menabilly	Pole Carew	
5757/2/68	17 Mar. 1807	J, Sowerby	Lambeth	Rashleigh	
DM1186-Eyles	21 Mar. 1807	Rashleigh	Menabilly	Sowerby	
Missing	*31 Mar. 1807*	*Pole Carew*		*Rashleigh*	*[see 3 Apr. 1807]*
CC/L/40	2 Apr. 1807	Rashleigh	Menabilly	Pole Carew	
CC/L/40	3 Apr. 1807	Rashleigh	Menabilly	Pole Carew	
CC/L/40	4 Apr. 1807	Rashleigh	Menabilly	Pole Carew	
Missing	*8 Apr. 1807*	*Pole Carew*		*Rashleigh*	*[see 11 Apr. 1807]*
CC/L/40	11 Apr. 1807	Rashleigh	Menabilly	Pole Carew	
CC/L/40	13 Apr. 1807	Rashleigh	Menabilly	Pole Carew	
5757/2/142	22 Apr. 1807	Gregor	Creed	Rashleigh	
Missing	*Apr. 1807*	*Pole Carew*		*Rashleigh*	*[see 24 Apr. 1807]*
CC/L/40	24 Apr. 1807	Rashleigh	Menabilly	Pole Carew	
Missing	*nd Apr. 1807*	*Pole Carew*		*Rashleigh*	*[see 1 May 1807]*
C/L/40	1 May 1807	Rashleigh	Menabilly	Pole Carew	
5757/2/83	1 June 1807	Mrs Powell		Rashleigh	
5757/2/91	**16 June 1807**	**H. Heuland**	London	Rashleigh	
5757/2/89	24 June 1807	W.E. Sheffield	London	Rashleigh	
CC/L/40	8 Aug. 1807	Rashleigh	Menabilly	Pole Carew	
Missing	*n.d. 1807*	*Rashleigh*		*Gregor*	
NHM Sow-47/22	24 Aug. 1807	Rashleigh	Menabilly	Sowerby	
5757/2/98-99	24 Aug. 1807	Gregor	Creed	Rashleigh	
5757/2/102	2 Sept. 1807	J. Sowerby		Rashleigh	
5757/2/161	**7 Sept.1807**	**H. Heuland**	London	Rashleigh	
DM1186 -Eyles	25 Sept. 1807	Gregor	Creed	Sowerby	
Missing	*26 Oct. 1807*	*Pole Carew*		*Rashleigh*	*[see 29 Oct. 1807]*
CC/L/40	29 Oct. 1807	Rashleigh	Menabilly	Pole Carew	
CC/L/40	4 Nov. 1807	Rashleigh	Menabilly	Pole Carew	
NHM Sow-23/141	18 Nov. 1807	Gregor	Creed	Sowerby	
CC/L/40	23 Dec. 1807	Rashleigh	Menabilly	Pole Carew	
5757/2/104	28 Dec. 1807	J. Sowerby		Rashleigh	

5757/2/77-123 contain 23 letters sent by Heuland to Rashleigh between 1 Apr. – 20 Nov. 1807

Reference	Date	Author	Place	Recipient	Comments
Missing (2 letters)	*n.d. 1808*	*Rashleigh*		*Gregor*	*[see 5 Feb. 1808]*
5757/2/107	**5 Feb. 1808**	**Gregor**	Creed	Rashleigh	
RASH/1/41	**15 Feb. 1808 E**	**Gregor**	Creed	Rashleigh	
NHM Sow-47/23	**7 Mar. 1808 E**	**Rashleigh**	Menabilly	Sowerby	
Missing	*n.d. 1808*	*Rashleigh*		*J.W. Williams*	
5757/2/108	23 Mar. 1808	J. Williams	Scorrier	Rashleigh	
Missing	*n.d. 1808*	*Rashleigh*		*Gregor*	
5757/2/143	26 Mar. 1808	Gregor	Creed	Rashleigh	

RP/17/46	**3 June 1808**	**Rashleigh**	Menabilly	John Rogers	
Missing	*4 Aug. 1808*	*Rashleigh*		*Gregor*	
5757/2/141	13 Aug. 1808	Gregor		Rashleigh	
5757/2/117	16 Aug. 1808	J. Carne	Penzance	Rashleigh	re sulphate of lead
5757/2/144	18 Aug. 1808	Gregor	Creed	Rashleigh	
5305/47	Sept. 1808	Rashleigh	Menabilly	Rbt. Ricard & R. P. Carew	
RASH/1/76	**3 Sept. [1808]**	**Gregor**	Creed	Rashleigh	
5305/48	3 Sept. 1808	J. Sowerby	Lambeth	Rashleigh	
5305/40	28 Sept. 1808	Gregor	Creed	Rashleigh	
Missing	*8 Oct. 1808*	*Rashleigh*		*Gregor*	
NHM Sow – 23/140	13 Oct. 1808	Gregor	Creed	Sowerby	
5305/46	14 Oct. 1808	Pole Carew	Antony.	Rashleigh	
5757/2/140	22 Oct. 1808	Gregor	Creed	Rashleigh	
DM1186 B Eyles	31 Oct. 1808	Gregor	Creed	Sowerby	
RASH/1/77	15 Nov. 1808	Gregor	Creed	Rashleigh	
Missing	*n.d. 1808*	*Rashleigh*		*Gregor*	
Missing	*n.d. 1808*	*Rashleigh*		*Gregor*	
5757/2/138	9 Dec. 1808	Gregor	Creed	Rashleigh	
5757/2/139	27 Dec. 1808	Gregor	Creed	Rashleigh	

5757/2/125 – 134 includes 22 letters Heuland to Rashleigh sent between 1 Feb. and Dec. 1808

5757/2/137	**18 Jan. 1809**	**Gregor**	Creed	Rashleigh	
5757/2/136	**11 Feb. 1809**	**Heuland**		Rashleigh	

5757/2/135 -149 includes 6 letters from H. Heuland to Rashleigh sent between 11Feb. and 30 May 1809

Paris (1819:29) refers to	21 Nov. 1811	Gregor		John Rogers	
J3/4/458	**30 June 1813**	**Gregor**	Creed	Hawkins	
RP/17/74	**10 June 1816 E**	**Gregor**	Creed	Rev. J. Rogers	
NHM R Beq 9/10	30 Oct. 1816	Gregor	Creed	Wm. Rashleigh	
NHM Sow- 23/139	**10 Dec. 1816**	**Gregor**	Creed	Sowerby	
DDG/1923/20	**8 Mar. 1822**	**Hawkins**	London	Miss Gregor	
5764/6	**No Date**	**C. Greville**		Rashleigh	memo re collection
5795	No Date	C. Greville		Rashleigh	memo re collection
5757/1/79	n.d.	Rashleigh		Scaddan	memo re localities

Letters Selected from the
Correspondence of Philip Rashleigh,
John Hawkins and William Gregor,
1755–1822

CRO, Truro, Rashleigh Papers: DDR/5300/31
Christopher Hervey to Philip Rashleigh at New College,
Oxford *Leipzig, 14 July 1755*[1]

Excuse my not having wrote to you before . . .

I am now the only Englishman at Leipzig as all the rest went away about a Month or two ago, some one way and some another. My Ld. Villiers and My Ld. Newnham and Mr Whitehead (The author of Creusa)[2] went to Hannover. However, I shall have the pleasure of meeting them again in Italy, for which place I shall set off in a very little Time, that is to say in about two Months or a very little more. I am to stay a Twelvemonth at Rome and I imagine I shall have a pretty large Acquaintance there upon my Uncle's Account.[3] I do not doubt but I shall be excessively pleased with the Country as every body talks a great deal of it. I shall I believe in my Way make a visit to some of the German mines, and if I find any thing of that sort I think may be worth your acceptance, I shall attempt to find a Method of conveying it to you. . . . .

Every body commends the Spirit of my Countrymen in having so quickly raised so formidable a Fleet. I hope from the bottom of my Heart that there will be no War, at least not yet awhile, as it will be very inconvenient to us Travellers, especially as I am in hopes of spending a Year at Paris. . . . .

Notes
1. This is the second of six letters sent by Hervey, a fellow student, to Rashleigh during a European tour he made between September1754 and his return to Cambridge in July 1758; for others see Utrecht (21 September 1754; 5300/26); Rome (15 May 1756; 5300/32); Verona (3 April 1758; 5330/35); ?Tenton (26 May 1758; 5300/34); Clare Hall, Cambridge (4 July 1758; 5300/35).
2. William Whitehead (1715–1785) poet & playwright, his play

Creusa, Queen of Athens (1754) was widely praised but his poetry was considered 'grand nonsense'.
3. This would seem to refer to George W. Hervey (1721–1775), the 2nd Earl of Bristol, who at the time was Envoy Extraordinary in Turin (1755-58).

CRO, Truro, Rashleigh of Stoketon papers: RS/1/910
Lord Edgecumbe to Philip Rashleigh
Bath, Friday 28th December 1764

I had the pleasure of seeing your Brother here yesterday, by whom I learn of your arrival in the West and visitation of Fowey, before your Antagonist got there. I understand he has a letter from Mr. Granville to the Lord Warden, who I know is not in the County, & if he were I do not apprehend he could be of the least [? help] to your Enemy, should he be so inclined. — I hear the young Trefray & Jonathan the Post Man met Mr. C. at Lostwithiel, in order to conduct him to Fowey, where upon his appearance, I hope he will be so little satisfied with his reception, that he will turn tail & pack off again to Town as fast as he came, & if that should be the case, his journey of hope will in the end turn out to our advantage. If my Intelligence be true this same Mr. C. has no very great quantity of cash to throw away but he will be very liberal of his promises in respect to Trade, if that will do.

You may easily imagine my Dear Sir that I am anxious to know how you go on, & therefore hope you let me hear from you soon; I shall stay here till the sixth of January, after that please to direct to me In Grosvenor Street. — I most sincerely wish you success & if you can point out any method for me to assist, you have only to mention it, & you will find me ready to follow any step you think necessary, being very desirous in this, as on all other occasions to prove the sincerity with which I am Dear Sir Yr faithfull & Obed. Servt.

Jones will be with you the latter end of the next Week

[Added Note] Mr. Crockett on 21 Jan 1765 stood for Fowey but was beaten by Philip Rashleigh, who succeeded on the death of Jonathan Rashleigh MP. Crockett bailed in about 5 years later for £6,000.

CRO, Truro, Antony: Carew Papers: CC//0/66/21
R. Pole Carew to Philip Rashleigh   *Oxford, 18 June 1775*

. . .

There is a Rumour that the Parliament will be summoned in July, but you will I believe hardly attend its Call; I sincerely rejoice that you have at Length escaped from a Place you have so little affection for.

CRO, Antony House, Torpoint, Carew Papers: CC/J/9/4
Philip Rashleigh to R. Pole Carew   *Menabilly, 20 July 1775*

. . .

As You have fixed your Tour, at least the beginning of it, I fear you will not wait for any Reply to such Answer as you may give to this, & yet I think it very probable that something may be omitted which ought more thoroughly to be consider'd; but my Bro'r. Charles will endeavour to Recollect whatever he thinks Material. If your Scheem [sic] is any kind of Secret, pray don't tell it me; for I am not fond of being Trusted with such things; but if your Plan is laid, & Publish'd, I should be glad to know in what Quarter of the World you are to be found at certain times, and it will give me great pleasure to hear often from You. Your Sister Pole has writ You that Mrs Parker would Recommend You to her Bro'r. in Spain, if you took that Rout [sic], & I think it would be worth your Accepting if you go into that Country.

The Station you once thought of, that of being in an Ambasador's [sic] Train, I have heard is by no means so desirable as You once expected, being very different to what it was formerly: I find it is now attended with much Expence & Dependance, without any Proffit [sic], & is Represented to me in such a manner as I dare believe would be disagreeable to You, & therefore I mention it for your Consideration before you engage too far. Should I have no Opportunity of Writing You again, I make sure of this for wishing You every Comfort & Satisfaction that Health and Variety of Amusements can Contribute, and if there is any thing I can add towards it you may be certain of having such

CRO, Truro, Rashleigh Papers: DDR/5302/133
R. Pole Carew to Philip Rashleigh
Vienna, 1 January/26 January 1777

I conceived that I had written both to you and to my Aunt Pole
from my Cabin as I descended the Danube, but as you do not
mention the receipt of my letter, and I have heard nothing from my
Aunt Pole I conclude that both my Letters must have miscarried.[1]
Tho' that is a case that seldom happens unless the person to whom
they are addressed is, as I have been, continually changing Place.
This deprived me of Yours which you say was directed to Berne.
Your Last has been a full month in reaching me owing to the
Badness of the Roads which are buried in Snow and have been so
for near Two Months indeed the first Snow that we had came in
the Middle of Nov'br. At present we have some appearance of a
thaw, but are by no means to hope for so speedy a conclusion of
the Winter.

. . .

I know not whether or no I can be of any Service to you at
Fowey. If I can I have reason to hope that you will make every use
of me that one Friend can of another that must ever be indebted to
him; or that a father can of a Son. I am a little upon the Horns to
know what has passed between my Cousin Charles & Mr. Elliott,
& whether he thought proper to deliver to him my Letter or no; I
begin to think that it was written too coldly, or too shufflingly – I
suspect that you do not state the Matter fairly, when you tell me
that a <u>Young</u> Lady lately come to a great Fortune &cc. &c. besides
I remember that that Lady all young & blooming as she is, had a
great Tendre for Menabilly –

I had already picked up a couple of small Specimens from the
Gold Mines in Transylvannia and had proposed to myself when
the Season will permit to make a Trip to the mines of Kremnitz
and Shemmatz in Hungary where my Pleasure will greatly be
augmented if I am lucky enough to pick up any Thing worth your
Acceptance. This Country is unfortunately so distant from any
Water carriage that I shall be obliged to limit myself to such Pieces
as I can dispose of myself.

. . .

The Dutchess of Kingston[2] has been here above two months.
Her Intention on arriving was to have been presented as such to
the Empress, but Sir R. Keith absolutely refused to present her
under that Title. At which she thought proper under Pretence of

Illness to keep to her Room, that she might have an Opportunity of affecting by some more sure Means her Purpose. This however has not succeeded; she was therefore driven on Friday last to the astonishment of the whole World to make a visit in public to one of the first Minister's ladies at whose House, the assembly was that Night. A very unusual step, and contrary to the Rules of the Place for no one is supposed to come into this Company (which consists of all the first Nobility) till they have presented at Court; last night she was at the Opera for the first time. How she means to conduct herself for the future, God knows. Her Behaviour &c. affords some [illegible] to the Conversation of this Place, which is other-wise [illegible] form enough.

Notes
1. From these comments it appears that several letters from both correspondents went astray.
2. Elizabeth Chudleigh, Duchess of Kingston upon Hull (c.1720-88); a beautiful bigamous courtesan, the cause of several scandalous escapades in British society.

CRO, Truro, Rashleigh Papers: DDR/5302/143
R. Pole Carew to Philip Rashleigh   *Vienna, 19 April 1777*

I am this Instant returned from the Mountains of Hungary after an Absence of Six Days only as the Companions of my Journey were in a great Hurry to leave them as soon as they arrived. Upon the whole I was disappointed in what we had to see there; we went down into the most considerable tho' not the richest mine in this Country . . .

The Collection which I told you of, proved to be rather a Collection of the different Chrystallisations of these Countries, than of the Metals, of which there were only a few Specimens and those I think not remarkably Curious, such as they were however the Professor Scopoli to whom they belonged was so obliging as to let me have one or two of each . . .

I met with by accident some other tolerable Bits of Gold & Silver Ore, and one Small specimen of Native Gold, some of the Silver is rich; but none of these are equal to the two small Pieces of Native Gold which were given me before my Journey & which came from Transylvania, from whence come all the richest Ores. Their Gold in the other Mines is for the most part invisible, and when any thing richer appears it is bought up at such immense Prices since our Countrymen travel this way, that they are soon disposed of in so much that I found an almost desert Country with regard to what I went in search of, such as they are. However I believe I shall make them my fellow travellers till I get to the Sea Side, & before that happens I hope to add something to them from the Mines of Saxony and those of Hartz. I shall not receive them here until the four & twentieth of next Month, when I will send you a Catalogue of them, but what made me take up my Pen in such a Hurry was, to give you an Account of the Chrystallisations &c.. They are all from the Mines of Hungary and Transylvania, and consist of a variety of Specimens of Spar, Quartz, as prettily chosen as I ever saw, many very Curious Pieces.

The present Possessor of them Mr. Scopoli,[1] at present Professor of Mineralogy and Conseillour of the Mines at Schemnitz, but named to the Professorship of Natural History & Botany at Pavia, means ... to dispose of them, and has already proposed them to the Academy at Pavia. As you mentioned to me Metals only and Semi-metals, I could not venture to treat on this Subject. His Price for them with his Ores, which are not very numerous, is fifteen hundred florins, about a Hundred and Sixty Six Pounds 14 shillings at the rate of Nine florins to the Pound Sterling, but as the Course of Exchange at present is against us does not amount to more than Eight florins & 44 Kreutzers it would amount to something more; a Sum which you may think perhaps too great for a Purchase of Matters which have no real Value. The Professor published last year a Book on the Subject in which he has given a Catalogue, and Prints of the most Curious parts of his Collection which he has since considerably increased so that he has as he tells me near four Hundred additional Specimens. I shall contrive to send you if possible by means of Sir Robn. Keith the Book, by which you will be well able to judge if the object is a tempting one.

The Specimens are not large, but I think very [page torn with loss]and well chosen. The Engravings tho' not very well done are I think pretty faithful. I believe him a very honest Man & have no doubt that many Amateurs would give the Money he asks for them, at the same Time the Sum appears considerable for things of no real Worth, tho' they are perhaps payed for at a much greater Price in detail; he has also a Collection of all the Birds & Beasts of this Country, stuffed and tolerably well done & some other Natural Curiosities. He would dispose of the whole together for

Two thousand florins, Chrystallisations, Metals, Birds, Beasts &c. But I do not think the latter is so much of an object to you. I shall be glad of an Answer immediately, as I have promised to give one as soon as possible.

. . .

Note

1. Giovanni Antonio Scopoli (1727–88); Professor of Mineralogy at Schemnitz; served as physician to the mercury miners at Idria; became Professor of Chemistry at Pavia and published *Crystallographia Hungarica* (1776), describing specimens collected on a visit to Hungary. His collection was donated to the Museum at the University of Pavia.

CRO, Truro, Rashleigh Papers: DDR/5302/149
R. Pole Carew to Philip Rashleigh   *Vienna, 2 June 1777*

[Contains List of 53 Mineral specimens with Latin descriptions]
The Specimens are all Small as you may suppose when I tell you that all together Box packing & all they do not weigh above Six or Seventy & Twenty pounds. I fear they will not answer Your Expectations but they are the best I could get. The two best small specimens of native gold I reserve to send to you from the Northern Sea but as I hope to pick up some other minerals in Saxony & at the Mines of Hartz, I thought it would be better to get these shipp'd off from Trieste, as well as to avoid the inconvenient researches of Custom House Oficers in the different Territories thro' which I should have passed and you will in all Probability have them sooner by this means than if you waited till I reached the northern Coast, the carriage from hence to Trieste is but [ten] Pounds and when once on Ship board the Expence is Trifling.
    . . . [further brief reference to Scopoli's Collection]
    I had an Opportunity of seeing the Whole Process of the Separation and Refining the different metals when at Shemnitz. The Ores being first stamped and Pounded and then washed as cleanly as possibly in Order to separate as much as may be the Earthy and Stony Particles, is thrown into a kind of Furnace or oven where a Gentle fire serves to carry off the Arsenic & Sulphur. After the Operation they add a certain quantity of lead in Order to vitrify the Earthy Particles which remains and which are now put

into a fierce fire to melt down together all the Metals that may be contained in the General Mass. The Gold, Silver, Lead &c. come out in one mass and the particles of Earth & Stone become vitrified & separate themselves from them. You are no doubt acquainted with the remaining process required for separating the different metals from each other. My Paper will not permit me to enter into the details at present. I will endeavour to let you know when the minerals are shipped & please to direct your next to me Messrs. Charles Heritiere de Feu, David Splitgerber Banquiers â Berlin.

CRO, Truro, Rashleigh Papers: DDR/5302/148
R. Pole Carew to Philip Rashleigh   *Vienna, 12 June 1777*

Your Box Dear Sir set off this day for Trieste where it will arrive in Six. It is addressed to the Care of the Count Zinzendorff, Governor & President of the Intendance at Trieste with a long catalogue of Title to whom a friend of Mine has written from hence to desire he will see it put into the first English Ship that may sail from there and give us some Acct. of it as soon as it departs: you shall not fail of hearing from me upon the first Notice I have of it. I preferred sending it by Trieste that I might make Room for whatever Fortune may throw in my way & at the same Time avoid the Importunities of Custom House Officers on the Road. I took Care to have it properly sealed here to prevent its being opened before Embarkation. My only Fear is that you will no be satisfied with them when they arrive, but you know how seldom one gets any thing Curious from a Trip like this from our Mines.

    . . .

    The Inland carriage from hence to Trieste is paid; so that you will only have the water carriage to pay which cannot be much as the Box does not weigh above 27 Pounds.
á Dresden á 16 de June 1777
This much have I written from Vienna Dr. Sir a Month Since. I delayed at that Time the sending my Letter being in Hopes to have been able at the same time to give you an Acct. of its Embarkation & Now hope if it is yet arrived; ... I left Vienna the ninth of the month and having stayed three days at Prague, arrived here last night. Our stay here will not exceed a Week; we have not yet seen a Soul! – the only objects worth Notice on our road here have been the several Fields of battle of the two last wars

between the Austrians & Prussians, the Principal of which luckily for Travellers, lay on the Road. – This Town & that of Prague bear very evident Marks of the Sieges which they underwent from the King of Prussia. He battered down a great Part of these Towns but the Military do not seem to give him great Credit as a Besieger tho' they allow him all possible Merit in the Field.

As your Letter can not probably reach Berlin till I have left it and I know not where I shall be stationary till I get to the Hague, I will beg you to direct next to me Chez Moliére et fils Banquiere a la Hague. Your letter should be directed I believe by Hand. I draw near to the Mines of Freyburg.

CRO, Truro, Rashleigh Papers: DDR/5302/150
R. Pole Carew to Philip Rashleigh   *Dresden, 3 August 1777*

I must sit down to give you some short Account of what I have been doing in the Mountains. My Acquisitions have not been very great, but perhaps I may have established a Correspondence that may be agreeable to you. I bought one fine Piece of Vitrified Silver, and others of Native and Dentrific which are tolerably good. One Grain of Diamond Tin from Bohemia, and a Piece of Cubic Fluor, I purchased here; the other trifling things which you may find in the Packet which I prepare for you, have been given me as Presents; I am uncertain whether the French Description has been added to the German, but I was unwilling to unpack them when once secure, and you are too well acquainted with the Ores themselves to need any other than the names of the Mines from Whence they come are all I believe, except the single Bit of Tin, from the Neighbourhood of Freyberg, about eight Leagues from hence, and the rich Ores are I believe from the Mine called <u>Himmelsfürst</u>, the Prince of Heaven.

The Case here is as in Hungary, there are two or three Collectors prowling about the Country, that pick up every thing that is curious; that it is no easy Matter to get at a minutes warning what one wants; among others is a Mr Wolff whom you may perhaps know, as I believe him to be one of your London Salesmen. But they have an Institution at Freyberg which is convenient for those who wish to make Collections, of every present Produce of the Saxon Mines. There is an established academy with Professors in Chemistry & Natural History, in Mechanics and Mathematics &c.

under whom are several young Practitioners, who are obliged to make Collections of every Produce of these Mines, which they sell, and every different Piece of Ore is estimated and valued according to a certain Rule by the Set of people sworn for that Purpose. A Collection of this kind costs between nine & ten Pounds, but amongst them one cannot expect to have the very rare Pieces, as the Horn Silver of which I have not been able to get any thing. Tho' I saw a very beautiful small Piece in the Collection belonging to the Academy which is a very good one.

As they are not very rich in English Ores, the Baron de Heynitz, who is the President & Chief of them all, proposes to you in the name of the Academy to make an Honourable Exchange of their Ores for English Ores; and in Case the Offer should suit you he begs that you would begin by sending them an Envoy of yours (for it seems they have several Times being deceived by Promises of this kind, particularly by the Swedes) and that you will name the Ores that you would choose to have, whether a whole Collection in General, or Particular Pieces, for tho' they should not have them in their Mines, if possibly they may have duplicates from other Parts they will be ready to furnish whatever they can afford, according to the Value of your first Envoy, and I believe they are People whom you may very well trust, and that they are very much in Earnest about it; the Baron Heynitz, is of a very good family & well known here, his Brother is lately appointed by the King of Prussia to the Direction of all his Mines.

The Piece of Vitrified Silver which I shall send you, should weigh 27½ Lots, or half ounces of their weight & is rated at about 15d per Lot, so that one is no great danger of being cheated, nothing being paid for the Ideal Worth except in very rare Pieces, which they themselves should pay dearly. They will also name the English Ores that they would prefer, or take the whole collection as you think fit – and they do not desire that you should trust them so far as to send the Whole at once, but a Part only, that they may show you in what Manner they would deal with you in return. – In case the things should be agreeable to you, they beg that you will direct what you may send a Minr. Monsieur Octavio Rudolph Schrödem Negociant á Hamburg pour le Compte de Madame de Heynitz neé Singlingen â Freyberg as Madame de Heynitz is an acquaintance of the said Merchant.

Inclosed I send you the Extract of a Catalogue of Fossils which are to be sold at Dresden, you will not be able to form any Idea from it of the value but it was all I could get. – the Professeur asks 1500 Dollars for the whole Collection. He tells me that Wolff has been bargaining with him these two Years for it, but offers him only 1300 – his only Reason for selling it [as] I understand it , that being appointed to one of the Places about the Electoral Cabinet of Natl. History, he is not suffered to keep a Collection of his own. . . . But I have no Doubt he would sell it for something less, as I had only Time to ask him the simple question, & no opportunity of feeling his pulse farther & I am told he wants the Money. Six Dollars make about the Pound Sterling, & now the Course of Exchange is against us, five Dollars & three Qrs; had it been at Six, 1000 dollars would have made about £166-13s-4d, but at present something more. I am by no means judge enough of them to be able to advise you to the Purchase. The Number of Specimens is marked opposite each Division in the Catalogue I think the Collection is a good one more solid than delicate in the choice of specimens, but how nearly it may be worth that sum I have no idea.

. . .

Berlin, 9 August 1777

P.S. I am just arrived at Berlin.

Your letter of the Third of July is this Instant brought to me.

I fear you will be much disappointed in the Specimens that I have sent you as I cannot say that there are any rare Pieces amongst them. I shall endeavour if possible to know by what Ship they go. . . . I have directed them to you at Mr. Watson's. What I have with me at Present will travel with me to the waterside. – I have just now delivered them from the Custom House of this Place; at a very small expence. When I have been at the Hartz, If I should be able to go there I will let you know your whole Expence, I have not ruined you as yet! I wish I had found more Opportunity of laying out your Money.

CRO, Truro, Rashleigh Archive: DDR/5302/154
R. Pole Carew to Philip Rashleigh
At The Hague, 28 September 1777

On my Arrival here Dear Sir I was much pleased to find your kind letter; and at the same Time one from the Gentleman I had written to in Bohemia, with the Account of the departure of the Box from Trieste and the name of the Ship & Master. They are on Board the

Thames Capt. Thomas Newstedt master, who thought of sailing about the twentieth of July as they make a kind of coasting trade. It is possible he may not arrive as soon as you expected.

I am really ashamed of what it contains particularly since I have [seen] so many beautiful Cabinets, tho' not much Gold. But considering the difficulty I was under of getting any Thing I hope you will pardon the unsuccessfulness of the Attempt. I was provoked to see that the finest Piece of Needle Antimony, which I had been promised in Hungary had not, either from forgetfulness, or from Wilfulness, been sent me. Scopoli had promised to give me the half of one fine Piece he had. It is possible he might repent of his Promise, tho' I think upon the whole he dealt very fairly.

Saxony seems to be the only resource for Purchasers for there one may get any of their present Productions at a rate which is taxed by their College or Academy; tho' I find that our Friends of Hartz accuse them of Taxing highly. I hope you will not find that I have paid much to dearly for the few Specimens that I was enabled to get there. – I saw only a part of the Saxon Collection and that imperfectly, being rather intent on what was to be got than seen of their Saxon Earths. I know they have large Collections. . . .

I forget whether they have any Petrifications, or not, nor do I know whether the Earths & Christals of other Countries would be acceptable to them or not, but I should think certainly the latter, if of curious form, and I think you can send them some that they are acquainted with, particularly those beautiful incrusted Chrystals, and indeed, I believe, they will be glad to have any [of] the Produce of England as their Intention is to make a general Collection of all the Mines of the World and I think they are rather Poor in our Mines.

I have seen I think larger Clusters of Fine Diamonds in all those Collections which come from the Mines of Bohemia than any I ever saw in England. I have no doubt that Mr. de Heynitz will let you know exactly what they would have.

. . .

I believe you would have liked some Twenty Specimens of Poetschs Native Silver of his Malachites & of his Pyrites, but the whole is rather a Good than an Elegant Collection. If Mr Heynitz should not understand English enough to carry on the Correspondence I will with great Pleasure become an intermediate one, and I am sure you cannot hesitate to make use of me being assured of how much Pleasure I have in endeavouring to convince you of my Gratefulness.

Since my last I have been at the Hartz and had the Mortification to see two very fine Collections, and not to be able to get the least bit. The Proprietor of the best of them, which is valued at 2000£ was unluckily not there, or it is possible he might have given me some Pieces of which he had duplicates – but the Master of the Mines who had the other Collection assured me that they neither of these sold a Bit and that their only Method was that of Exchange and that unless I had something to offer in that Way, it would be impossible for me to deal there and that two or three Collectors monopolize every thing that is Curious that the Mines produce. By this means Woulff and a certain Forster become entirely Masters of this Commerce. The Second Collection is a very good one particularly rich in Silver Ores and he assures me contains a Specimen of every Mine in the World. He asks seven Hundred Pounds for it and warrants two hundred and fifty Pounds <u>worth</u> of Silver in it. –

...

CRO, Antony House, Torpoint, Carew Papers: CC/J/9/6
Philip Rashleigh to R. Pole Carew
Menabilly, 16 October 1777

Abundance of Thanks are due to You my Dear Sir for contributing so largely to my Collection of Minerals. Had you Expended Ten times the Sum you have on my Account for these Matters, be Assured I should have repaid it with Pleasure, & if my Pocket had been loaded as much in proportion as my Head is with these [Nugs], I should have been Mad enough to have taken some of the Offers which have been made you for whole Collections:

Woulfe[1] & Forster are the only People in London, who make Tradeing Voiages [sic] for a Profitable Account; I have dealt with both of them, the latter is unreasonably high in his Demand for Specimens any way Curious, I have had two or three good things from him in Exchange, but suppose Mr. Heynitz would have given me ten times as much; Woulfe is much more Reasonable, but he will not part with his best Specimens as he wants to Sell the whole together; his Collection is the best I have seen by far, but kept in a very dirty manner, He says it is the best in Europe and asks 1200 Guineas for it. I hope you have had some Amusement in your Search for the things You have procured me, & I conclude if I had been of your Party, I should have thoroughly despised the little Collections of this Country: What Size do their Specimens generally run to? Did you observe many pieces of White Tin Diamonds? Woulfe sold a Single Crystal of this Sort for 8 gs. it was very perfect & I suppose Weigh'd 3-oz.

From Scopoli's not sending the Neidle Antimony he promised you, I suspect other things would have been found wanting, if attention had not been given to the packing. Did you observe any of the Mineral we call Mundic among the Collections? You see what a Number of Questions you have put, by having answered others, but I will dismiss the Subject & Expect the Boxes.

. . .

Partridges are Remarkable scarce all over this Kingdom, I have not killed 3 for the Year. I have been in Dorsetshire to Shoot Pheasants, in some places they are as plenty as in France, I kill'd 4 Brace last Monday at a place call'd France near Blandford, where Mr. Portman was so kind to carry me for a Days Divertion [sic] we kill'd in all 7 Brace of Cock Pheasants in 3 hours: I return'd home this Evening.

My Sister Gould has Innoculated her two Young Children, as the Small Pox was broke out in their Neighbourhood. . . .

Should You send any Boxes or other things to England for yourself or Friends I do not think it a good way to order them to be left at the Custom House till call'd for; as we have several ingenious Gentlemen who can Personate others upon occasion & the People at that Office are very free in their Examination of the Contents, & not very careful in re-packing. I have begun a Correspondence with Baron Heynitz, but as he is a Dignified Man. I do not know his proper address, should any inconvenience arise from the want of Linguist in our Correspondence, it is very probable I shall accept your profer. Pray let us know what stay you make at the Hague & where you proceed next.

Note
1. Peter Woulfe (1727–1803); English chemist, who with his brother John became a mineral dealer in both London and Paris.

CRO, Truro, Rashleigh Papers: DDR 5302/162
R. Pole Carew to Philip Rashleigh

a La Haye, 24 March 1778

I am quite ashamed of my heedlessness at one Time no date at all,
at another the wrong month, this does not speak as the man of
Business; tho' I cannot help laughing within myself at the Excess
of my Stupidity, as I well remember that I had taken the pains to
write the last in large & legible Characters to convince you that I
meant to be more exact for the Future. I will however flatter myself
that I am less Blunderheaded with my other Correspondents, &
for the very Reason perhaps that I pay less attention to it.

. . .

I am much obliged to you for a Box full of Commissions w'ch
arrived the day before Yesterday. I might have told you what pistols
I preferred, these will do very well. – as a further Proof of the extent
of my Recollection I must own to you that I am uncertain whether
or no I mentioned to you that I was desirous of purchasing the
London Chronicle from the beginning of our unhappy Troubles.
I think from the Beginning of 1775 & continuing it on; it might
be sent regularly to Antony, unless you know of any Friend that I
might oblige by the Reading of it till I return, in a perhaps distant
Period, . . . – I would be glad also (& you will say that I am
inexhaustible in giving Commissions) of Almon's Parliamentary
register[1] from its Commencement, with the Continuation of it, to
undergo the same Fate as the Chronicle. . . .

. . .

Amid our distracted Scenes at Home, I received some Comfort
from the spirited Address of the House of Commons this Mg on the
Communication of the French [ambassador's] Insolent Paper, may
it be the united Voice of an injured People, & I fear nothing from
the Wiles, nor the Power of a rancorous irreconcilable detestable
Enemy; I would not see that Carthage destroyed, least we should
fall to pieces ourselves by our domestic Broils, when our foreign
Enemy was no more, but I w'd. have their Panic Faith punished,
tho' I like them better now that they have Courage enough to
declare themselves, than when under the Mark of Friendship they
did us every Injury in their Power. The pressing Circumstances
of the Times hasten that Mask from them, fearing that England
should in good Earnest reconcile herself to her Colonies, she has
taken that step w'ch. she thought might still prevent it by declaring
her Connexion with America; she has talked big in hopes to

encourage the one & to brighten the other. But later, Posterity will cry Shame on the Americans, if they hesitate to break so un-natural a Bond, they cannot be the Allies of the French, if they have any British Blood in them, & can but cool Reflection succeed for a while to the heated rage which hath dictated such a Step, they must return to a Mother Country, who opens her willing Arms to receive them. I am transported when I think of this anxious Subject. —

The Opposition are not I fear aware of the great detriment they do their Country by laying open its nakedness by pointing out its every weakness, & by cavilling at every best intentioned Step of the Minister, meerly [sic] because it comes from the Minister. They put Swords into the Hands of our Enemies, for not a Word that it is said in Parliament but is read in every Court of Europe & particularly those Parts w'ch are a Satire on ourselves, for to any merit our Misfortunes, the whole Tribe of Gazetteers throughout Europe (a Powerful Troop) are our professed Enemies, we have taught them to rail at us, & they do spit their Venom, that it makes one Sick with Anger. You find me a little warm on the Subject, it is impossible to be otherwise, at this distance from the Scene of Action. I am daily witness of the bad Effects of the Discussions of those Abusive Speeches that are made in so intricate Moments. May we but join Heart & Hand in the Cause we are entered on & I have the Surest Hopes that England yet shall triumph over all its Foes & make France rue the day that she so wantonly provoked the Lion's rage. She has not the least Credit; their Friends the Dutch won't trust them for a Stiver.

Note
1. John Almon (1737–1805); book and pamphlet seller; radical political journalist & supporter of Wilkes; contributed to the *Gazetteer*; became proprietor and editor of the *General Advertiser* in 1784.

CRO, Antony, Torpoint, Carew Papers: CC//0/66/24
R. Pole Carew to Philip Rashleigh
á la Haye, 5 Janvier 1779

CRO, Antony, Torpoint, Carew Papers: CC/J/10/88
Philip Rashleigh to R. Pole Carew
Menabilly, 25 January 1779

[These two letters discuss Tithes, the Church, the Clergy and the value of Money]

CRO, Antony, Torpoint, Carew Papers: CC/J/10/191
Philip Rashleigh to R. Pole Carew
Menabilly, 2 September 1779

From the Various Reports in Print & Conversation You are scarce able to Credit anything. In the Place of the English Fleet, we have lately been Entertain'd with seeing the Combined Fleets of France & Spain on our Coast; Yesterday Morning our Fleet return'd having been kept at the Mouth of the Channel by strong East Winds; a few Hours after the Enemies Fleet appear'd likewise. The disparity of Numbers must be Ballanced by the Skil [sic] & Resolution of our Sailors, but 80 to 40 are such odds that every thing is to be Apprehended; & England once Subdued on the Sea, let other Nations look about them, & when too late lament the Strength & Power of the Family Compact; & being on this Occasion so Unjustly Exercised, what Nations will think themselves safe, if this Power thus Combined should please to Disturb them.

Plymouth has been greatly Strenthen'd lately several Batteries have been Erected, particularly one behind Crimble Passage House, by which Ld. Edgcumbe has lost some Trees: Camps are Form'd about Maker as well as Plymouth, & the whole Country is Arming for its Defence. The Gentlemen of this County have Proposed to Raise 1000 men at their own Expense, to Serve for three Years, be Paid by the King, not to go out of the County unless there is an Invasion, & the Officers to be Named by the Subscribers & Approve of the King; which Terms his Majesty has consented to. General Haviland & Sr. Wm. Draper have the Command at Plymouth.

. . .

Baron Heynitz has sent me a Box of Minerals which are Arrived in the River Thames; I expect some good Specimens among them, though I have poor ones of most part of his Catalogue: he has desired me to send him some particular Minerals, & among the rest he says '*des echantillons du Roc et des Ganges dans lesquelle se trouvent vos Minereaux*'. I do not know what he means by Ganges; will You Interpret it for me. We are in such continual hurry about the Fleets that I have not had time to send your Sister Sally's Account

CRO, Antony, Torpoint, Carew Papers: CC/0/66/30
R. Pole Carew to Philip Rashleigh
Hague, 12 October 1779

. . .

I hope you will be satisfied with Baron Heynitz, & that he will have treated you with ye same Liberality, which occasioned his exclaiming on ye Pleasure & Astonishment w'ch. was expressed on ye Arrival of your Minerals at Freyberg. — Gangue signifies merely the Mother Stone or Rock to which the Metal is found fixed in the Mine.

. . .

Paul Jones you will have heard is come into the Texel with ye *Seraspis* & *Countess of Scarborough* as his Prizes, the Fight which those two ships sustained agst. Jones's Squadron, consisting tho of one 50 Gun-ship, one 36 Gun Frigate, one 32 & one Brig of 12 [,] does them & their Country the highest Honour; the *Seraspis* Captain Pearson was hooked by his Anchor to ye *Bon homme Richard* an old French East India Man made into a 50 Gun Ship for three Hours & the Muzzles's of their Guns touched during the Whole Time; one of the Frigates was during the whole Time laying at his Stern & raking him fore & aft, tho' he could not bring a single gun to bear on him & it was this Vessel that did him the most Injury & obliged him to strike after the loss of 140 or 150 killed & wounded & after Summoning the *Bon homme Richard* to yield, which he must infallibly have done, had he not been thus supported by the other Frigate, as he went to the Bottom the next morning before they could get out all the Wounded; as far as I can find, the Loss aboard Jones's Ship is as great 306 killed & wounded. The Fight between the *Countess of Scarborough* & the

2 other ships was in ye mean Time very warm tho' unequal, their Loss considerable tho' not in ye Proportion of the other two. Jones & the French Captain Cotineau of ye *Pakas* of 32 Guns are upon bad Terms together owing to the latter not having shown any great forwardness to fight; Captain Pearson who is still Prisoner on Board, says that if the day had lasted, he should have taken the whole Squadron, as it is, he perhaps distinguished himself as a brave and gallant officer.

You will observe that this Squadron of Jones's came out of L'Orient at ye Moment or a day or two before the combined Fleets came into the Channel, & was destined to make a Diversion & to harrass [sic] the Coasts to the West, North & East while the French & Spaniards pushed us to the Wall as they fondly hoped to the South;

Jones was then evidently destined for Texel & that for two Ends; they have all along affectedly called his Squadron the American Squadron & Jones, the American Commodore, & I have seen Certificates given under his Hand to Master's of Ships w'ch he has ransommed, where he stiles himself 'The Honourable Paul Jones, Esquire, Commandant in Chief de l'Escadre Americaine en Europe'.

All this is done to give certain Reliefs to American Affairs in Europe & they were sent into Texel to embarass [sic] the States General, & to widen the Breach between England & Holland, by Salutes, giving Succour afforded, Stay permitted, Rebel Flags &c suffered to fly in their Ports, &c on some Sides, & the Complaints w'ch the English Embassadors [sic] might be obliged to make to reclaim the Prizes brought in by Rebels & Pirates, (Jones being a Subject of ye King's) by the Demand of Jones's Parson, which by the Treaties he was authorised to make, &c. &c. In Short in ye unhinged State of this [Intervention] the French had fair Hopes of bringing it to a Quarrel & indeed the Field is a good one; that this is their Intention & that they hoped by this means, perhaps to push the Dutch to some <u>actual</u> avowal of ye Americans, is Evident, since tho' Nothing was more simple nor more expected than that they should declare themselves under French Commissions w'ch w'd at once put an End to all Dispute; they persist in calling themselves American, & one of ye French captains let the cat out of ye bag, by saying he knew very well what embarassed [sic] them at the Hague, it was – said He, because we will not declare ourselves French. Another Object they had in view was to escort the Dutch Ships loaded with Naval Stores for France, w'ch have long been laying at Texel & this was to have been done during ye Confusion in the Channel, but Jones has played his Part & the combined Fleets have not played theirs. We are to see if ye Second Representation will be better executed. – Oct. 15 1779

CRO, Antony, Torpoint, Carew Papers: CC/J/10/139
Philip Rashleigh to R. Pole Carew
Menabilly, 28 October 1779

In Answer to your favour of the 12th Inst. I shall send You an Acct. of the Principal Sums Subscribed towards the Provisional Regiment of 1000 Men; It is generally thought they will cost nearer 15,000 than £12,000, in Raising & Subsisting before they are Complete; till which time they are not to be taken into Publick Pay. Beside the Subscriptions Sir Fr. Basset & St. John St. Aubyn agree to raise two Companies which will go a great way towards the business, but I do not believe many others will be found to part with their Money as these Gentlemen do; nor do I know any Gentlemen who has such Abundance, unless Mr. Hawkins's Trustees have made a Bag for him. Notwithstanding these Offers I do not believe 12,000 £ will be Raised, & when Raised I do not see where the Officers will come from; Subalterns are much Wanted in our Militia, therefore I think the New Regiment will be in the same State .—

Future Ages must certainly be Astonished at those Nations who have any Colonies of their own, Joining with those belonging to other Kingdoms in Severing them from the Alegiance [sic] of the Mother Country; but if All Europe are United against us in Declaring America Independant, [sic] I had rather this Claim should be Acknowledged by the general Voice of All Europe, than that France should claim the whole Merit, if it is a Merit. But if other Colonies should hereafter make the same Claim what can their Mother Country alledge [sic] against it the President is made & Approved on by themselves.

Paul Jones certainly meant to Draw the Dutch into a Declaration, but if a Friendly Power Acknowledges & Countenances those who are at Rebellion with their Neighbour, such an Act must take off the Mask of Friendship, which can never remain with those who Violate another by Encouraging Acts that tend to Maim & lop off its Limbs.

. . .

Your Definicion [sic] of Gangue answers Exactly what others have Construed it. The Specimens that Baron Heynitz & Mr. Charpentier have sent, are of the midling [sic] Class, they are very Acceptable as some of them are better Specimens than I had before but none of them Capital. I shall send him one more Box of very fine Specimens which I collected this Summer in the North of England.

[List of 24 Names of the Subscribers for raising 1000 men = Total of £3293"17"9]

[List of 15 Names of the Principal Subscribers for conducting The Tinners to Plymouth = Total of £929-10]

There are many other Places have Subscribed towards Volunteers for the defence of their respective Towns in Particular & their Neighbourhood: but in all the Subscriptions throughout England the Placemen & petitioners who ought to have been most Liberal have been rather Sparing of their Money upon such an Occasion. Our Fleet is again Sail'd, & it is said have orders to go off Brest & see if the French will face them. The Odds are much against us.

Messrs. Watson & Rashleigh have been very fortunate in geting [sic] their Ships home Safe from Halifax with large Remitances [sic] —

When You have Settled the Plan of your long Journeys, pray let us know which way you Steer. The disposition of all Europe seems to take off much from the Pleasure of Traveling [sic]. My Brother talks of Settling with a Lady, and only waits for a Comfortable Living to Fix at.

CRO, Antony, Torpoint: Carew Papers: CC/0/66/38
R. Pole Carew to Philip Rashleigh   *Hague, 11 April 1780*

You have made me happy by your Declaration relative to the present sitting members for the County. Nothing I own would be so agreeable to me as the peace of it, the Seeds of Dissension which were sown by the last General Election produced very nauseous Plants, & I could wish to see them trodden down. Those Scenes are however likely to be repeated with greater Violence Seven Years hence, we must then do the best we can to prevent it. In the mean time I am highly obliged to you for your very kind & candid Frankness to me on the Subject.—

I should always vote strongly against any Limitation of the

Power of acting of Members of Parliament; Nothing can be more contrary to the Genuine Spirit of our <u>well educated</u> & <u>enlightened Constitution</u>. There exists in G. Britain a certain Class of Gentleman who are brought up, instructed, & informed in a Manner fitting to enable them to consult for the Good & Advantage of their Fellow Subjects, to become the Legislation, of the People in <u>General</u>. If instead of these, we are to receive our Laws from the Coblers [sic], Tinkers, & Excise officers of a certain disproportionate Number of Indifferent Towns, woe be to the Ruled! It is then that the Other Parts of the Kingdom, our great Manufacturing Towns, who send no members & who might justly say, they are not represented, in short the Consequences of it are too obvious to you as well as to myself to be dwelt upon.

The States General of the United Provinces, are just in this case, the Consequence of which is they are a Body mearly [sic] existing for the Form & Late Business is in fact done in the separate Provinces, & in each Province Resolutions formed from the Deliberations of each Town Council, generally composed of a set of very ignorant & illiterate Fellows; & their Productions are very highly tinctured with their Origin. —

When I say that I do not think the Influence of the Crown sufficiently great, I speak to the present Moment, when most certainly Faction has reared its Strength to a dangerous & almost ungovernable Height; Crisis of this Importance gave Dictators to the Romans, & require in my opinion, extraordinary Powers of Authority in the Chief Magistrate with us; I am still, however in Hopes that this Fermentation will subside of itself; Innovations are dangerous, & in Times of Tranquillity I should be sorry to see the Executive Power increased by an Iota; but I am sorely grieved also to see the necessary Exertions of Government daily hampered & obstinated by a worthless set of Incendiarys, to see England, the only honest Man amongst nations, traduced & blackened by her own inconsiderate & frequently unprincipled Offspring, It is difficult to form an Idea of the Effect of their foul Language, throughout the Continent, without having been daily Witness of it; they alone furnish Argument to all our Enemies against us, & the Speeches of Opposition are continually cited upon us by all the French Productions, as Proofs of our Evil Designs & reprobate Measures &c.. It is in Moments like these, that the Influence of the Crown, should be lawfully increased by the firm Adhesion, of the Worthy & Independent, unhappily many of those whose Intentions are the purest, become unwaringly the Tools of Faction.

— but I am impertinently troubling you with my Preaching on a Subject where I have only to listen to the Voice of Your Instruction – sure am I however that you will not be displeased with me for delivering to you my Sentiments undisguised –

CRO, Antony, Torpoint: Carew Papers: CC/0/66/40
R. Pole Carew to Philip Rashleigh

Copenhagen, 4 July 1780

I was honoured two Posts ago with Your letter of the 10th Ult. & congratulate You on being got into the Country to breathe a purer Air & in more tranquillity than you would have done in London: I sincerely hope that much vigour will be shown in punishing those who have endeavoured so fatally to disturb the Security of its Inhabitants & who carried perhaps their designs to the most treacherous Lengths. I was at first induced to think it was only the Mad Work of a Mad Man, who had inflamed a mad people, & I had despatched him to bedlam, but later Accounts seem to insinuate other Views, Money Given, &c.

I am just got so far in my long projected Tour towards the North, & as I shall probably see the Mines in Sweden, I shall be glad to receive your Orders relative to any Specimens of ore that you would wish to have in case I am so lucky as to meet with those you wish for. You will be so kind as to name those which you prefer, & I will make it my Business to search them out & that I may receive your Commission in Time be so obliging as to write by the return of the Post & direct to me chez Mons'r Wroughton, Envoie Extraordinaire de la Majesté Britannique auprés du Roi de Suêde à Stockholm.

It is possible that when I reach Gothenburg I may think it worth while to go forward to the Silver Mines in Norway, & in that case I shall venture to purchase for you should any thing very curious offer. – A Native of Iceland has made me an offer of a Collection of the Various Stones of his Country, the only Expence, which they will occasion is that of the Transportation. If they should be an Object of curiosity to you, I will accept the Offer & if the Commission is copiously executed, I would then beg to have Specimens of such Pieces as would afford duplicates this Commission cannot be executed in less than a Twelvemonth I understand there are no Minerals in the Country, at least no mines worked, but a great variety of Stones, some of which of the finer Sorts, as the Jasper, Agate etc. The Chief Mines in Sweden are Iron & Copper.

. . .

Yesterday & the day before arrived in the Road before this Town 15 Russian Ships of the Line & 4 Frigates. They are going in Three Divisions, the One into the Mediterranean, the other off Lisbon & the Coast of Spain & the third to arrive in the North Sea for the Protection of their Commerce. I am Confident they have not above a Third as many Merchant Ships out of the Baltick. They are to return to Petersburg to Winter, which will be no easy Matter for these ships destined for the Mediterranean.

CRO, Antony, Torpoint, Carew Papers: CC/J/11/32
Philip Rashleigh to R. Pole Carew   *Menabilly, 20 July 1780*

The Rioters who lately did so much Mischief in our Metropolis are now trying and many of them Executed & others Condemned: it is a Extraordinary thing that an Unarmed Mob should do so much Mischief unmolested, & no Person of any Consequence appeared to Head them, except Ld G.G. who seems to have been the Speaker on Religious subjects at several Meetings of the lowest Class of People, and was become an Enthusiast in that Cause; he is not yet tried, but under Confinement in the Tower, & it is said charged with High Treason.[1] You can have no Idea of the Ruin & Desolation this Mob created before the Cityzens recover'd their Astonishment: Messrs Watson & Rashleigh have for sometime past engaged with several other Gentlemen in a Horse Military association; my Bro'r was with me during this Disturbance, & Mr. Watson Mounted Guard for several Nights & Days; everything at present seems Quiet, but the Military are still Quarter'd in several parts of London & the Change cover'd with Straw for their beds, which looks as if further Mischief was apprehended, but I see no likelyhood of Danger now the Inhabitants have Recover'd their Senses.

Your Bror Edward was in the Midst of the Bustle, & saw the Gaol of Newgate, Ld Mansfield's & other Places on Fire, at a very small distance from the City you would have concluded the whole to have been in Flames.

. . .

You may depend I should not omit to fulfil your injunction of Answering you favour, . . . when it so much concerns the kind offer you make me of procuring those articles I am most desirous of. I am less acquainted with the Production of the Swedish Mines than any other Country. I shall therefore only give you a few general directions such as all Crystalline Regulus Figured Ores of Copper or Iron will be Acceptable. Looking Glass iron Ore of which the best Steel is made, Iron Ore with Asbestos, both from Dannemora; The Tungsten of the Swedes, something like our White Tin Grains, on Garnet Stone; Red or Blue Crystallized Copper Ore, or fine Malachites. Should you Visit the Mines in Norway, you may be able to procure me some beautiful Silver Ores, I have only 3 or 4 Specimens of the common sort of Native Silver from that Country, & wish very much for some fine pieces, unless at an Extravagant price.

I know nothing of the Stones of Iceland, but if any thing Curious in Figure, Colour or Crystal should be produced in that Country they will certainly be Acceptable, & you may depend on having any part you please. As you have thoughts of going to Russia, if you Visit the Mines of that Country some very fine Malachites are found in them, resembling short Iceacles [sic] of Green Velvet, & many others such as I dare say you have seen in many Cabinets, I have some pretty good small specimens from that Country; they have a more Curious species of Lead ore there than in any other place I have heard of. It is Red Crystallized Lead ore almost Transparent, I believe it is very rare, this is found near Cathrinebourg in Siberia, I have a bad Specimen from thence, & should be very glad of a good one if it comes in your way. I am likewise told Horn Silver Ore is found there, what I have under that name from thence is not the right sort, it should be soft enough to admit a Pin being stuck into it. I have as You desired mention'd some of the Principal Things I want, but like all, other Collectors, anything Curious in the Mineral Kingdom will be Acceptable, either Metals, Semi-Metals, Crystals or Fluors; Perfection in the Points & Edges of all Crystallizations is a Material circumstance.

I have sent Baron Heynitz another very large Box of English ores &c. which I hope he will receive safe. There have lately been several Foreigners Collecting in this Country, a Baron Lining is now in some part of Cornwall & said to be Recommended by St. Joss. York. I have not seen him, & therefore conclude he has no Recommendation, without which Strangers are liable to Suspicion. Baron Pominouski[2] has likewise been in this County lately to collect Minerals but I do not find either of these Gents have been successful. Don't object to the largeness of any Crystals if Clear or Perfect, or with Skirl Hair or Moss.

Be assured I shall be well pleased with any Purchases You make for me, & likewise think myself happy in the business being undertaken by a Friend whose Judgement I can depend upon. If any Ship comes from these Places to Falmouth the box may be directed for me to the care of Mr. Carne Merchant in Falmouth, if sent to London Messrs. Watson & Rashleigh will be answerable for it. I hope you will excuse my Trespassing so much on You, but such an Opportunity seldom offers.

Added: 'I most heartily wish All the maritime Powers would adopt a Code of Laws for Trading in times of War. I think it might be done for the Advantage of all or be established as a Law of nations.'

Notes
1. The riots referred to are the five days of the Gordon Riots that began on 5th June 1780 – see C. Hibbert, *King Mob: The Story of Lord George Gordon and the Riots of 1780* (London, 1958) and also comment in Uglow, *The Lunar Men* (2003), 338-9; for eyewitness accounts by Susan Burney of these riots see Constance Hill, *The House in St. Martin's Street, being Chronicles of the Burney Family* (1907), 257-8, and C. Harman *Fanny Burney: A Biography* (2000), 153-5.
2. Probably Baron Podmaniczky (1772–1833); Hungarian aristocrat and mineralogist; his collection was acquired by the National Museum in 1842.

CRO, Truro, Rashleigh Archive: DDR/5757/1/7
R. Pole Carew to Philip Rashleigh
                                        Stockholm, 13 October 1780

Tho' I have taken much Pains & spent a good Deal of Time in executing the Commission which you were so kind as to honour me with. Yet I am very fearful lest you should not be satisfied with the Manner in which I have hitherto acquitted myself: & that for two reasons, the First that I have not been able to meet with any Fine Pieces of Native Silver, which I think you were particularly desirous of purchasing, & the Second that after Reflection I think I have paid very Dear & put you to a great Expence for what Minerals I have got together. But in fact I was obliged to take as a Favor what I have procured; & was too far advanced with Professor Engeström upon that Footing to be able to retreat with Common Civility. All I can say is that If you should think I have been extravagant, or should you be already provided with specimens of what I send you, or be indifferent about them, I shall then have no objection to them myself.

You will receive directed to yr. Care of Messrs Watson & Rashleigh, Two Boxes. The one containing 232 Specimens of Ores which I have purchased from Mr. Engeström (the same who translated Cronstedt's Chemical Mineralogical Book into English). If the Professor has cheated me I am sorry for it, indeed he was fair enough to own that he esteemed his own Trouble & Expense about them as much or more than the value of the Ores, as many of them are foreign to Sweden – & he had taken much Pains to get them here & has since laboured in writing Catalogues, packing &c. In Short all this is to tell you that he made me pay him 100 Riks Dalers Specie for them, or according to the present course of Exchange with Brokerage &c. Twenty-five pounds Sterling, which I really think an Enormous Sum now I have got the Minerals & only congratulate myself that I did not put you to the Expense of 50 Dalers more, which the Professor would willingly have done, tho' he assures me, that I have these much cheaper than any other Stranger has procured them. You will judge of that when you see them.

In the Second Box are 49 Specimens of Ores &c. which I picked up myself at the Mines, which as they cost me little or Nothing & may be worth the Carriage, I would beg Your Acceptance of. – I cannot say much for the Beauty of the Specimens in General, but they were the best I could procure & I have been frequently directed in the Choice of them, by the variety of the Mixtures, or by the Place from which the Ores may have come, which stamp now & then a Value of Rarity upon them. I shall be obliged to send the Catalogues to my Cousin P[eter] Rashleigh by the Post, to prevent its being of any use to Persons who might open the Boxes, & I shall leave Directions here that he may be advertised of the sailing of the Vessel which carries them in order to preventing any confusion at the Custom House. – I have got a Specimen of Horn Silver which appears to me pretty Good, but the Chrystallisations are so small that it would be difficult to submit it to the Proof of a Pen. – You will find amongst other Things some Specimens of Serpentine Stones from Saxony, & Swedish Marbles. I knew not whether they are matters of any Curiosity to You, if not, I shall very willingly take them off your hands. –

Mineralists & Chemists here are not agreed about their Tungstein or Heavy Stone. You will find 3 different Specimens. The one from Lorraine, the other from Bohemia, & the third of this country which Mr Engeström asserts after Cronstedt to be the true, or at least to be that which Cronstedt denominated Tungstein – tho' Engeström gives that appellation to the other two as well, & indeed from their Weight they seem to deserve it, but both Cronstedt & Engeström require a Basis of Iron to form the Tungstein, whereas the famous Professor Bergmann shewed me another Species much like that of Bohemia, which contains no Iron, & therefore he asserts that Iron is not essential to it. If the Specimens of Asbestos arrive unhurt, I think you will be pleased with many of them, they are in great variety, mixed with Iron &c. – You will receive likewise many Iron & Copper Ores from Russia & different parts of Germany – some good Specimens of Mica, Cobalt, Bismuth &c., and two small specimens of Malachite but I hope to procure you better in Russia.

The Looking-Glass Ore is esteemed here merely an Accident of a Water &c. which has flown over a polished, as it were, the surface of a pretty rich ore, but is by no means looked upon as a Proof of the best Iron, nor of that of which the best sheet is made, tho' in fact the Ore must be tolerably rich to put on this Appearance, & it is a pretty general Rule in the Iron Mines that the Richest Ore is also of the best Quality. – You will receive some specimen of this; tho' not I think very extraordinary. – In fact there are very few Collectors in this Country, & the Swedes attach themselves very prudently to the knowledge of yr. different varietys [sic] of Minerals &c. & put themselves to no great Trouble to procure beautiful specimens of any Thing. Chrystals are scarcely attended to by them & their Mines seem to produce very few.

. . .

One Thing I forgot to mention which is the manner in which the Swedes draw Maps of their Mines, which is preferable to any thing I have seen & my Affection for Cornwall has induced me to purchase one of them to show the manner in which they are executed, tho' in Truth they are expensive things. A very small one has cost me four pounds Second Hand – of a large Mine they will be not less than 10 or 12 Pounds – but they give a better idea of the Manner of working the Mines &c. than any I ever saw. The Sections are Parallel to the Horizon, as well as Perpendicular to it & every Bottom has a Section. I reserve myself the Pleasure of shewing you this when I may have the singular Satisfaction of taking you by the hand. . . .

[On an Accompanying Slip] I should think that a map of the Great Mine of Zaprun would be a proper Acquisition for All Souls Library, if Peter Rashleigh is of the same opinion. I can easily order one to be made. The Price as above 10 or 12 £. There are some other curious Books in the mechanical Line to be procured here as Thunberg's Method of Working under Water at Carlsnöna – Chapman's Ship Building &c. which I think very well worth their having a proper Library of Books.

CRO, Antony, Torpoint: Carew Papers: CC/J/11/33
Philip Rashleigh to R. Pole Carew in St. Petersburg
Menabilly, 18 November 1780

By your esteemed favour of the 13th Ult. rec'd last Post, I fear I have Engross'd too much of your Time in pursuit of Subjects You are but little Interested in, but I am for that reason the more Obliged to You. Whatever success you have had, the means you have taken for procuring fine Specimens of Minerals has been the most reasonable & likely to obtain them: I depend as much on your own Judgement as upon the Great men who are Stiled Professors of the Science, they frequently descend into the Minutæ of no use; however there are many Eminent for their knowledge, and You seem to me to have Selected such for your Advisers. Be assured my Dear Sir I shall be Exceedingly Pleased with the Collection you have purchased for me of Mr. Engestrom: for though I have in the last two years increased my Collection exceedingly. Yet I dare say you would think it very deficient to those you have seen. I have had a small Collection from Russia in which Dr. Guthrie presented a piece of the famous Native Iron from Siberia, among others were some small pieces of malachite & some of the Wood Mineralized with Copper or changed into Copper Ore, which I am told abounds so much in some parts of Russia that a Whole Forrist [sic] overthrown & changed from Wood into Copper Ore is to be seen in some part of the Empresses Dominions: should You meet with any Mineralists in that Country Pray Enquire into the fact, as I am rather an Infidel.

I dare say the piece of Horn Silver you have got for me is a fine

Specimen, those Crystals are never large. I am told this Ore is found in Russia, but doubt it. There certainly is red Crystallized Lead ore found there which I have only a poor Specimen: it is found near Catherinaburgh. You seem to have fix'd the Coldest Season for Traveling [sic] in the Coldest Climate. I should think Russia at this time of year would only Exhibit Views of Ice & Snow, & that You would be wholly confined to Domestic Life.

I hope Mr. Engestrom will send the Boxes in some neutral Ship. The Crystals I have rec'd from Foreign Countries have been exceeding bad, Except a few things from Saxony: The Hartz is the best place I know of for Crystallizations of all kinds, particularly the red Ruby Silver Ore which I have not been able to get with fine Perfect Crystals.

Cornwall & Derbyshire are very Rich in Crystals of Quartz, Fluor & Spar, in the latter County is found a Substance like Spun Glass & others like Milk White Feathers finely Curl'd; Pray have you met with any thing of this discription [sic], some have try'd it & call it Gypsum, I cannot bring it to such a consistence. I have some fine Specimens of it.

I have greatly increased my Cabinets & seem as if I should soon want another Room.

. . .

CRO, Antony, Torpoint: Carew Papers: CC/J/11/36
Philip Rashleigh to R. Pole Carew in St. Petersburg
Northumberland St., London, 23 February 1781

Least my former Letter should be lost by Accident in these dangerous times, I write a few Lines to say I readily accept the Proposals from Mr. Pallas of Exchanging Russian & Siberian Minerals for those of this Country, and that I will endeavour in the Course of the ensuing Summer to procure such Specimens as he is most desirous of obtaining; some of them are not to be had, the Mines which produce them being out of work.

I should be glad to know if Mr. Pallas is well furnish'd with the variety of Spars and Fluors from the Northern parts of this Country as I have some duplicates which would be acceptable to him, if he has not got them: I have also some tollerable duplicates of the White sort of Minerals I mention'd formerly & which are not to be procured at present, it is a sort of Gypsum.

Our Miners are become so Expert in Manufacturing their Specimens & so Extravagant in their Demands there is no dealing with them, but I can send Mr. Pallas as curious Specimns as any he can return me from Russia or Şiberia. I am not desirous of the variety of Stones which turn to no use, unless their Elegance in Colour or Crystallization make them Valuable; my chief desire is to procure Specimens of the different appearances of the Mettals [sic] & Sem-Mettals with their Crystallizations, & all the very Beautiful formations of metals, Spars, Crystals, & Fluors: I do not run into Earths, Clays, & Sands, which would extend my Collection beyond my Limits; I find it very difficult to confine these objects of amusement within reasonable Bounds, the connection which Metals have to other matter makes some of them necessary.

In the Cornish Mines we never find Spar & very seldom Fluor. In Derbyshire both Spars & Fluors abound; the Lead Ore is Generally found in Limestone, Tin Ore never – Mr Pallas mention's some kind of Lead ore found in Cornwall which I think is not to be procured, I have never yet seen any Yellow Lead Ore found in that County; But unless Mr. Pallas is particularly desirous of these specimens from particular Mines, I shall be able to furnish his Cabinet with them from others.

I have sent several letters with a second very large Box of Minerals to Baron Heynitz, but can hear neither from him or his Substitute Mr. Charpentier though I have Accounts of the Box being safe deliver'd to his Friend at Hambro. I shall expect a few Capital Specimens in return; the last they sent me were good specimens but not very fine, but a sufficient Ballance for those I sent them at first.

. . .

My Bro: Peter is about fixing his Abode in Kent and in the Spring will probably take a Partner for Life, having fix'd upon one for that End. In his Travels this year in Yorkshire he has picked up a piece or two of remarkable Slate with Vegitating Mundick on it resembling Embroidery like branches of Oak, such as I never have seen; but it is a misfortune in Mundicks that they are very subject to Decompose.

I forgot to mention that I have no good Specimen of the cellular Iron Ore, or that which resembles the Cauliflower. I am Oblig'd to You for the Account of the Petrified Wood impregnated with Copper & Vitriol, yet I cannot help suspecting this Matter to have been Originally Wood, tho' I have heard of branches of Trees being impregnated with Silver & Copper. Pray what language has

Mr. Pallas writ in on what Subjects? Having exhausted my best Duplicates for Baron Heynitz it will at least be the end of the Summer before I can procure such as I wish to send Mr. Pallas under your recommendation.

CRO, Antony, Torpoint: Carew Papers: CC/J/11/38
Philip Rashleigh to R. Pole Carew in St. Petersburg
Menabilly, 13 April 1781

We have had so little of your Company in this Part of the World that I can scarce guess whether you will be surprised at the contents of this Letter or not. I have frequently recommended Matrimony to your Consideration, & therefore You may conclude I had no Objection myself to that state of Life, but Numberless Obstructions have hitherto prevented me from Joining Hands with one who has long Possessed my Heart; though it has been my fate to spend many Solitary Years without a Companion, it has not been my Inclination, some of these Obstructions being Removed, will probably be the Means of making me Your Uncle in the Course of this Summer by an Union with your Aunt with whom I have Lived in the most intimate Friendship even before you was Born; I think we know so much of each others Tempers & Dispositions as to Render a Prospect of Happiness for the few Remaining Years of Life, even though we have no Prospect of being Blessed with Children, but Content will be the Means of looking over Misfortunes which cannot now be Remedied, & make up for a Number of Deficiencies.[1]

. . .

The Minerals from Mr. Engestrom are safe in my Custody, & many of the Asbestos Specimens Exceeding pritty [sic] & I believe very rare; many of the other Specimens are New to me, so they will make a great addition to my cabinet. One of the Specimens I cannot find, it is that in the Catalogue Lapis ponderosus albus martialis, Minera Stanni alba impropria dicta. This was a piece I should have prefer'd to many of the other Stones, but I believe by some Accident was omitted to be sent.

Duplicates of Foreign Minerals are frequently very useful, by enabling me to Exchange with others which is the best & Cheapest way of having a fine Collection. You say if I think you have been Extravagant, or if I am indifferent about them, you should have no Objection to them yourself; Neither of these Circumstances exist, but if you are the least desirous of having the duplicate You have certainly a fair Title, & I will reserve many of them for You, if you will give me directions so to do. I have an Engagement for another Exchange besides Mr. Pallas, but this will enable me to assist your Friend Mr. P. if he is desirous of Specimens from our Lead Mines. I hope soon to hear from You on that point; if he is not well provided I shall send him some things that must Please him. I have bought a Cup of the Bristol China for him which I shall send with the Minerals. That Manufactory is totally knocked up, which I wonder at, as the Materials are Cheap & the China allow'd to be the best of English Manufactor; this being the Case, I have purchased a Tea Set, being willing to have this Production of our Moorstone.

Note
1. Rashleigh married Carew's Aunt Jane Pole a year later on 17th April 1782.

CRO, Antony, Torpoint: Carew Papers: CC/J/11/39
Philip Rashleigh to R. Pole Carew in St. Petersburg
Northumberland St., London 27 April 1781

Having made an Excurtion into Hampshire for the Easter Holydays where I rec'd your two kind Letters dated 12/23 March & 16/27 of the same Month for which you have my Respectful acknowledgments, & to which you should have had an earlier Answer by the last Post, but many things prevented it & I hope the short delay will not be material.

[Several paragraphs dealing with family matters & discussing Livings & Carew's financial affairs]
 I still expect to hear my Box of Minerals got to the Right owner, but if I do not hear that soon I will trouble you on the Subject when you get to that part of the World; but I have my Suspicions of a little Deceipt [sic] about them, but not from your Saxon Friends.
 I am much Obliged to you for introducing me to a Correspondence with Mr. Pallas; I have rec'd his Letter & Memorandum, & inclose an Answer: the hints he gives about his Collection will be very useful to me in selecting Specimens for him. I am not well

enough acquainted with the French Language to Read it with satisfaction.

The Box from Mr. Engestrom is safe Arriv'd. & after some difficulty clear'd from the Custom House, who would not grant it to me on the usual application by Petitioning. The Duty on these things is ad Valorum, which must be Sworn to, & the Value being Ideal renders it very difficult to ascertain, & if the Commissioners chuse to add 10 Pr.Cent they have a right to pay the Money & take the Goods; however the Box is safe in my Custody, but by what means it got out of the Custom House I know not. The Specimens of Asbestos are very fine, the Mica of a Green Colour in Calcareous Spar is very Rare, & some of [the] Crystallizations very Curious & Perfect; many of the other Specimens are different to what I have & will be a Considerable addition to my Collection: I do not think there were many Elegant Specimens among any of the Ores, but some of them are Curious & not Common. I should have tempted the Gentleman with a Sum of Money for his Drawer of Silver Ores as you say they are very fine. I wish I may be able to send Mr. Pallas the things he wishes for, I shall endeavour to give him Satisfaction if I can. The Post is at the Door.

CRO, Antony, Torpoint, Carew Papers: CC/J/11/40
Philip Rashleigh to R. Pole Carew in St. Petersburg
Menabilly, 25 June 1781

Your very Obliging letter of the 7/10 May gave me more Pleasure than you can easily conceive & the kindness you express demands my grateful acknowledgement; I hope you will never have cause to change your sentiments, as it will always be my wish &endeavours to promote a mutual Friendship between our families. Your Aunt still continues a good deal Indisposed with a Violent humour about her Head & Body; Dr. Gould saw her this Morning, says there is no Danger, but it will require time to get rid of it; he advised a Milk & Vegitable [sic] Diet, with some other Medicines, which he hopes will carry it off in a Fortnight. But this is an unfortunate time for such a Complaint.

Should you receive this at Petersburg You may tell Mr. Pallas I have look'd out some Specimens of our Minerals for him, & that I am going to the Mines this Week to see what I can pick up for him. I shall send him some Lead Ore which I think very good & some of them very Elegant. I do not recollect to have seen many beautiful Specimens from the Russian Mines, except some of the Malachites; I own I long for the Piece you mention, but the enormous Price alarms me; If it is a large square Lump without any fine velvet Surfaces, or other beautiful Appearances I should not think it Valuable, but if has an extended Surface of velvet or Sattin Green, without being interrupted by pieces being broke in the middle; or if it is Stallactical like Icicles, or otherways beautiful, I should probably be tempted to Purchase it; but it is impossible to be any Judge without seeing of it, but you may be assured I shall be well pleased with whatever You do about it; but I think from your Acct. of the other Specimens & the Crystallized Red Lead Ore, that I should like them at the price they Ask. I think from Mr. Pallas's Memorandums, I am acquainted with what things will suit him, & shall Endeavour to procure as many of those things he mentions as I can.

Should you correspond with Mr. Engestrom, I wish You would mention that his No. 108 *Lapis Ponderosus albus Martialis, Minera Stanni Alba impropria dicta* – was not to be found in the Box, & as it is a Specimen I want, I should be glad if he has an Opportunity that he would send it.

In a few Days I shall expect your Authority for Selling the next Presentation of Drewsteington by the return of one of the Letters of Attorney I sent You, in the mean time I shall be looking out for a Purchaser; & will get as much as I can for it. – I shall do nothing without your direction notwithstanding the Powers you may give me by the Letters Of Attorney, unless any unforeseen accident should make it Necessary.

. . .

[This is My] Last to Petersburg.

CRO, Truro, Rashleigh Papers: 5303/16
R. Pole Carew to Philip Rashleigh
No. 47 New Bond St., London, 28 May 1782

I have been favoured with Your Two Letters of the 16th & 20th Inst. & return you my thanks for their Contents.

. . .

I am told that almost all the Lord Lieutenants were averse to the idea of arming the People, a Measure which more than all others must tend to increase the disorder of this very disorderly Country. I do not find it is likely to be very warmly entered into, unless where it is as dangerous indeed as any where, in the City of London, & perhaps among Charles Fox's Rabble at Westminster, whom willingly arm to support him. He may be Fox Populi, a Man of the People, but he never can be a Popular Man. — he is the most undignified Minister that ever spoke in the House, & has lowered his Country more in one Fortnight's Administration, than he will ever be able to raise it, by either War or Peace which he has talked of so much & so improperly.[1]

It is very certain that a great Man at the Admiralty received Ld. Cranston, who brought the News of Rodney's Victory,[2] in a very scowling Manner & upon his asking for a 50 Gun Ship he was told there were a great many People to be served & tho' it is a rule scarcely ever departed from but by the present Lord, to give a ship to the first lieutenant of any of our King's Ships which has taken an Enemies Ship, & Ld. Cranston as the Admiral's Captain would certainly have had the Command of one of the vacant ships in the West Indies, if Rodney had not thought he sent him on a better Errand.

The very extraordinary Measure of Rodney's Recall will be very frequently in the Ears of those who advised it, & it is said that Keppel stood alone in insisting upon it.[3] No one can persuade himself that they will push the Fatal Step to the utmost, but suppose they will or have recommended to Pigot[4] to serve under Rodney; I do not find any Grounds for this conjecture. Had they named a Howe, a Barrington, a Kemperfeldt to succeed him, there was some Excuse to be made but —

. . .

Notes
  1. At this time Fox was involved in several Parliamentary battles and was particularly hostile to the King but a great friend of the Prince of Wales – see S. Ayling, *The Life of Charles James Fox* (London: John Murray, 1991), Chapter 7)
  2. Rodney: a further reference to his exploits, particularly the Battle of the Saints where he captured the French Admiral de Grasse; subsequently received thanks of Parliament & was raised to the peerage.
  3. Augustus, Viscount Keppel (1725–86); Commander of the Grand Fleet, 1778; First Lord of the Admiralty, 1782-83.
  4. Hugh Pigot (1722–92); Admiral; made Commander-in-Chief of

the West Indies to supersede Rodney, 1782. MP for Penryn (1768-74), Bridgnorth (1778–84).

CRO, Truro, Rashleigh Archive: DDR/5757/1/23
R. Pulteney to Phillip Rashleigh
Blandford, 23 December 1783

Permit me to renew my Thanks to you for the agreable present you made me of Cornish Fossils; the inspection of which has given me much Entertainment & Instruction, & they will fill up many important [pages torn with loss].

I am particularly pleased to see the <u>Killas,</u> the <u>Elvan</u>, & the <u>Erisay</u> Stones. I also much wanted a good specimen of the <u>Feldtspar</u>, & the Cockle or Shirl; in both which, you have made me rich; & have afforded me also a fine opportunity of [acute] completing the variety of <u>Granites</u>. The fine large piece of <u>Chalcedony</u>, the Tooth Tin Ore the Gossan, & particularly the <u>Wolfram</u>, (which I much wanted to see), & the fine piece of <u>Zeolite</u> have added equally to my cabinet & to my Information.

In distributing my Granites, I had taken it for granted, they they were all of Cornish extraction, but, when I came to No. 45. <u>Red</u> <u>Feldtspar</u> <u>spotted</u> <u>with</u> <u>black</u> <u>Cockle</u> <u>in</u> <u>larger</u> <u>spots</u>, I became doubtfull whether that Number was not <u>Oriental Granite</u>; it is so exactly like a small specimen which I long since received from Da Costa, as <u>Oriental</u> <u>Granite</u>, that they must be the same thing, from whatever place they were both brought.

I have just been much delighted with Bergman's *Sciagraphic Regni Mineralis* but as yet his scheme is much too brief to be of use in arranging a Cabinet. He has reduced the <u>Primitive Earths</u> from nine as they stood in Cronstedt, to five species; one of which is a New ore, which he calls (1) <u>Terra</u> <u>ponderosa</u>, & which is produced from the <u>Marmer</u> <u>Metallicum.</u> The others are (2) Calcareous, (3) Magnesia, which he makes the Basis of all Soap Earths, (4) Argillaceous, & (5) Siliceous. He has introduced several new Acids, particularly one procured from <u>Molybdone</u>. He has brought the <u>Manganese</u> into the Metalline Class, having produced a Regulus from it: & has mentioned another Metal, heretofore called an Iron ore, & which has since most aptly been called <u>Siderum</u>. He has found the <u>Garnet</u> <u>Earth</u>, the <u>Zeolite</u>, the

<u>micaceous</u> & <u>asbestine</u> Earths of Cronstedt, to be compounded of various proportions of some of his own five primitive Earths.

As you were so obliging Sir, to give me room to hope for another Quantity of Fossils, sometime when you were at leisure; may I beg to ask, if you have in Cornwall, any Stone that you call <u>Basaltes</u>; exclusive of what is called <u>Shirl</u>? (for they are, I apprehend improperly included, in Wallerius, under the same generical Term). If their [sic] is such at hand, I would beg the favour of a sample.

Should you have it in your Power to send me any Ores, permit me to inform you, that I have no specimen of the Ores of <u>Nickel</u>, <u>Bismuth</u>, & <u>Antimony</u>: And that I am very poor in those of <u>Arsenic</u> & <u>Cobalt</u>, as well as in Variety of <u>Iron. Copper</u>, <u>Tin</u>, & <u>Lead</u>.

I most abound with, by the Favour of Mr. Seymer.

The radiated appearance of No. 74 from which you say a little Tin is obtained, is so like what is seen in a substance which I have from Derbyshire, under the name of <u>Cauk</u>, that I should think it the same substance; but the latter kind is much heavier & abundantly more compact, & I judge its Basis to be the <u>Terra</u> <u>ponderosa</u>.

I know not whether you ever see Mr. <u>Raspe</u> or are within his Reach; if it should be so, I would beg the favour of you to ask him whether He sees in Cornwall any Stones that answer to the <u>Corneus</u> of the Swedes. If he does, I should hope He would be kind enough to communicate a Specimen or two: particularly with his opinions which of the species in Wallerius, it answers best. He has four under the names of <u>Corneus nitens</u>, <u>C. fissilis</u>, <u>C. spathosus</u>, & <u>C. Trapozius</u>. I exceedingly want to [illegible] than any, the <u>Trapp</u>. I should equally be pleased to know whether there is in Cornwall what the Germans call <u>Kneis</u>, or <u>Gneiss</u>.

I will not expect an Answer to this letter, as I know Sir, your Engagements must be many, & Important. But, if you will give me leave, & anything further occurs to me, by which I can assist you in your obliging design of favouring me with any further samples of Fossils, I will take the Liberty to write again to you: Yet, as I know not what Cornwall yields, except from Mr. Borlase's Book, your own judgment will be the best rule. I thank you for your intention of sending me some polished substances. I am not very anxious in that head as I love to see them, as Nature produces them.

CRO, Truro, Rashleigh Papers: DDR/5757/1/24
Walter Synnot to Philip Rashleigh   *Maythe, 7 May 1784*

I had the pleasure of receiving your favor last post and am extremely obliged to you for sending me so valuable a Collection of Fossils: I see many articles that I much wished for in the Catalogue, and shall send you my opinion of them as soon as I receive them; I hope you have ordered your Merchant in London to inform Mr Deare in what Vessel they were shipped, as you omitted informing me of its name.

The busy scene of Life I have been engaged in ever since my residing in Ireland has prevented me from applying myself so much to the study of Mineralogy & Chemistry as I would wish, but my Love for these elegant amusements is not in the least diminished, and I sigh often for the time when I can devote myself more to them; I have a Collection for you that I hope you will think some ornament to your Museum.

You ask me some questions concerning our Volunteers which I shall answer as fully as I am able the Irish first learnt the use of arms when this Island was in the midst of War left without troops & liable to be insulted by every Enemy: it was a spirited undertaking such as neither the History of Greece, or Rome furnish us with a parralel [sic]; The real number was then about 6,000, they are at present not so numerous but certainly would be more so in case of a War. The Irish obtained a sort of Freedom when armed, which they are certain they would be deprived of if they were to lay them down; they would be again left destitute of Troops and exposed to every hostile attempt. We are a Loyal People, but we will not be imposed upon; The different Bunglers who have been lately Ministers in England have never understood her interests in regard to Ireland; they have all seemed to think that the prosperity of this Country must be the ruin of Britain, but they are greatly deceived, for what is the interest of the one is the interest of the other. The Minister in England has perhaps at all times a greater influence in the Irish than in the English Parliament, and sorry am I [to] say that that influence has been basely exerted, not a law has been proposed for the advantage of Ireland this last Sessions but has been rejected, not one has been proposed that was oppressive and injurious but it was carried by a Great Majority; publick discontents are great but believe me Sir our Volunteers are Loyal and though they have been treated in the worst manner have never betrayed the least mark of resentment;

I will not say they would suffer themselves to be made Slaves, but it must be great injuries indeed that would make them act in a different manner from what they have hitherto done.

You think Sir that much time is lost by learning the use of Arms; it is not so great as it appears to be [and] is generally a day of parade except in Ulster where are [both] Men and Dissenters; when my Company were first raised they met once a Week, now they are disciplined they meet once a month except in the busy times of harvest and sowing. My whole regiment meets perhaps three times in Summer; in peace time we bring 1000 Men into the Field; we have six brass six-pounders; the Canon [sic] were given by Ld. Charlemont; the expence is moderate, the privates pay Sixpence a month for powder. When the Regiment meets the officers treat the men with only bread, cheese and Porter, and dine with them on it. We are dressed in Scarlet faced with white; the Men buy their own Cloaths which are at first expensive but last long as never worn but on parades; we have all short blue jackets faced with scarlet which we wear when only in single Companies; Our Privates are rich young Farmers and behave themselves remarkably well; the Officers are at the expence of furnishing Serjeants from the regulars to discipline them; my Overseer is an old Serjeant. I have thus given you a full account of Our Volunteers It will be little interesting you, but it is not a subject I should have taken up if you had not desired it.

CRO, Truro, Rashleigh Archive: DDR/5757/1/25
R. Pulteney to Phillip Rashleigh   *Blandford, 8 May 1784*

I have for a long time owed you my Thanks for the Favour of your obliging letter of the 21st of Feb. Accept them now Sir both my gratefull Acknowledgements for the Intelligence that your Letter conveys to me.

We are in hopes that M. Bergman will find time to fill up his Chasms & give us a more complete Work on Mineralogy in due time. That Author thinks the Terra ponderosa contains a metal although it has not yet been reduced to a Regulus it was not chemically investigated before the year 1774 & is found as yet in very few substances, as he says, except the Barium metallica & Lapis hepaticus. I never saw the white Tin Ore, but I find there is a German Author or rather a Russian who has lately written on Tin Ores & He says the spathose Tin Ore is the same thing with the ponderous Spar, & indeed Wallerius says it contains more Iron than Tin. The same writer says also that the striated or amiantheiform Tin Ore of Wallerius found in Siberia, is a Shirl.

The new Metal which is called Siderium was discovered nearly at the same time, unknown to each other both by Mr. Bergman & Mr. Meyer & they describe it to be of a White Colour and as being the thing that gives fragility to cold Iron. Hitherto this new metal has been intimately united with iron & it was but since the publication of the Sistem graphic that Bergman has proved it to be a distinct metal.

I also have been exceedingly puzzled by A [page torn with loss] ,ing confounded together the two substances Basaltes & Shirl. This the Swedish Mineralogists particularly seem to have done by including them both under one & the same generical Name. But indeed since I attended to Native Fossils my opportunities of seeing both have not been enough frequents to enable me to speak on this subject. I much wish fine well chosen Specimens of the true Irish Giant's Causeway, or that of Staffa or Iceland in order to get a good Idea of that substance.

M. Saussure who is writing the Natural History of the Environs of Geneva & has prepared a Description of the Earths & Stones seems to have distinguished these two substances better than the Northern Mineralogists. On the Whole I understand the basalts to be a true Volcanic Production or semivitric fixation of Earths & Stones by subterraneous fires; & the Shirl to be a native production though often contained in Basaltes.

Your Opinion if [Caak][1] confirms a surmise of Wallerius the Swede,[2] who calls it spathose Gypsum but nevertheless suspects that it belongs to the Fluors: this, if I mistake not, is also the opinion of Da Costa who censures both Cronstedt & Wallerius for placing these heavy substances & the [Bononian] Phosphorus all with the Gypsums. [page torn with loss] no substance among the Stones that I wish more to have ascertained to me & to possess specimens of than the Corneus of the Swedes, since their Authors speak of it as a common Stone with them & they make it in their writings the basis of so many others in compound and Rock Stones.

I do not think that Da Costa can make any thing of it, & it is evident that the French Translator of Wallerius's Book in 1753 did not understand it & that Author complains even in his last Edition in Latin of 1778 that Foreigners yet mistake him relating to it. Saussure finds it in Switzerland but says [page torn with loss] difficult to define. Mr. Ferber[3] says Horn slate is properly the [Denomiliation] of a Rock consisting of Quartz & [Glimmer] or Mica thoroughly & internally blended so as not to be distinguished 'by the Eye'. I shall be much obliged to you for a specimen or two of such Variety as you may meet both of what you take to be <u>Corneus.</u> I should suppose that Mr. Raspe who translated Ferber's Book would instantly know it. The Corneus of the Germans is, as I understand it a Flint in a Petrosilex & is very different from the Corneus of the Swedes.

I never saw a Tourmalin except, I think, in the British Museum. It has been long since well known on account of its electrical Property of which many Experiments are to be seen in the Phil Transactions, & till very lately [page torn with loss] found in Europe. Mr. Bergman says it [page torn with loss] covered about 5 years ago in the Tyrolese Mountains where Chrystals of it had been found superior to any brought from Ceylon or S. America. Wallerius seeks it among the Zeolites & Bergman – thinks it has a great affinity to the Shirls. Wallerius thinks the Gneis of the Germans is the species of Jasper which he calls Sinopel – the Sinople of the [Shaps] a well known name in authors & a substance I greatly wish to see. Ferber describes Gneis or kneis to be a schistose Stone composed of Quartz & Mica; but that is [page torn with loss], little. If you should Honour me with the favour of your Correspondence on any these Subjects in future, may I beg the honour of knowing in your next letter what Mineralogical Author you are in the use of that I may have the Conveniency of referring to Science in any future Letter the better to ascertain what I mean by any particular substance as well as to save trouble.

P.S. Upon recollecting that it was probable you might soon pass through Blandford to Town & being willing to transmit to your Hands & beg the Favour of your Acceptance of the Volume that accompanies this I thought it better to leave this Letter &c. under the care of Mr. Watson than to send them into Cornwall. I lament that your stay is so short in your passage through this place. But shall be happy in every opportunity of having the Honour of paying my Respects to you.

Notes
1. 'Caak' refers to 'Caulk' – the Derbyshire miners' term for the massive white variety of barytes.
2. J. G. Wallerius (1709–1785); Swedish mineralogist & physician; published *Mineralogia* (1747) after visiting the mining districts of

Sweden to obtain specimens for his mineral collection; both French and German editions were produced later.

3. J. J. Ferber (1743–1790); widely-travelled Swedish mineralogist; became Director of the Mining Academy in Berlin; published accounts of his journeys through Europe (1774) and in a volume of letters (1789); his descriptions of Naples and the eruption of Vesuvius were considered to be the finest of eighteenth-century scientific writings.

CRO, Truro, Rashleigh of Stoketon papers: RS/1/1046
John Rashleigh to Philip Rashleigh
Ballinado, Ireland, 28 July 1784[1]

I was honoured with your letter for which I now return you my most sincere thanks and am happy to find you are in good health.

At a late Review of the Volunteers in the North they came to a resolution of giving the Roman Catholicks a right of Suffrage, tho' I have a great respect for them, agst my Judgement as Will as it is hitherto informed, will not suffer me to agree with.

You seek why we wish for a more Equal representation; can it be said we are properly represented when the majority of the House of Commons are returned from Boroughs with perhaps eight or ten Votes, and which are now made properties by a few great men, who either foster them for Aristocracy, Or perhaps standing forth, the Patriot of their country which I am. Sorry to say very seldom happens not very long since two gentlemen meeting at a gaming table, one of which had bad success ventured to play a Seat of one of his Boroughs where he lost & is now foiled by his respectable antagonist this puts me in mind of a Story told of one of our Members, who was returned at a Contested Election when he was applyed to by his constituents to vote against a Bill. 'What!' says he: 'have I not bought them very dear & will they not allow me to dispose of them as I think proper!'

The Aggregate meeting of the City of Dublin are requesting the Severall [sic] Sheriffs all over the Kingdom to call meetings, to petition his majesty to dissolve the present Parliament.

It makes me exceedingly happy at the opportunity I took on making myself acquainted with you, having no family of my own, nor one of the name, I believe in Ireland, . . .

Note
1. This letter reflects a transitional stage in Irish history after the much earlier rising of the Gaelic Irish in 1641 that had been quelled by Cromwell in 1649–50, but before the United Irish rebellion of 1798 seeking an independent Irish republic. In 1782 the Protestant 'patriots' of Ulster had won legislative independence for the Dublin Parliament, but these 'Volunteers' refused to disband and were demanding parliamentary reform. Although this subsided the complex situation that prevailed in Ireland 'of agrarian poverty, of religious discrimination, and of nationalist radicalism', all led to the subsequent violence (Ayling, *Fox*, p.115). As an MP, Rashleigh would have been interested in the information that the letter provided.

CRO, Truro, Rashleigh Archive: DDR/5757/1/30
R. Pulteney to Phillip Rashleigh
Blandford, 27 November 1784

Your obliging Favour dated the 17th inst. came to hand & then on the 25th the Box of Fossils arrived safe. Permit me to return you my very grateful thanks for the Favours: You have overwhelmed me with Riches, & furnished me with subjects of speculation & Entertainment for months to come; & I may add of instruction too; for several of them are such as I had no competent idea of from Books. I feel ashamed that you should apologise to me for not sending me gaudy specimens: those you have favoured me with are in my opinion, very fine & probably sufficient to exhibit & characterise the subject, as far as any thing detached from the Bed or stratum can. I am particularly obliged to you for the Trapp, since that is one of the Cornei of the Swedes; & had it not been for your kindness, I knew not how I should have procured either that, or the Black Corneus, both of which will give me much Instruction, as I find that kind of Stone is very much unknown in England; & I had in vain desired da Costa to procure me some: He even does not know the species. The specimens of the Kneiss is also very interesting to me, as I now see it is a micaceous Stone but I think there is yet wanting a good Arrangement of the Stony Class, as far as they are simple & not reduceable to the Class of Ores. I much regret that Mr. Kirwan had not done it more particularly in his Book; & reduced the Synonyms of former Authors to his Species.

I marvel to see the <u>Toad</u> <u>stones</u> are so various an aspect as apparently to forbid their being called by the same Name. The green sort is extremely like what has been described as a <u>Vein</u> <u>Stone</u>, or a <u>Carpolithus</u> by some Authors; & is very like which I had received under the name of <u>Vein</u> <u>Stone</u>. I have lately been informed that the intelligent Miners of Derbyshire do not adopt Mr. Whit[e]hurst's System which he has so much laboured in that County. I much lament that I have not had the Pleasure of waiting on You at my House for a time sufficient to beg your Inspection of the small number of things I have; from which I should also hope for much instruction: I wish it too that you might see whether I have any Article that you would desire to make your own.

Could you make it convenient Sir, at your next attendance at Parliament, to favour me with a Call, I should hope to have it in my power to offer you a Specimen of the Rowley Rag Stone which (if I am not out of luck) I hope to secure from a Gentleman of the County where it is found, very soon.

Mr. Seymer has not been very well of late; but it is a Pleasure to see how keen his taste for his favourite Pursuits remain, & with which Impatience He expected the Box I delivered to him from you.[1]

I am mortified to think that your time & attention should be taken up in any degree with subjects of so disagreeable a Nature, as those you particularly mention, that might otherwise be so much more agreeably employed; & I cannot but most sincerely wish you a good riddance of such troublesome Intruders.

Note

1. In a letter of 4 January 1784 (RIC, RASH/1/44), Seymer had acknowledged minerals received from Rashleigh.

[5 letters Rashleigh sent to Thomas Pennant (1786–1787) in answer to his queries are in Warwickshire CRO: TP/12/19-27.]

NHM, Mineral Library, Russell Bequest, John Hawkins Letters: No. 13[1]
Philip Rashleigh to John Hawkins
Menabilly, 25 February 1789

If your Friend Mr. Jacquin does not come into Cornwall, he may not have an Opportunity of Collecting any Minerals from that County. I should have no objection to Exchanging some of ours for those of Hungary if you think that by that means we may increase the Varieties in each of our Cabinets: I have several Hungarian Minerals already, but unless the Mines in that Country are destroy'd they produce much finer Specimens than any I have. As this Gent. is of your Acquaintance I should be very glad to see him at Menabilly & shew him my Cabinet. Having some reason to Complain of the Returns I have from Foreign Countries in Exchange for the Produce of our own, I am a little cautious of making open Engagements unless through the knowledge of some Friend & therefore should not make this Offer unless by your Advice. As you are engaged deeply in this pursuit, I shall be very ready to give You my Assistance & should be glad to know what You are particularly in want of, that I may lay aside for You such things as I put my hand upon.

[reference to workings at the Loe Pool][2]

We have had very bad Weather ever since I came home & it now blows a Storm & has carried away part of the Pattent Roof of my Stable, which I thought would have resisted any Wind of this part of the world. My remaining in this Country will depend on what business comes before Parliament, but at present I suspect nothing Material unless the Joy of [the] King's being able to undertake the Publick business before a Regent was appointed.[3]

Notes
 1. This Letter is not addressed but it occurs with other Hawkins letters in the Russell Bequest; it is referred to (see Sir A. Russell, 'Philip Rashleigh of Menabilly, Cornwall and his mineral collection', *Journal of the Royal Institution of Cornwall*, New Series, 1, 2

2. (1952), 4); it is obviously not the first communication between them.

2. 'Loe Pool' = Russell has described this as the lead mine at Huel Pool, Helston.

3. Rashleigh was undoubtedly aware of the situation for the Minutes concerning the King's indisposition reveal that 'an entire cessation of the King's illness' was recorded on 26 February; on 28 February the Privy Council ordered that a Prayer of Thanksgiving for his recovery should be given throughout the country. On 10 March, His Majesty sent a commission for the opening of a new session of Parliament and submitted his estimates for the coming year (*Gentleman's Magazine*, 59, 1789:175, 265-6).

NHM, Mineral Library, Russell Bequest, Hawkins Letters: No. 14/15
Philip Rashleigh to John Hawkins

Menabilly, 22 March 1789

You are very kind in giving Yourself so much trouble about my Cabinet. I will certainly endeavour to add a variety to Mr. Jacquin's; I have no particular desire for the Package traveling one way rather than another, but wish to have it directed for me to the Care of Messrs Brook, Watson & Co., London, as I believe few Ships come to Falmouth from that Country, otherwise Falmouth is the most convenient Port, as being so much nearer.

The Person I meant at Freyburg who had such a fine Collection of Horn Silver was Mons'r. Pabst von Ohain, I did not know his collection was on Sale. I never heard any of this Ore being found in the Emperor's Dominions, but it sometimes happens that Duplicates of Foreign Countries get into Private Cabinets. I have a poor Piece or two of this Ore, one which Baron Heynitz broke from a specimen in his Possession, but I think they are very indifferent, nor do I recollect seeing any large pieces Except one in Dr. Hunter's Museum.

I believe Mr Scopoli has been the means of my getting most of the Common Minerals of the Hungarian Mines, & I have since procured a few Specimens much Superior to his: The Crystallizations he sent were very insignificant, but in the last Box I had from Baron Trebra, I had some very Perfect & I believe not Common. If I mention anything particular it is because I am in want of it, not because I Expect to have it, for other Collections may be Poor in the same Article as well as mine: I have one Good Specimen of Crystallized Gold Ore.

I am Obliged to You for offering to Purchase some Specimens for me in the Collection coming to England for Sale; I think it would be very difficult to describe what I might want & Catalogues are not much to be depended upon, I should like to see the Collection when it arrives, but though I have not determined to remain in the Country all the Spring; I have not resolved to go to London unless some particular business I do not expect should call me there. When we left Mr. Forster's in Covent Garden, I forgot to ask You whether his English or French Collection was to be prefered [sic]. I think our Mines never produce so little Variety as at Present, I Expect something New when the Lead Mines are put to Work.

I am very much inclined to think with Mr. Werner that Basalt is formed by Moisture, which being withdrawn leaves the Substantial Matter in the form we hear of, for I have never seen any of these magnificent Works of nature: I have many times observed in Clay Countries after a great deal of Rain & then much Sun, that the Ground has Crack'd in similar Forms in a small degree, to the Gyant's Causway [sic]. The *Ludus Helmontii* seems another argument to strengthen this Idea, I have a Specimen which indicates it so strongly that I have scarcely a Doubt to the contrary. Were these Forms occasion'd by Fire, the Angles in general would not have been so sharp as represented, especially in such large Bodies, which could never have been formed by Fire without some Cinerous marks more conspicuous than the little holes in these Substances. One should have been at Staffa to have argued on this Subject, & I have seen the top & bottom of the Pillars as well as the Country around them.

Minerallogy [sic] so much the Taste of the Present Age that if ever the Philosophers Stone was to be discover'd now is the Time. From what Stone or Substance has Mr. Claproth discover'd the two new Primative Earths?

I think we shall Refine Minerallogy too much.

CRO, Truro, Rashleigh Letters: DDR/5757/1/58
John Hawkins to Philip Rashleigh

Upper Brook St., London, 10 May 1789

I am obliged to you for several fine specimens of Fluors & calcareous spar which in consequence of your information I purchased of Mrs Powell. Before the receipt of your letter I had not heard a word of this sale so that the best specimens had already been picked. I thought the prices not unreasonable and it gave me pleasure to lay out my money with so intelligent and genteel a female mineralogist from whom I shall expect every year an accession of interesting specimens.

. . .

It is a favourite principle with me in collecting that one good specimen is worth a hundred bad. I would not engage to pay the freight of many collections which were offered to be sent me in exchange by persons abroad. Of the two divisions of Mr. Forster's Collection I know not which is to be preferred. The Ohain collection at Freyberg is perhaps equal to any existing & to be sold reasonably. The Specimens of Horn silver are superior in number & variety to any other that I have seen in any cabinet. Every thing that Saxony has produced since 40 years is to be met with here in the greatest perfection. The Collection too is arranged & described by Werner in the compleated [sic] manner.

I will not assert that basalt has been formed in the humid way but nothing can be weaker & inconclusive than the arguments advanced in proof of its fiery origin. The disposition to divide into a prismatic form is by no means peculiar to this fossil. It is common to porphiry & I have observed it in the Tufa near Rome & in the Gypse Quarries near Paris. I will shew you next winter the most regular columns of true Porphiry. We find some species of rocks allways divided in the quarry in Rhombs others allways in Trapezoidals, so that each species of rock has its particular method of dividing, but some approach more to geometrical regularity than others.

The fossils from which Mr. Claproth has produced his two new earths, are the Adamantine Spar & the Jargon. I hope to collect in Cornwall some other rare fossils for the examination of so good a Chemist which may form a kind of supplement to his essay on the Min. Histy. of Cornwall.[1] I should be glad if you would lay aside any thing that occurrs [sic] to you as fit for this purpose.

I am on the point of beginning a tour into the Midland

Counties & Wales previous to my journey into Cornwall. I shall visit Anglesea. I am in hourly expectation of the arrival of the remainder of my collection from the Adriatic & the Archipelago, and am in hopes of procuring a very good house in a central part of the town in which I can place myself & my collection for which few batchelor [sic] houses have room enough.

I have seen the whole of Mr. Soper's collection & must own that I expected to see something better. Mr. S. mentioned not one word of disposing of it. Mr. Hanley is gone with Mr. Torkelin & Mr. Horne to investigate the natural history of Iceland. Count Andreani of Milan is gone for the second time to the highlands of Scotland and the Western Islands to write the nat. history of that Country. Raspe intends to spend this summer in Scotland.

Note
  1. In 1787, Klaproth published 'Observations relative to the Mineralogy and Chemical History of the Fossils of Cornwall' in a Berlin scientific journal.

CRO, Truro, Rashleigh Letters: DDR/5757/1/109
John Hawkins to Philip Rashleigh
                                 Buxton, 14 September [?1789]

Any mineralogical news from such a country as Derbyshire must amuse you therefore I shall make no apology for troubling you with a few observations made in the course of my present tour. For their purpose I availed myself of the advantages afforded by an occasional visit of Sir Joseph Banks to his seat in this county, and accepted his invitation to meet him there. His hospitality has not interrupted my pursuits. This Gregory Mine into which I twice descended actually passes under his house and several veins of Lead are exposed to view in his gardens. Overton Hall[1] therefore may be called a Mining Villa and the fit residence of a Mineralogist.[2]

Mr. White Watson, whom you know, was here to be my Cicaroni, but unfortunately neither he nor any others of Sir Joseph freinds [sic] would follow me under ground. A Scotch Professor indeed had once the curiosity to accompany me but in spite of his zeal for mineralogical information I believe he has had enough of it. You would have been as much amused as Sir Joseph Banks was, to hear me and this gentleman Dr. Hope disputing two whole days on the Huttonian Theory myself a Neptunist, the Dr. a Plutonian.[3] This contest ended not till we parted, each perhaps more firmly convinced than before of the rectitude of his opinions.

The principal objects of my Tour have been to acquire a distinct idea of what are called here Pipe works, to ascertain the alternating Strata of Toadstone & Limestone, & whether the Lead Veins are really cut off by the Toadstone Beds as Whitehurst pretends and lastly how far the sections he has given are accurate.[4] We have nothing similar to the Pipe works in Cornwall and it would be difficult to give you a clear idea of them. They seem to be peculiar to this county. They may be called <u>Deposits</u> of <u>Ore</u> which accompany the Cross Veins at a certain depth and in a direction parralel [sic] to the Strata. The Limestone & Toadstone Measures really alternate but have neither that regular parralelism nor straightness that Whitehurst has described, nor are they broken in that manner, for instance under the bed of the Derwent they are entire. Nor is it true that the Toadstone wholly cuts off the Veins, it deranges them indeed and alters their nature so far that the Galena ceases & the veins are divided into strings or small fissures of spar which the Miners think not worth pursuing and for this reason they say 'the Vein is lost or cut off', which expression means no more than that the ore has disappeared. It is curious however that these Veins resume their former breadth & contents in the second Limestone. Usually however they are not pursued to their depth. It is likewise remarkable that the veins are equally disordered and impoverished when they strike into the shale above and that they are never observed in the superior Gritstone Stratum so that had the hills been covered every where by this Gritstone & Shale the rich & numerous Veins below them would never have been discovered. Mining Adventure is farther limited in this country by the great inclination of the Strata for the veins cannot be pursued far after they have dipped under the shale.

This is just now the situation of the Gregory Mine. The State of Mining Industry here is much on the decline. The produce of this Derbyshire mines being reduced to one half of what it was ten years ago partly in account of the low price of Lead during the greater part of this period &c. &c. in consequence of the greater depth & the exhausted st[ate of] most of these Mines. The lead produce of Yorkshire is said to be infinitely greater at present. I find a considerable number of German Mining terms in use here which proves I think the introduction of German Miners perhaps in the Time of Elizabeth. We have some of these terms in Cornwall.

Considering the declining state of the Derbyshire Mines, it is not to be wondered at if they produce so few chrystallizations [sic]. In fact I have collected allmost nothing except a few bits of Elastic Bitumen which are allso [sic] scarce. The sandstone which forms the superior crust of the hills in this county is of a very remarkable quality for it consists of a mixture of grains of Quartz & & Felspar; the latter assuming nearly its chrystalline form. These Grains therefore could not have been formed by attrition and united by subsequent agglutination. About 12 or 15 years ago several Cornish Miners wandered into Derbyshire for employ[ment]

When you read in the papers of the riots in this neighbourhood in consequence of the high price of provisions you will naturally conclude that the harvest has been unfavourable but the reverse is the truth & the price seems to be kept above its natural level by the very general practice of forestalling. It is easy to perceive that the time is not far distant when the Proprietors of Mines & Manufacturys, which employ a great number of people, will be reduced to the necessity of becoming Purveyors of Corn for them. The Population of the country is increasing in consequence of the numerous Manufactorys lately established in it and the effect on the agriculture of the country is very [......]cptable. The Hartington Enclosure will rescue 26000 acres from heath and Moor game.

On Thursday I spent four hours under ground at Ecton. This famous mine is now fairly exhausted and the miners are reduced to the necessity of picking its bones. Less than 100 tons of copper are produced here.

Ecton is certainly the deepest Mine in England being 150 fathoms under the level of the deep Adit. The Ore lies in what is called a Pipe Work but which I think ought to be called by a new name for I question much whether there is any thing similar to it in the world, I shall therefore not attempt to give you a description of it in the compass of a letter. Nor is it easy to reduce to words the idea which I have of this curious mineral Deposit altho' it is by no means so irregular and capricious in its form & direction as is pretended.

I shall proceed in a few days to Cheshire where I have several visits to pay and in this manner I propose to spin out the remainder of the year. Next summer shall be devoted to my friends in Cornwall and to a mineralogical tour thro' that County. I look forward with pleasure to my visit to Menabilly

Notes
1. 'Overton Hall, Ashover – the Derbyshire estate owned by Sir Joseph Banks' – see S. R. Band, in R. E. R. Banks (ed.), *Sir Joseph Banks: A Global Perspective* (1994), 213-16.
2. Banks was essentially a botanist and would never have considered himself a mineralogist; Torrens has clarified his interest in the earth sciences (ibid., 49) but acknowledged that it was essentially through exploration and the patronage of surveyors prompted by the economical exploitation of his estates.
3. Huttonian theory – see Introduction
4. A reference to Whitehurst's work *An inquiry into the original state and formation of the earth*' (1778) based on his investigation of the strata in Derbyshire. T. D. Ford, 'The growth of geological knowledge in the Peak District', *Mercian Geologist*, 14 (4), 1990:161-190, discusses the interpretation and occurrence of this assemblage of basaltic lavas known as 'toadstones' (at 170).

CRO, Truro, Rashleigh Letters: DDR/5757/1/60
John Hawkins to Philip Rashleigh
Chandos Street, Cavendish Square, 31 December 1789

I have just been favoured by the receipt of your letter and suppose that your stay in the country will still permit me to answer it. I paid visit a few days ago to Gen'l. Rainsford[1] who after some difficulty in finding shewed me the specimen of copper that you spoke of. It is about 2½ inches square and I think exceeds any specimen that I have of this kind in the size and length of the fibres. It comes for certain from Botallack but, I doubt whether you will be able now to procure a single bit. The Large specimen which I was fortunate enough to procure is now lying in my desk ready to be delivered to you. Some large specimens of the vitriolated Lead spar from Anglesey are arrived greatly injured by careless packing and you shall see them & take your choice. I expect also some large specimens of the Beeralston fluor the object of your late disappointment. Not one of my foreign minerals is yet unpacked. My Cabinet will not be ready till February. I shall be able to accommodate you with some cinnabar ores from Idria which I have just received. In Airshire [sic] they have lately discovered a large vein of plumbago but which is not so good in quality as the Cumberland pencil lead.

Claproth has just sent me the analysis of the Jargon and

Adamantine spar in each of which he discovered a new earth. Since that he has published the discovery of a new Semi-metal in the Pechblende which I employed him to examine some time ago. The Chemical operations of this man are more to be relied on than those of any other whom I know. His acids & alkalis employed in his analysis's are prepared with the utmost care & precautions to prevent errors in the result and he is remarkably candid and diffuse in the statement of his experiments. With a family and other vocations he has not been able to devote that time to the analysis of mineral bodies which the mineralogical world could wish. Strongly impressed with a sense of his merit after I quitted Berlin I sent him a sum to enable him to prosecute his pursuits in mineralogical chemistry and with my freind [sic] Werner sent him many minerals to examine the Jargon & Pechblende were of the number.

Mr John Wedgwood & myself resolved the other day to contribute 20 £ each to prosecute this purpose in case Mr. Claproth should have leisure to accept the proposal which I am about to communicate to him. It is our intention to send him a number of English minerals for examination. Have you any Cornish production which you would particularly wish to have analysed and in this case will you contribute something in addition to our subscriptions.

In my journey up, I passed thro' Callington from whence I took a ride to Kit Hill where I not only found an abundance of Wolfram but allso [sic] many specimens of sulphurated tin. I was equally deceived as yourself in the black columnar crystals collected by Mr. Wedgwood & said to be of iron, of this however I still withhold implicit beleif [sic] the form so perfectly resembles the long prismatical tin found in some mines.

Since my arrival in Town I have translated from the German a Catalogue of all the minerals, which have hitherto been analysed and by whom with remarks and structures. I will communicate a copy to you on your arrival, and if I have time will translate Werner's paper on the forming of mineralogical Cabinets.

Harris has now two fine specimens of the Auvergne Antimony the ends of the Xtals in perfect preservation for the largest about 6 or 7 inches square he asks 2 guineas for the other 1½.

Count Reden writes me from Derbyshire that he shall come to town in February previous to his journey into Cornwall & he spent a long while in Scotland. . . .

Note

1. Charles Rainford (1728–1809); army officer; MP for Maldon (Essex) 1772–4, Bere Alston (Devon) 1787–8, Newport (Cornwall) 1790–6; promoted colonel 1774, major-general 1777, lieutenant-general 1782, general 1796; various scientific interests; elected Fellow of Royal Society 1779; Fellow of Society of Antiquaries.

NHM, Mineral Library, Russell Bequest, Hawkins Letters: No. 42/43
Philip Rashleigh to John Hawkins   *Undated [January 1790]*

You will give me great Pleasure in the Expectation of seeing your Cabinet, & I shall have a Considerable addition to mine by the good Things You are so kind to Reserve for me. I shall make all the Enquiry Possible for the Botallack Copper & if any is to be procured I am in Expectation of geting [sic] it. I am convinced it is the same as Gen'l. Rainsford shew'd me, & which I have been Enquiring for ever since I saw it: a good deal was raised I shall think myself unfortunate if I should not procure a Specimen to save Yours.

Jacobs has been here with a Box of Ores, chiefly Red Copper, some large & Rich Pieces Crystallized between two flat surfaces, they were better than what I possessed before but the Walls of the Load had destroyed the Crystals on the sides in general. He had two or three good pieces of the Blistered Ore with Hexagonal Tables on the top, & nothing else of any consequence. I have sent to Naniothan about the Shot Tin which by Klaproth I find is not round like Shot, but like Shot split in two, or Hemispheres.

I am much Obliged to You for the Translation of Werner's System of Minerallogy [sic], & as your Spe'ms are to be all Arranged, I know of no System so good to adopt: I shall obey your Commands on not communicating a Copy of it. I shall be very glad to see Werner's Paper on the different Cabinets as I conclude he has seen many & been inform'd of others, & I suppose he never found one anything like Perfect, & it is probable there is no such thing.

I thank You for what Trebra says, The Horn Silver I conclude was the Specimen he prefer'd to all his Cabinet. The finest Piece I ever saw is in Dr. Hunter's Collection, & I believe few can equal it. I shall always think Baron Trebra has acted very Honourably in our Exchanges, & I believe each now Possess most of the productions from the other's Country. Pray give my Compliments to him when you write.

The Instructions You left me at Menabilly will be of Service to me, I shall make enquiry after the things I want. Some fine Specimens of Tin Ore were formerly found on the Mount, & I believe are now in Mr. Gawler's Possession, unless Sir Jo. St. Aubyn has found them among his Ores.

When you returned by way of Tavistock You might have gone to Hiccory Bridge & seen the Cobalt ore there frequently intermixed with small Capillary Native Silver. I have often wonder'd this Mine has not been Work'd again, tho' the Water is very powerful in it.

I have procured a small piece of the Ore Mr. Wedgewood got for Iron Ore, mine I am told is much inferior to his. This Ore resembles Tin Crystals so much that I cannot persuade myself they are Iron, my Specimen is too small to make any Expts. upon with accuracy, & at present I cannot procure more; but will have another trial in Summer. Is it not Schirl ?

Report say Sir Jo. St. Aubyn has gain'd over many of the Fishermen in Paul by favoring them in the Fishery at the Mount, but I do not give Credit to these Reports.

In consequence of your telling me that some Fluors of a different Colour to mine were flung away on the Shammels at Beer Alston Mine & that Cap't. John Vivian knew where to find them, I writ to him desiring he would procure me some, he properly applied to Mr. Gullitt for his liberty, who writ me a most Impertinent Letter on the occasion on which I shall have no further intercourse with him.

You would have had this letter some time since had I known where to Direct; I sent to Your Bror. for Information but gain none, in a day or two after you left the County. Having this Minute rec'd. a Direction to You from your Bror. I no longer delay.

NHM, Mineral Library, Russell Bequest: Hawkins Archive /54

John Wedgwood to John Hawkins   *Bath, 1 January 1790*

I sent you last night by the London waggon a box of the Bath Stones. I thought it better to send a single large piece than many smaller ones. I hope you will be able to make your pieces to your own size

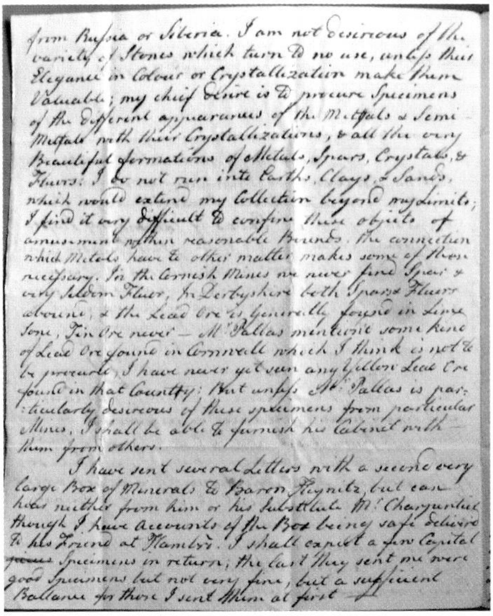

Fig. 1 Letters from the Carew, Rashleigh and Hawkins archives in the CRO:
Top left – Rashleigh (23 February 1781); Top Right – Gregor (8 January 1791);
Bottom left – Carew (31 December 1775) – **not selected**;
Bottom right – Gregor (25 July 1805).

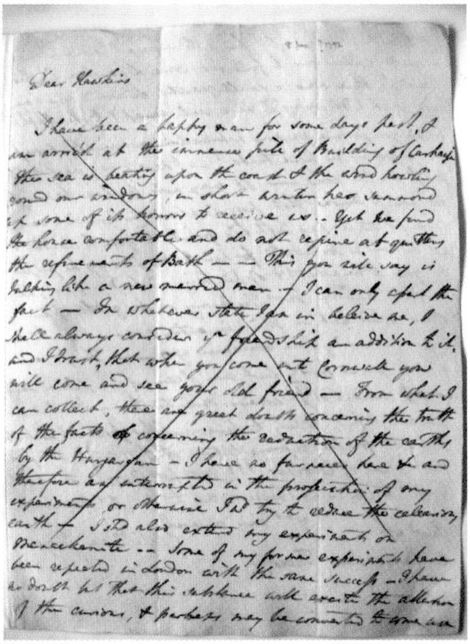

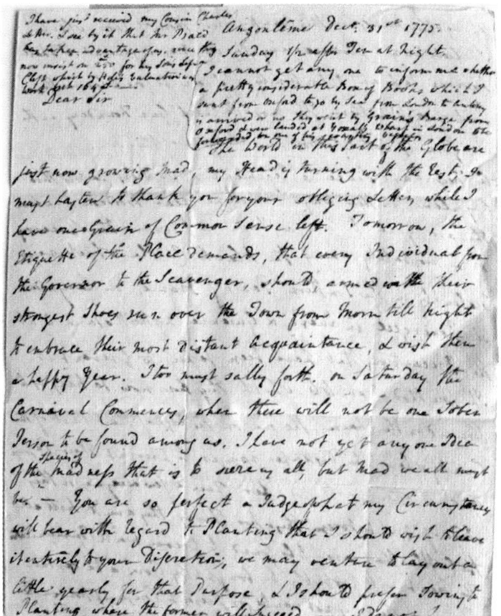

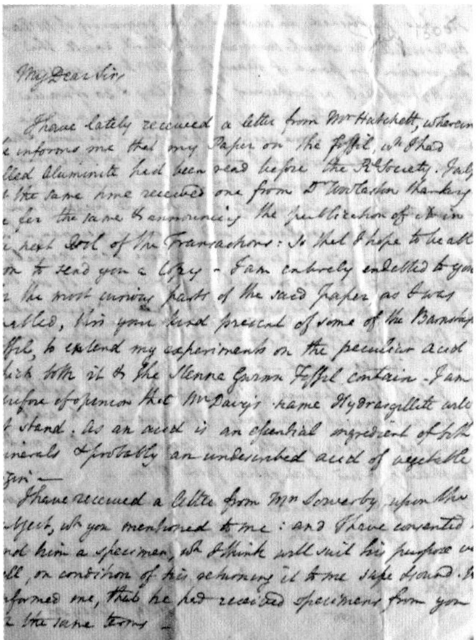

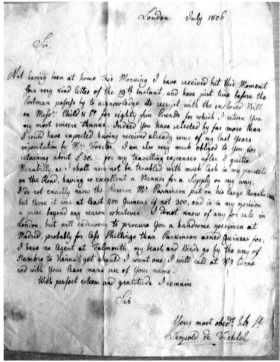

Fig. 2.   Letters to Rashleigh from Dealers.
Top – Mrs Forster (25 June 1805) with a list of specimens & their prices;
Bottom – Leopold Fichtel (c. 19 July 1806) – **not selected**.

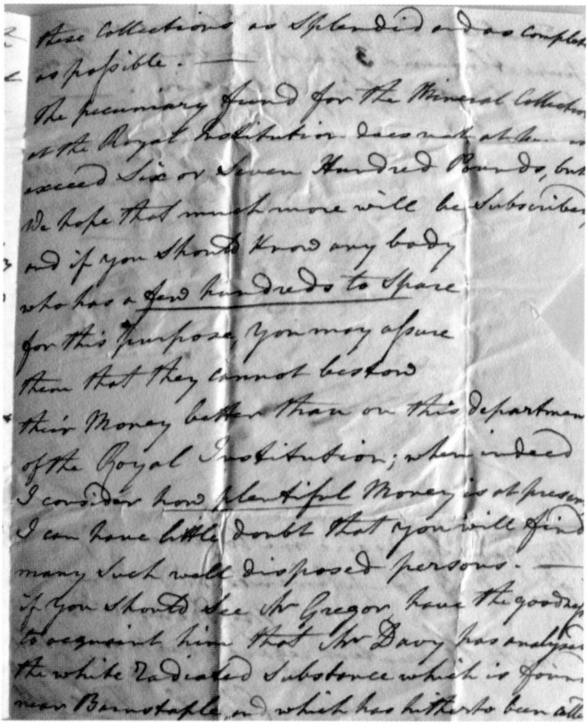

Fig. 3. Letter from Charles Hatchett to Rashleigh (19 November 1804)
on various mineral topics – **not selected**.

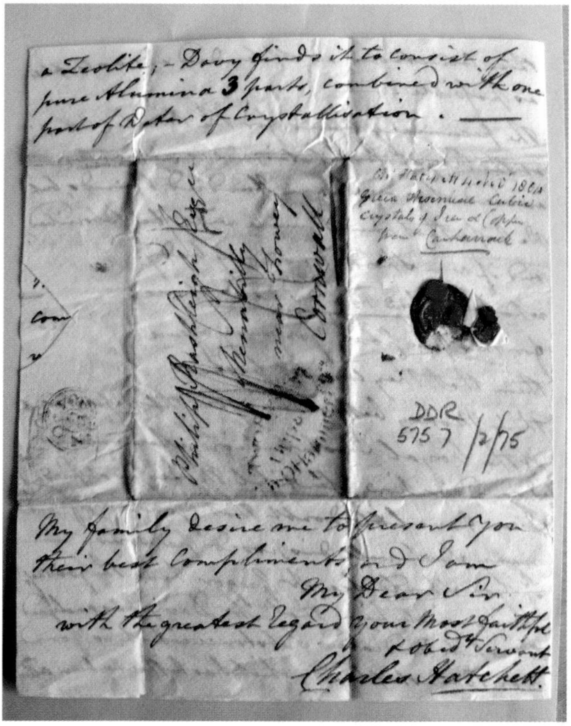

I will here mention a very convenient but simple improvement on the Blow pipe which mr Hatchett has made. it is nothing more than the addition of a Bladder to the common Blow pipe By means of which when filled & pressed with the lip against the mouth of the pipe, the stream of air is continued without interruption

& the practitioner is enabled to draw his breath as frequently as he pleases.

Fig. 4. Use of the Blowpipe.
Top – 19th century illustration;
Bottom – sketch by Rackett in a letter to Dr. Pulteney (24 January 1793).

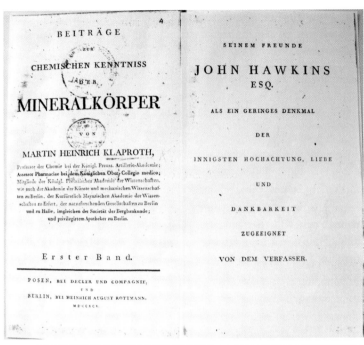

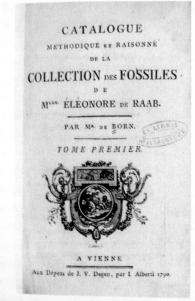

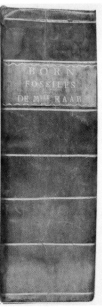

Fig. 5.   Publications by European collectors with whom the Cornish trio
corresponded and cooperated.
Top – Klaproth's volume of Mineral analyses (1795) dedicated to John Hawkins;
Bottom – Catalogue of Mlle. Eleanore De Raab' Collection (1790)
– (see p. xxxiv & xxxvi).

Fig. 6   Rashleigh's specimen of Liroconite – Mss Catalogue No. 1114:
Top – NHM photo; Bottom – original drawing.

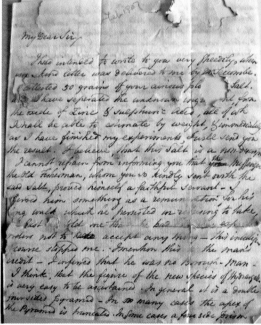

Fig. 7 Top – Sowerby's figure of Gregor's 'new specimen
of Hydrargillite' – in *British Mineralogy*, vol. 3, pl. 243;
Bottom – Gregor's letter to Rashleigh (11 February 1807) about this.

Fig. 8.   Meteorites:
Top – Gregor's letter (23 August 1804) referring to "Thunderstones" – **not selected**
Bottom – Sowerby's published print of the Yorkshire Stone (1812).

from the block. I have sent the fellow of it into Staffordshire for my own use.

I met here in the rooms of Mr Townshend of famous note in Cornwall.[1] I made myself known to him & we had a good deal of conversation together. He tells me that a well has been sunk here about 30m fathoms deep thro' the Pistolite in Bath Stone that they came to a hard & solid marble. In Wiltshire too in sinking very deep wells about two years ago they dug thro' the Chalk & came to a sandstone very white & hard & that this seems to be the basis of the chalk in that country. Large blocks of this same white sandstone are found scattered about the country on the surface. This is the only information I got from him on mineralogical subjects but I easily perceived that he was a true English Mineralogist considering petrifactions as one of the most interesting branches of the science & for the better knowledge of this branches has been at the pains of studying conchology. Otherwise he has no idea of any classification but has that inherent confusion so learnedly displayed by those two masters of the science Kirwan & Magillan, the former of whom I believe he looks upon as the *ave plus ultra* of this science but enough of him.

I was agreeably surprized yester-night to meet Count Andreatki in the Ball room.[2] He was just arrived from Town & has not left Paris more than three weeks. – I don't hear that he has brought any thing from the Continent, nor new discovery of any kind. He has been all over Ireland & Scotland & now he is going to North America & so on to South America to visit those almost unknown regions. He sets out in a short time.

. . .

Notes
1. Probably the Rev. Joseph Townsend, Rector of Pewsey, but living in Bath in 1790s; one of the earliest investigators of the mineralogy and fossils of British geological formations.
2. Probably Count Andreossy (1761–1828); French military commander who had a beautiful collection of minerals.

CRO, Truro, Hawkins papers: J3/2/37
John Wedgwood to John Hawkins

Etruria, 16 January 1790

Yours of the 16th came to hand in proper time & I am much obliged & I hope edified by your mineralogical information in answer to the questions I put to you – In the course of the classification of my fossils I discover every day fresh instances of my ignorance & I don't know how in this barbarous part of the world to gain any information not a soul having the least idea of the science – When your cabinets shall be arranged I hope to profit more by them than I could by reading a whole library of mineralogical books – Another thing which renders my work more disagreeable is the immense chasms that I find wanting perhaps a whole dozen families in some genera & having no decent regular suite at all – But Patience as the Italians say – As far as my present collecting goes I advance rapidly in assorting them.

I take it for granted that all the Agates come under the family of Chalcedony – I am totally at a loss about the Hornblendes having my mineralogical knowledge chiefly from French Mineralogists & their work. I confess myself at a loss to comprehend what is the substance the Germans call Hornblende. I shall send you some of the Pierre de Corne of Saussure which may perhaps prove to be the very thing – I don't know the pure Argil earth. The alum stone I suppose to be that from near Rome – Mountain Wap[1] & yellow earth are both totally unknown to me as well as stone marrow.[2]

I lament extremely my ignorance of the German language but I am resolved to begin again my attempts to learn to read it[;] to speak it is beyond my ambition unless I were in the country – I know that I lose immense pleasure in not being able to read it but cannot tell the extent of it & we have no translations of the German books to assist the unlearned – I am sorry that Mr. Hopton meets with no encouragement in his translating Riesman's mining dictionary.

I shall be equally well pleased if you send the £20 to Werner as if you – sent it [to] Claproth. You may count equally upon my promise & you may call upon me at any time for the money: the No. of the Mining Journal that I have is the Viertes Stuck for April 1789. Pray did Jacquin leave No. of the Physical Journal for November last which I lent him?

. . .

We have been very gay here this last fortnight having had one

Assembly & two private dances in that time & are going on Monday to another – This I confess deranges me a little for it is impossible to settle the day after a dance – I find it so at least –

Have you had any tidings of any of your boxes from Cornwall? I shall in a short time make up a box for you.

Notes
1. 'Wap' may refer to water deposited alluvial sediments.
2. 'Stone marrow' might mean a fine-grained 'floury' rock

CRO, Truro, Hawkins Archive: J3/2/151
J. W. Hawkins to John Hawkins
Batworthy, 17 February 1790

I expected ere this to have had an opportunity of paying my respects to you in London; but the cause of my intended journey being removed; I am now to apologize to you, for the apparent neglect shewn to your very kind letter of the 4th Dec'r. last.

. . .

Our deep adit, which we continue driving, is yet nearly one hundred fathom from the load. We have just compleated a water engine; the wheel thirty six feet diameter; stroke of the crank six feet; to lift a column of water, in diameter twelve inches and an half. I should have been happy to have seen your models, before the outlines of this machine were determined; it may however, from what I know, be tolerably proportionate; yet I shall reserve my opinion, to be regulated by your judgement, when next summer, you do me that pleasure you promise.

. . .

Our tinners tell me that our ore is too rash to smelt alone, which having been corroborated by the ill success of a Mr. Warren, one of our late adventurers, who attempted to melt it with a blast furnace. I have since sold some parcels of black tin, in Cornwall: but the disadvantages there will induce me to endeavour to be better acqua[inted] with the subject. For which reason I have reserved different samples for future assay, and experiment. The 'rashness' I attribute, not to pyritous matter, which might be sublimated; but to a great portion of ferruginous particles; which we cannot separate from the black tin, by any process in dressing that will pay cost; If which, being mechanically united infusion, produces a too friable and impure ingot for merchantable metal. The ore bears tin metal generally a large proportion in twenty. May not this be fused with advantage, by a reverberating furnace, by attending particularly to the affinity of iron, and by careful separation of the fluid tin from the scoria?

I mean to erect a small assay furnace, to have it ready for you, to make a few assays, if you should have liesure [sic]. If I was satisfied that the plan would be practicable; I should propose to our owners a melting house to be erected at Tavistock; which is distant only three miles from Morewelham Quay for coal and shipping; and is also a coinage town.

Mr. Kingdon of Exeter informed me that he has sent you some curious specimens of crystallized ore of manganese, and desired me to present his compliments to you. I shall hope to be indulged with an early reply.

CRO, Truro, Rashleigh papers: DDR/5757/1/61
Baron de Lindenthal to Philip Rashleigh   *23 March 1790*

Now it is nine years ago that I have send you over a box with several minerals, which I hope shall be safe arrived at that time.[1] I hope you shall be pleased with the contend [sic] of the said box & if this my supposition shall be the right, I wish you should send me now some of your english [sic] minerals of which I shall be very glad to receive. Fine copper, lead, tin & the different Zink ores, as likewise fine pieces of different Spars, if there are in not & all too little size shall be very agreeable to me, particularly the lime, fluor & zink Spars of different colours, figures & transparency from Ulverston, Matlock, Lady Walsh and other mines, likewise as certain nob. transparent large crystals of lime spar who commonly have the figure of six sides & two, three or more inches in there diameter & in generally what your self find worthy for collecting.

Since I have leaved England I have traveled in the remothest countrys of the asiatic Russia where I have served as engineer officer of mines & collected a great deal of natural curiosities, in which regard I am able to send you in the future, if you desire many fine pieces which
[the continuation of this letter not preserved]

Note
1. There are lists of Minerals sent to Baron Lindenthal dated May
   1790 & Nov. 1790 (see RIC Rash/1/19 & 20); Rashleigh included
   his name in the key to donors in an Mss catalogue (see R. J.
   Cleevely, 'The contributions of a trio of Cornish geologists to the
   development of 18th century mineralogy' *Transactions of the Royal
   Geological Society of Cornwall*, 22, 3 (2000), 103, fig.5.

NHM, Mineral Library, Russell Bequest – Hawkins
Archive: 52-53
John Wedgwood to John Hawkins   *Etruria, 22 July 1790*

Now that the hurry & bustle of the Election is over you will I hope
have time enough to read a letter from a friend who always wishes
you well. I have seen with pleasure that Mr. Gregor has gained
his Election: & with so good a majority too.[1] Pray when you see
him present my best Compliments to him & tell him that I did not
receive his letter till the day of Election was over for my father had
received it in London & its being directed to Joshua Wedgwood
instead of John. He did not give it me till I accidentally saw it.

I have been in Derbyshire this last week & have visited most
of the shops where minerals are to be purchased & have met
with some few good things., particularly a selenite in the form of
flowers which the miners call Snow. – I have the finest piece that
has ever been found. – the calcareous cristals are become very
scarce. Some cubes of lead & some fluors I have picked up as well
as some blende cristallised. In a month's time I shall receive some
more things out of Derbyshire & I expect they will be some of the
best sorts. I shall delay till then making up this box of fossils I
have for you. I have been very careful about the sizes of my pieces
& you may be sure of having all your of a proper size for your
Cabinet. Tho' I will answer for their being of sufficient excellence.
If they are not you must take the intent for the deed. I have not
been able to meet with any specimens of the clastic bitumen worth
bringing away. – But I have promises from the different people
that they will provide me some.

I have all my boxes from Cornwall except one & that I know
to be safe at Redruth waiting till another is ready to accompany
it. If you meet with any specimens which I have not & you have
duplicates of I shall be obliged to you to put them by for me till

you can have an opportunity of sending them to me. If you would procure me a piece of the Restormel manganese I should be very glad of a good specimen of it. I have laid by the famous piece of red Copper ore for you & will send it to you as soon as I hear of your return to London.

Soon after I left Buxton I was informed of a circumstance which I was sorry I did not hear of before – near Buxton about 2 miles on the Macclesfield road the country is crossed by a vein of earth of a brown colour, this on being washed is found to contain cristals of rock with the pyramids perfect at each end. Some of an amethestine colour, some clear white, opaque – yellow. There are found also cubes of fluor solitary & perfect opaque & milky white. I shall have some of this earth sent to me & will send sample of it. This vein extends many miles & is every where filled with these cristals – Some of these cristals are an inch long by one half broad. Some of them very small. All sorts of good specimens are now very rare in Derbyshire. The mines in general turn out but indifferent – the best trade in the Vases of Fluor. – the greatest manufactory for them is at Derby & belonging to a Mr. Brown & his son. – They have their lathes turned by a large water wheel & can regulate the quickness & slowness of their motions with the greatest facility – this gives them a very decided superiority over every other who opposes them in this branch. They want good forms & don't seem to be in the regular way of getting them for they have nobody about them who [seems] to know anything about the matter.

Note
1. Francis Gregor became an M.P. for Cornwall after a contest in the summer of 1790; Thorne (1986:82) stated that this had cost him £20,000.

CRO, Truro, Hawkins Letters: J3/12/1372
Philip Rashleigh to John Hawkins
　　　　　　　　　　　　Undated [shortly after 22 October 1790][1]

I was sorry to find by your Brother that You had left Cornwall, as I flatter'd myself with Pleasure of seeing You at Menabilly before you return'd to London, but your readiness to Serve your Friend was of more Consequence & I hope has been of use to him. During the time you spent at Helston I conclude you examined the Lead works in that Neighbourhood, & have probably secured some good Specimens of White Lead ore, as I hear some large Pieces have been found there, particularly one in the possession of Mr. Robinson, but whether Solid or xtallized I could not learn. What is it the Germans call <u>Lead Spar</u>? Is it the White Spatose Crystals of Lead Ore? Lead Crystals of all sorts, or Calcareous Spar.

My Bro^r Charles tells me you have found a New xtal pray tell me of what sort; I have seen some Fluors of different forms to any I had before, & have got some very fine Specimens of Copper Ore since I have been in Cornwall: I dare say you have been successful in Collecting this Summer. I have an Account of some Curious Minerals from Siberia which are coming to me, but have no Account of their Arrival or the vessel which was to bring them

Mr. Williams of Anglesea has offer'd to take all the Copper Ore of Cornwall not exceeding 40,000 Ton between All the Copper Companies at 76 £ pr. Standard & 50s. Returning Charges, or 74 £ pr. Standard & 45s. Returning Charges. Sir Fr. Basset desired a Month to Consider of these Proposals. Mr. Williams's proposals were not to be carried into execution unless half or ¾ths of those concern'd would agree.

Next Friday there is to be a Grand Ball at Tregethnan, many Cards of Invitation are dispersed & many Excuses return'd. On Thursday Mr. Glanville & Miss Masterman enter'd into partnership with a very large Capital.

Two Days since I met with some small xtals at Polgooth resembling Cobalt Ore in Colour & Figure they are formed upon hollow Crystals of Quartz; the Quantity is too small for any Proffit to arise and scarcely enough for Experiments in the moist way; it may be only Mundick as it certainly contains Sulphur & Iron, & neither Silver or Copper, but some other matter, as Nit. Acid takes a deep Yellow tinge with it: I have desired the Captains to look out for more substantial pieces. Among the Specimens of Copper Ore I have a small piece very much resembling a White Feather. Though I could not have the Pleasure of seeing You I hope to be favour'd with a line to Dear Sir Your much Obliged Friend Phil Rashleigh

Note
1. The letter can be roughly dated by the fact that the marriage of Mr. Glanville and Miss Masterman took place on Friday 22nd October 1790 at Lanlivery. Hawkins replied on 4 November 1790.

CRO, Truro, Hawkins Archive: J3/12/1354
Rev. William Gregor to John Hawkins

Undated [c. 25 October 1790][1]

I am ashamed that I have so long delay'd thanking you for your very kind letter from Helstone which gave me intelligence wh. surprized me indeed. If the facts be true what a revolution will there take place in systems, & opinions! I have sent for Lavoisier's *Elements* and shall read them with particular pleasure and prejudice in his favour from the acuteness he has shewn in prognostic by facts wh. other philosophers wd. have treated with contempt. The certainty wth. which Mathematicians can foretell eclipses, demonstrate that the theory is true on wh. they found their prognostications and the same argument may be applied in favour of Lavoisier's Hypothesis.[2]

I sent you a letter to Freuthe which arriv'd just after you had left it. – I sent you also a long account of Menackanite where there are many facts relating to it, which will not escape the notice of the Phlogistians & Antiphlogistians.

I mean to send a copy of it to Crell and I shd. be oblig'd to you to send me his Direction immediately you receive this. I shall be at Bath in Mrs. Gwatkin's [illegible] House.[3] If I make any stay at Bath I may possibly take a short trip to London when I hope that I shall be so fortunate as to find you in London. . . . You w'ld receive my memoir before you receive this. There are probably inaccuracies in Phraseology, & language from the hurry in which I have scribed it. I wish you nevertheless to shew it to my friend Dr. Pearson. The power, which the Calx of Menackanite has of preventing the Prussian Alkali from producing Prussian Blue and Tincture of Galls Ink, when Iron in its metallic State is digested in its solution, and the power of the Black Calx of Manganese of restoring these worthy Precipitants to their former Privileges, is a fact wh. will I dare say be taken Notice of by Lavoisier & Priestley. I am in some difficulty with respect to those papers which you were so good as to send me, of that ingenious friend of yours Klaproth. They are too big to send in a letter, but I hope to have an opportunity of transmitting them to you before it be long.

I had the honour of destroying Miss Masterman in the Parish Church of Lanlivery last Friday and presenting her to Mr. Glanville.

Present my best Compts. to Dr. Pearson[4] and tell him that I shd. have written to him expressly on the subject of Menackanite, but thought it better for him to see the paper, than what can be crowded with confusion into a letter.

Notes
1. The wedding referred to took place on 22 October 1790; Gregor's request for Crell's address in order to send his account of Menackanite indicates a date prior to 1791; and it is known that Hawkins was in Cornwall in the later months of 1790.
2. Lavoisier's "*Elements*" was published in 1789.
3. Mrs Gwatkin, Bath; presumably the mother of Charlotte Anne Gwatkin, whom Gregor married in December 1790.
4. Probably George Pearson (1751–1828); physician & chemist; elected Fellow of the Royal Society 1791; one of the first Englishman to accept the theories of Lavoisier.

CRO, Truro, Rashleigh letters: DDR/5757/1/62
John Hawkins to Philip Rashleigh
Sunbury, 4 November 1790

Many thanks for your obliging letter which business and engagements prevented me from answering sooner. My Call to Cambridge frustrated my intention of visiting you. It wished for an opportunity of communicating the extraordinary chemical news which I received just before my departure from Cornwall from Vienna. My freind Pennant wrote me that he had seen at Baron Born's, the Regulus of calcareous magnesian and baritic earths and of manganese and molybdœna each *sui generis* & procured by the simple addition of Phlogiston. So that as he says, there remains now only our primitive earths viz. the silicates of which the argillaceous is only a modification. The discovery had lately been made in Hungary by a Neopolitan.

Of this extraordinary discovery I received the other day a confirmation in a letter from Baron Born referring me to the 3rd volume of his description of Mad'lle de Raab's cabinet for a description of the regulus of each metal. This new work of Baron Born is printed only for the use of his freinds and the proprietor of the Cabinet and contains a very interesting enumeration of all the mineral productions of the Austrian States many of which have never found their way to England. Madlle de Raab proposes to sell this collection for an annuity of one hundred pounds per Annum.[1]

All the silver ores of Saxony are now amalgamated. A collection of the volcanic productions of the neighbourhood of Rome has been just sent me, which contains fine Xtals of Hornblende. Dolomieu has published an Italian translation of Bergmann's Catalogus productions of Volcanos with a long commentary.[2] A very good descriptive Catalogue of the Volcanic productions of Naples has just been published there. So much for foreign mineralogical novelties.

I have been very unsuccessful this year in my Cornish collection. Hearing that you had found our freind Moses too dear to deal with I resolved not to be the occasion of this increase of price and have not even purchased a specimen of him or spoken to him so that I hope he will either abate his demands, or that you will encourage some one in opposition to him.[3] Neither have I found any thing at St. Agnes. But at Helston I picked up a specimen from the Great work which tho' small is so original that should I not be able to procure you a better[;] it will be at your service. One of the Cap'ns Isiah Broad of St. Hillary has faithfully promised to look out for more. These are rhomboidal Xals of common Felspar with the angles uncommonly distorted. And on the same specimen is a fine little Xal of Apatite or phosphorated Calcareous earth. These two fossils together with cubes of yellow mundic lie on a druse of small quartz x'als. I hope Cap'n. Broad will succeed in procuring a larger specimen this is the only one that I have yet seen and the mine will probably be soon given up never to be reworked.

I have some specimens of pure white lead in bar shaped separated parts (no perfect xallization) but I neither possess nor have seen fine specimens of white lead. Lead spar is the denomination given to white lead ore by the Germans. I have lately seen some from the Lead hills milk white transparent and lamellar like heavy spar; Allso [sic] of a beautiful apple green.

The Xals from Polgooth are probably Arsenical pirites [sic], the smallest specimen with the blow pipe is sufficient to discover the presence of Cobalt. Or you may try to produce the sympathetic Ink. I am anxious to see the white feather-like copper ore. The post is now going excuse haste.

Notes
1. Born's catalogue was followed by William Babbington for his *"New System of Mineralogy"* (1799).
2. K. W. [Dolomieu], *Beschreibung einer Sammlung von meist vulkanischen Fossilien* (1790), see W. E. Wilson, 'The history of

mineral collecting 1530-1799', *Mineralogical Record*, 25, 6 (1994), 168 and 210.

3. Russell identified 'Moses' as the Jewish dealer Joseph Joseph of Redruth.

NHM, Mineral Library: Russell Bequest No. 18/19
Philip Rashleigh to John Hawkins
Menabilly, 15 November 1790

Though I could not have the Satisfaction of seeing You at Menabilly I had much Pleasure in hearing from You the 4th Inst. & am very thankful for your endeavours to procure me a Specimen of the Curious Fossil you found at Helston; the piece you have secured seems so much adapted to your own Cabinet that I cannot think of depriving you from it. Raspe has talked so much about his Tungsten that many People are enquiring for it, but I could never be satisfied that he actually discover'd the Substance or knew the spot from whence it came: I think at least he should have inform'd his benefactors.
. . .
If you are not already acquainted with the Cabinet of Madlle de Raab I conclude you will take a view of it in your next Tour of the Continent; had I been 20 or 30 Years Younger nothing would have given me more Pleasure than to have seen some of the Foreign Curious Cabinets. I wish we had Baron Born in Cornwall.

Strangers who come into this County now and then seeing a Specimen which appears beautiful, give a great price for it, & the Dealers then think every thing they can procure is inestimable: There are two or three Persons in Redruth who pick up a Specimen sometimes and ask even more than Moses: I have endeavour'd to get some Miners to Work a little in order to procure some more specimens of Fluor, my Brother Charles has been to St. Agnes & set them to Work under a careful Person and I soon hope to proffit from the adventure & if they succeed you shall have a supply, but I fear they differ to what I have got, which though New to me may not be so to You. You may form some Idea of these Crystals from a scratching of them below. [Brief description of five items] If you have seen the originals you will say what a sad Idea I give by the outline.[1]

I tried the xtals from Polgooth immediately on bringing them home by the method, You mention, but could produce no sign of Cobalt, nothing but Sulphur & Iron, and some other Earth: so that I believe they will prove to be nothing but Mundick with the outside tinged with a thin coat of Iron.

Next Thursday our Miners are to settle a New Contract with all the Companies for their Copper Ore: the Proposals are better than the present but whether they are so good as they ought to be I cannot Judge: the proposals are a Standard of £76 & 50d; Returning Charges or £74 & 45d Returning Charges, this will make a difference whether the Ores are Rich or Poor.

Though I had not the pleasure of seeing You in Cornwall yet I hope you will not leave London before I get there, which will be some short time before our Petition gets to a Committee after Xmas.

I find Baron Linden that has been Traveling so much & is so fond of it that he has injured his Fortune in the 10 Years Tour, & now wishes to Assist any Young Gentleman unacquainted with the Customs of different Countries where he thinks he can be useful.[2]

Notes
1. Russell stated that these specimens of Fluorite were obtained from the Trevaunce & Pell Mines at St. Agnes: see Russell, 'Philip Rashleigh', 6.
2. Probably a reference to Baron Lindenthal

CRO, Truro: Hawkins Archive: J3/12/1355
Rev. William Gregor to John Hawkins

undated [?January 1791][1]

Had I known that you were still in London, I wd have troubled you with a letter long since. On My Brother's arrival I have learnt this agreeable piece of Intelligence.

I have not much in the Mineralogical way to write to you. – One thing however I cannot help asking you about. – I was not long ago informed that near Helstone there was some appearance of a Salt in the side of the road. – I went to see it. I cd. not discover much traces of this appearance as the white particles wh were in the road appear'd to me to be Mildew. But on Examination I found [the] earth wh I collected from the road to contain some

Salt. . . . [account of various chemical tests made by Gregor] These
Chrystals have puzzled me much.

[Further detailed account of experiments on this and the results
and his thoughts]

. . .

I have lately met with a Mineral wh is very heavy, wh appears
from the very few experim'ts. I have made with it to contain Tin,
Iron, & some traces of Cobalt. I have met with slags of this kind
more than once before mixed with Arsenick, more of which distiled
water took up a small quantity consist'd of Tin united to the Acid
of Arsenick. The Mineral I mean above was given to me as coming
out of a Lode. Of this you shall hear more when I write next.

I have not prosecuted my inquiries on Menackanite. I at one
time had an idea that the calx might consist of Tin & Manganese,
but I have not tryed [sic] with yet w'th this view. The Silver ore as
they call it, of wh. you have heard no doubt & seen specimens is
very difficult to procure. A very little piece wh I had, I found to
contain Iron, Lead & silver united to some Acid. Let me hear from
you soon.

Note
  1. The reference to the Helstone earth indicates the letter was written
     c.1791.

CRO, Truro, Hawkins Archive: J3/12/1397
Rev. William Gregor to John Hawkins
undated [?January 1791]

[Part letter]
I return you many thanks for your very kind & lively letter, the
spirit of which was kept up with considerable ingenuity. Your
congratulations are not considered as words of course. – I enclose
you another Manuscript of Klaproth's. – I sent you by Mr. Carlyon
the Analyses of the Adamantine Spar by the same ingenious
Chemist and also the printed memoir on the Jargon. I had also
a lame translation of the Analysis of the Adamantine Spar. As
you have the original, I shd suppose that you stood in no need
of it, & if that be the case I shd be oblig'd to you for it. – If it be
inconven't, however to you to part with it, I will send it you by the
post directed to my Brother. – What you assure me concerning Dr.

J. Bank's observations on my paper for Menackanite for exceed
my ideas of it. If Sir J.B. really thinks it worth insertion in the Phil.
Transactions, he is wellcome [sic] to do what he pleases with it,
persons who read my short experiments on the sand will wonder
that I had not made many more, which will naturally occur to
them, as they did to me. But time & some chemical substances
failed me.

I have found the calcareous stones in this parish and there is also
a very black earth very frequently to be met with, whose Nature I
know not. As I have no apparatus of any kind. – I have no doubt
but that by a little labour & examination, a very good vein of lime
stone might be found in this Neighbourhood which wd be a great
object. –

I am exceedingly sorry that you will turn your face towards the
Continent soon. Yr. Mineralogical observations must be valuable
from the experience you have gain'd from so many different
sources & I am glad that you intend communicating them to the
world. – I hope that I shall now & then hear from you & whatever
I can do for you here, or whatever I may chance to observe, I
shall be happy to please you that I have not forgotten the many
favors I have received from you and how much I esteem your
friendship.

You promised to procure me a small quantity of the Ore of
Emery and some Molybdone. The former has not been sufficiently
examined & I wish'd to see whether some particular qualities
which I had found to belong to the Calx of Tungstein, applied also
to the Calx of Molybdone.

CRO, Truro, Hawkins Archive: J3/2/186
Rev. William Gregor to John Hawkins
Carhaise near Tregony, 8 January [?1791][1]

I have been a happy man for some days past, I am arriv'd at the
immense pile of Building of Carhaise.

The sea is beating upon the coast & the wind howling round
our windows, in short winter has summon'd up some of its horrors
to receive us. Yet we find the house comfortable and do not repine
at quitting the refinements of Bath. – This you will say is talking
like a new married man. – I can only assert the fact – In whatever
state I am in beleive [sic] me I shall always consider yr. friendship

an addition to it and I trust, that when you come into Cornwall you will come and see your old friend.

From what I can collect, there are great doubts concerning the truth of the facts concerning the reduction of the earths by the Hungarian – I have no furnaces here &c. and therefore am interrupted in the prosecution of my experiments, or otherwise I wd. try to reduce the calcareous earth – I shd. also extend my experiments on Menackanite – Some of my former experiments have been repeated in London with the same success – I have no doubt but that this substance will excite the attention of the curious, & perhaps may be converted to some use. Mr Woulfe has expressed his astonishment concerning it. I shall endeavour to find out some Lime stone in this Parish, there was a small quantity discover'd some time ago, such a discovery wd. be a real benefit to the Neighbourhood.

Can you procure me any information concerning the process for engraving in Aque tinta? – I have a very neat rolling press on the road – It may not, perhaps be amiss for you to know that poor Captain Carlyon in a very derang'd state has left his friends & gone to London. As nothing is too absurd for him to do, it may be proper for you to be advert'd of his being in London lest, he might alarm Mrs Trelawny or be guilty of any other mad act – This is entre nous – I hinted something to you concerning him sometime ago. –

The papers which you so kindly lent me, I can, if you please, send under diff't. covers directed to my Brother – We are, I find likely to have another poll at Lostwithiel but not for the representatives of the County but for the office of Cororner!!! [sic]

Note
  1. Probably January 1791, as there are several letters dated later that year which are sent from Caerhayes.

NHM, London, Mineral Library: Russell Bequest No. 24
Philip Rashleigh to John Hawkins

undated [?24 July 1791][1]

Yesterday Mr Hailstone brought me your Letter of Introduction, I am obliged to you for the Sight of Gentlemen who have any delight in Mineralogy, but such persons should give themselves a little more time. Mr Hailstone came just at Dinner time, & after that was Concluded, walk'd into the Cabinet Room in the Evening when I shew'd him a few of the Principal things there & he took his leave, not being persuaded to spend the Night here. You had given him such full directions to Guide his Tour that he wanted none from me. I believe he had never seen many Collections, but the very short time he stay'd gave me very little opportunity of Conversation with him. I shew'd him our New Silver Ore which I think is composed of Hornetz & Ochre of Lead, it has the appearance of a Gossan, but on near inspection some parts contain minute Crystals of a Greenish Colour & Cubic form, this part of the Lead is very tender & of a loose texture, other Veins have been found more Solid & easily cut with a Knife, these Veins are very thin; I could not see any of this sort at the Mine, but had a small piece given me by one of the Adventurers, I believe it to be the true Hornetz it leaves a silver appearance on the Touch Stone.

The Captains are pretty strict in preventing sampels [sic] from being carried away, as much of it would be Stole if they were not on the Watch, it being very easily converted into Silver. The Proprietors were all very civil in permitting me to see the Mine. They suppose enough is raised to enable them to build a Furnace, I wish they would consult you upon the most eligible Form of it. This Mine being in its infancy no Judgement can be form'd of its future Produce.

I expected to have heard you was on the Continent instead of being in Chandos Street, or I should have congratulated You, as I now do on your Brothers being a Baronet.

I believe you have heard of the Productions of a New Mine call'd Huel Noble in Ladock, the Appearances seem to be only Sulphur & Arsenick, but I am told it will run easily into a Regulus, either you or Mr. Wm. Gregor suppose it to be the same as the new ore in Germany which I have never seen or heard of.

Note
1. Hailstone visited Cornwall in July and August 1791; see letter from Hawkins to Rashleigh (27 August 1791) and Hailstone's letter to Hawkins (18 September 1791) following his return to Cambridge with his apology explaining that the 'transient glance' at Rashleigh's mineral collection was owing to a keen desire to get 'amongst the Mines' the source of such fine specimens'.

CRO, Truro, Hawkins Archive: J3/2/177
John Wedgwood to John Hawkins

Etruria, 12 August 1791

I am much obliged to you for your present of Volcanic fossils which arrived very safe & were very acceptable to me. Young Watt was with us at Etruria when they came & was much pleased with them after inspecting them. Tho' a pupil of Werner's he is become a convert to the igneous formation system of Basalt.[1] – He tells me he means in the next Manchester memoir to give a Statement of the two doctrines extracted from the works of the different supporters of each system. He will afterwards leave every one to form their own opinion on the subject with out any bias from his reasonings for he will give none. If this is executed with judgement & impartiality it will be a very acceptable present to all lovers of mineralogy for such a thing has long been wanted. We have lately melted platina here into a perfect malleable button or regulus by fusing it with Nitric & glacial acid of phosphorous & giving it a strong fire for about 5 hours. – Mr. Arnold the famous watchmaker was here & it was for him that the experiment was made & he says it is likely to be of the greatest advantage to him. He had meant to have laid out £100 in a lens but this fusion was equal to any thing he could have expected from the sun's rays so that expence is saved to him. – This is all the Chymical & mineralogical [information] I have picked up since I was last in London.

The two kernels of the dates which I had from you are now two trees near 9 inches high & thrive very fast.

Note
1. Gregory Watt, son of the engineer and scientist James Watt, read a paper at the Royal Society 'Observations on Basalt, and on the transition from the vitreous to the stony texture, which occurs in the gradual refrigeration of melted basalt', *Phil. Trans. R. Soc. London*, XCIX: 279-313. There is a memorial plaque to him in Exeter Cathedral.

CRO, Truro, Hawkins Archive: J3/2/138
Rev. William Gregor to John Hawkins
Killiow, 26th August [?1791]

I have just time to write to you a few lines to thank you for yr. kind letter & the communication of your excellent observations on the refining [of] our Tin. Your hints are so judicious & wd. so contribute to the credit & advantage of those who are so concerned in Tin, moreover they appear so little to shock the narrow prejudices of the Smelter, by deviating so slightly from the common mode, & thereby costing little to make the improvement, that one is much mortified that yr. plan was not eagerly adopted as soon as you suggested it. The lightness of Tin is a lucky quality wh. it possesses for it easy refinement & on that you founded yr. observations. I intended to have made some particular comments on yr. valuable Paper, & to have asked some questions concerning some [erasure] points, but I find that I have left yr. letter &c. at Caerhayse. I have never made any assays on our Tin Stone, [erased] being discouraged by the difficulty it attends its decomposition by Acids. But the slags wh. I have examined from the upper Blowing house at St. Austell are contaminated with the Calx of Wolfram & Iron, the solution of it in Marine acids forms a most beautiful Blue colour. I think also that it contains something analogous to the Plumbago consisting, as I shd suppose, of charcoal & Tin.

Mr. Giddy's acquaintance, I shall, I assure you for my own sake assiduously cultivate, he is a wonderfully acute man, & will be a great treasure to this or any County. He was so good as to spend a Day with me, Dr. Beddoes was with him, whom I dare say you are acquainted with. He is a great [stickler] for the cause of Fire, in the formation of Loads, basalt &c. He is certainly a very ingenuous man & the world is indebted to him for some very useful publications. –

I am much oblig'd to you also for yr. introducing Mr. Hailstone to me. I was very much pleased with him. I attended him to the Parish of St. Stephens. – We thought that [we] were led a fool's errand by a man there to see an old work wh. contained some ore wh. 'no body knew what it was' – we were much distressed on coming to it – we broke off some stones wh. appeared to contain nothing promising. I put one however into my pocket and on opening it on my arrival home, I was much pleased to find that where it was broken it was covered in many places with efflorescences of the colour of peach blossom I conclude therefore that it contains Cobalt.[1] This I have not been able to prove by experiment, wh. I must certainly shall when I return. –

I mean also to resume my expts. on Menackanite, as I hear, that Mr. Benellack has found out that it consists of various metals. – whether compound or simple it certainly is a curious production. I want very much to see Mr. Keir's paper on the menstruum formed by Vitriolic acid & Nitric.[2] There are some facts recorded in that paper wh. strike me as bearing some resemblance to wh. I have observed in Menackanite. But I have only seen a short extract in the Review. [? Tennant], I hear has done wonders – he is a very clever Man.

I wrote you that I had met with a curious soil containing some saline substances – Selenite, a salt in the form of Parallelopids wh. agrees in most respects married with lime, except in not deliquescing, as I have kept some unstopped in a paper for more than three weeks without its losing its figure. it shews traces of Vitriolic acid also – so that I think it a triple salt and [salited] Manganese – and a good deal of vegetable extractive matter. – If you have Rose de L'Isle, I shd. be oblig'd to you to let me know what figure muriated Lime assumes in its Chrystals. – The Salitic Manganese is also curious.

Lavoisier's Theory spreads. I have not seen Kirwan's recant, if he has [recomposed], he has done Credit to himself & the French Philosopher whose works are truly scientific I think.

I have now some commissions to trouble you with & questions to ask you. – I shd. so be oblig'd to you to buy for me one of the little pocket microscopes that you use to examine ores with. They are, I believe called 'Linnen tryers' & you of course know what is proper for the purpose. – Are any crucibles made of Porcelain such as Klaproth uses to be procured in London or does Mr. Wedgewood make any vessels for the same purpose? – The microscope I wd wish to be sent as soon as possible and if you will let me know its price, I can pay Mr. Chilcott who has, I shd. suppose, an acct. current with you. You promised me also a specimen of Emery & Molybdena – Have you any of the new earth from New South Wales that Mr. Wedgwood has analysed? Have you seen Mr. Gilpin's new work 'Forest Scenery'.[3] I ask your opinion of it before I buy it, as I have all Gilpin's other works. – I have now tired you.

. . .

Notes
   1. 'Peach blossom efflorescence' – pink powdery coating due to surface oxidation of the cobalt mineral Erythrite.
   2. James Keir (1735–1820) chemist, industrialist, poet and author; elected Fellow of the Royal Society 1785; Fellow of the Society of Antiquaries.
   3. Reference to Rev. W. Gilpin's *Remarks on Forest Scenery and other woodland views* (1791), based on his tours during the closing decades of the eighteenth century; editions of the work were still being published in 1834. Gilpin's notebooks and the MSS are now at the Bodleian Library.

CRO, Truro: DDR/5757/1/64
John Hawkins to Philip Rashleigh

Sunbury, 27th August 1791

I blame my freind Hailstone exceedingly for not having avail'd himself of your kind reception to examine one of the first rate collections that I know. He wrote me from Penzance[1] that your collection had astonished him, but that he could only take a glance at it being impatient to proceed into the heart of this mining country. For the same reason he passed by the Gregors. Your observation is just, he has seen very few things and has at present more zeal for Geognosy than the study of minerals, little aware of the impossibility of making much progress in the former without an accurate acquaintance with the latter. Pr. Hailstone who sides with me in referring the general strata of the earth to an aquatic formation met with the Fire-spouting Mineralogist Dr. Beddoes at Mr. Giddy's. Mr. Edwards who received these gentlemen at the Copper house wrote me a witticism of Dr. Smith of Pembroke, one of the party, "that they had Hailstones & Coals of Fire".

You generally gratify me with some Cornish mineralogical news. The silver ore from your description appears to be Horn ore as you say. Grey is the colour of this mineral which sometimes but rarely has a greenish cast, the cubic form of Xallization is common to this & vitreous silver ore but if very minute that is another circumstance in favour of your conjecture. This Horn ore is so soft as to yield an impression to the nail & so fusible as to melt at the flame of a candle. Claproth who lately analysed it found in 100 parts 67 of silver a little iron still less vitriolic acid & the rest muriatic acid. It is only found on the trail of lodes & in the most gossany part & as you will know in very small quantities.

Should the lode in working deeper be found to contain <u>real silver ores</u> & not merely argentiferous Galena I would recommend the adoption of Baron Born's new process of Amalgamation as now practised in Saxony. The Machinery & Apparatus may be made as small as they please. But it is not advisable for the managers to put themselves so much out of the common way before they have given a very effectual trial to the lode & ascertained the continuation of its rich argentiferous contents. Wm. Gregor writes me[2] that the little peice [sic] which he procured, was found to contain Iron, Lead & Silver united to some acid. Perhaps this was not a fair specimen, the lead might be merely adventitious.

I have received two specimens of what appeared to me to be common mundic from Huel Noble. I think all the mundics in that neighbourhood should be tried for gold.

I have receiv'd the two last volumes of Baron Born's catalogue of Miss Raab's Collection. The chemical part is conformable to the new Nomenclature, most of the new analysis's are cited & the Crystals described according to Rome de Lisle. But the arrangement is not such as will satisfy a Naturalist most of the external characters are slightly pass'd over and a number of artificial combinations are admitted, so that the author has no fixed & philosophical principle of arrangement. Among the rarities in this cabinet are muriated Antimony from Przibram in Bohemia of which I believe you have a specimen, Antimoniated Lead, the new white Gold or Gold mixed with a new metal from Transilvania & Silver alloyed with sulfurated Molybdena from Deutch Pilsen in Hungary. Of this last I have a specimen. B. Born beleives [sic] that the common Tin stone contains the Tungsten acid; from its specific Gravity.

I find by the German Revisions that Werner's Catalogue of Pabst von Ohain's Collection so long expected is now published. This in my opinion is the model of good arrangement and description.

A pupil of Werner's, young Watt of Birmingham, intends to publish in the next volume of the Manchester memoirs an impartial statement of the two doctrines of the formation of Basalt. Although I know that he is become a convert to the Igneous Theory we may expect something much [more] satisfactory upon this subject than what is contai[ned] in Dr. Beddoes paper.

I have not yet sent off my Cornish specimens to Miss Raab so if you have any very small duplicates I shall be very glad to receive them & send them in your name, any solid bits of the more rare

Cornish Minerals would be very acceptable to my freind Claproth for Analysis. My German boxes are yet unopened but contain many large specimens intended for your cabinet & really collected with that view. I believe now that I shall defer my journey to next year.

Notes
1. Hailstone's letter from Penzance has not survived, but see that of 18 September 1791 (NHM 156-157).
2. Gregor's undated [January 1791] letter (J3/12/1355) (reproduced above).

CRO, Truro, Rashleigh papers: DDR/5757/1/65
John Hawkins to Philip Rashleigh   *12 September 1791*

In answer to your enquiries dated the 31st of August I assure you that any thing which is tolerably well chosen & preserved will be acceptable either of Cornwall or of the northern counties and that you will greatly oblige the lady from whom you will probably procure a copy of her Catalogue. The size I have marked over leaf which she gave me but precision is not required.[1]

I know now for certain that Baron Born is no more, his decease was sudden and after he had experienced a suspension of pain for some weeks. The disease which has put an untimely end to his existence arose from an accident in descending a mine which he describes in his Letters on Hungary. It was a nervous affection which settled in his feet and for eighteen years had persisted at short intervals to torment him. Since I have known him he has scarcely a day free from pain and never a fortnight without paroxisms during which he suffer'd excruciating agonies. His life has certainly been prolonged some years by medical skill but I fear that the suddenness of his death must be attributed to the prescriptions of a Quack which afforded him some temporary relief. And so flattered his hopes of existence that he wrote me & Mr. Greville in terms unusually sanguine for a man so emaciated by disease.

He is a character whom I can never contemplate but with admiration, he deserved to live in a better age and to wear a crown, for of all the men whom I have known abroad he possessed the quickest conception of thought and the greatest comprehension of mind with a heart very sensible to the calls of humanity. He was all intellect if I may so describe a man whose body was wasted to a shadow & whose mind was incessantly at work.

In consequence of a foolish match made in a very early time of life he has been a stranger to domestic happiness and he has experienced all that envy & malignity could effect, in his profession and public concerns, insomuch that he is said to have left his affairs in a very embarrassed state.

I find by Miss Raab's catalogue that Tin has been lately discovered at Monte Rey in Gallicia and there are some specimens in the collection from thence. This discovery confirms the assertion of Pliny which before I much doubted.

Note
1. Hawkins had drawn a rectangle 2" x 1½" as a template for the size of Miss Raab's specimens.

NHM, Mineralogy Library: Russell Bequest 156-157
John Hailstone to John Hawkins
Trinity College, Cambridge, 18 September 1791

I have every reason in the world to be delighted with my Cornish Tour & thankful to those who contributed in so unreserved a manner to my profit & amusement. The attention of the Gregors was extremely flattering to me, from the chemical abilities of one & the great & patriotic mind of the other. Cornwall as much in store. My Apology to Mr. Rashleigh must be my extreme desire to get amongst the Mines which the transient glance of his immense collection served to increase. It requires months & not days to view it as it deserves. Mr. Edwards offered me all his assistance & gave me an introduction to Mr. Benallack of Redruth which was of great service to me. The hospitality of Mr. Giddy of Penzance & of the family at Tredrea I shall always remember. David Giddy's acquaintance is very valuable & I hope to cultivate it to a greater extent.

The story of my conversion at Cooks Kitchen is as you observe a trick of the Fire-spouters. My observations during 5 hours that I was underground at that work were of an opposite tendency. Dr. B[eddoes] is much attached to Hutton's theory & it was the report current of your Countrymen that he was come to prove their county made by Fire & that my Errand was to shew it was made by Water. He fancies that he sees a confirmation of his ideas in the Copper Gossans many of which seem to have undergone the Fire, & it was his luck to meet with Mr. Gullet at his first entrance into Cornwall who has made a collection of Gossans with this very view & who was surprised to hear that Dr. Hutton had been beforehand & had published the very same Hypothesis which Gullet wished to assume the merit of inventing. Dr. B. says that he has imitations of all sorts of Stones from Granite to Flint from the Iron works in Shropshire so like the originals that they cannot be distinguished. Every kind of blue Rock & especially your Frestone he calls by the comprehensive name of Basaltes. You may suppose we had some differences in opinion upon these subjects but notwithstanding I passed some days very pleasantly in his company. There is a Freedom of Thinking about him which inspires one with esteem. I have a project to consult you about in this letter which will leave no room for any thing but a naked Journal of my transactions after writing from Penzance.

. . .

The project I allude to is to read a set of Lectures in the University on these subjects but as it is a new theory it will be right to publish beforehand a sort of Plan of the manner of treating the subject. My intention is to divide it into two parts. 1st Mineralogy strictly called & the 2nd Geology – to this latter I shall refer all that [was] said upon the Taxa & Petrefacta. In the first part I [make] a chemical arrangement & Werner's method of Description [illegible] this view his Tables ought to be translated & annexed to the Syllabus. I have the French translation of his Essay & have already translated his Terms of Art tho' not entirely to my satisfaction.

The introduction of technical mineralogical Language would be of great advantage but then the terms must be well chosen and precise to ensure it any reception. Each article besides its Nat. History might be rendered interesting with an account of its oeconomical Ores. You will perhaps urge to me that the Collection is not splendid & extensive enough for such a plan but you know the People here know nothing of the matter & the defect would be growing less & less. The Post is ready to set out I must therefore conclude by desiring your thoughts on this matter when you have leisure.

NHM, Mineral Library: Russell Bequest No. 26
Philip Rashleigh to John Hawkins *[?] October 1791*

Least a further delay in sending the Minerals to Mademoiselle Raab should be thought neglect, I have pack'd up such as I could lay my Hands upon & sent them by Russells Waggon & hope they will get safe to Your Address in Chandos Street. Perhaps many of them are too small to be admited [sic] into Miss Raab's Collection, & if so, I shall be glad to receive them again without displeasure. I think for the Number & Seize [sic] they are a Valuable Collection, as most of them are in good preservation they will, at least, be some addition to what you have collected for her. As I know you can add the Wood-like Tin Ore, I have sent none of it. I could not find just now a better specimen of the Pointed Fluor, that Mineral being very difficult to get Perfect. The Catalogue is inclosed & as the Lady may not understand English, I dare say she will apply to You for a translation. As I am unacquainted with what the Lady has got, I have sent such as are most scarce here, if You think they are not worth sending you will detain them.[1]

I really know not what to send Mr.Klaproth, as he has seen most of our Minerals.

[A separate sheet lists the Mineral specimens.]

I have been to the Lead Mine at the Low Pool, but found nothing Curious there, or any way tending to it, but Mr. Rogers gave me a very pretty Piece of Ore with White flat Crystals of Lead Ore of an uncommon form such as – [Rashleigh has drawn a small sketch of crystal faces] which came from Penrose mine.[2]

I wish I could find a good clever man to Draw & Colour some of my Minerals, as I think some are worth Notice; I would hire such a person, if to be found on moderate terms, but I should not like an indifferent hand. My time is drawing fast to an end, & therefore if my Friends propose to favor me with any New Subjects of Curiosity for my amusement, they should not postpone them long. I have had a box ready pack'd for two if not three Years in expectation of an Exchange with Denmark. I have likewise many things laid by for Mr. Jacquin: but by your Advice I do not send them away.

I am told Tungsten is to be found in large Pieces in this County, but it has escaped my Search. Raspe has set many enquiries on foot after it, but I doubt if he ever found it.

This is a very busy time of Year with us by Mayors Chusing & Feasting, not the most Pleasant way of spending a Week.

Notes
   1. Letter annotated 'Answd. Nov. 23rd'; the specimens appear to have
      been sent to Miss Raab in 1791.
   2. Russell, (1952: 7), identified the mineral referred to as Anglesite
      and stated that the locality should be Wheal Rose, Sithney and
      not Wheal Penrose – but P. Golley, P., and R. Williams, *Cornish
      Mineral Reference Manual* (Truro: Endsleigh, 1995), list it under
      both.

CRO, Truro, Rashleigh papers: DDR/5757/1/66
Rev. William Gregor to Philip Rashleigh
Caerhayes, 27 October 1791

I received your kind letter. I wish I cd. give you any information
concerning the Mineral you enquire about. I have never met with
a specimen of Tungstein which was decisively the production of
this County. I have heard Mr. Raspe say that he had discovered
it in a mine on the land of the late Mr. Spernon, but I never saw
any of it, nor talked with any person who had seen it. Had I ever
discovered any, you may depend that I shd have informed you
of it, & contributed some of it to yr. very valuable collection of
Minerals, wh. the private Property, I consider, as a public Benefit
to this County. – The Other Ores, in which the metallic Calx
contained in Tungstein is found, occurs very frequently, I have
some specimens of Wolfram from Perran & that neighbourhood.
And lately at Kitt Hill I picked up some very pure pieces. – So
that if Tungstein is ever found to be useful in the Arts we may
expect to derive advantage from our Wolfram. When I am in
the Neighbourhood of Huel Fortune I will make enquiries about
the Tungstein said to be raised there. I have been informed that
Mr. Bennallack has asserted that Menackanite, wh. I thought to
be a simple Metallic Calx, is a compound & a pretty complex
compound too. He says that it consists of Cobalt, Tin, Calx of
Wolfram & Manganese & Iron.
   I have made some experiments wth a view to these Metals
but I cannot find any trace of Tin, Cobalt or Wolfram in this
Calx. I therefore do not intend to make a recantation till further
experiments force me to it. I shall believe that the Black Sand of
Menackan consists of Iron & a small portion of Manganese, united

to nearly half the weight of a peculiar metallic Calx <u>sui generis</u>. – I think it very probable that it may be found to be of use.

. . .

The Proprietors of the Silver Mine have been in doubt concerning the proper Processes for smelting the Ore & their Caution shew'd. their Wisdom. As it is well known fact, that in smelting Luna-Cornea & some other Silver Ores the Metal is volatilised & lost by improper Management. I have written to Mr. J. Hawkins to inform me of the usual Process in Germany &c & he has informed me what he can collect, wh. I shall send to Mr. Hennah. –

We had no extraordinary fall of Hail, at least that we can recollect, on the Day you mention[1] The size & figure of the Hail you describe is very remarkable. I much wonder that your glass in the green House resisted so well the 'Pelting of the pityless Storm'. From the shape of the stones wh. was parallelopipidon, they must meet with more resistance of the Air in their descent, & therefore they wd. lose some of their forces from that circumstance, but I shd. have thought that wd. have been fully compensated by their extraordinary weight. I shd. have thought that few panes of Glass in Menabilly wd. have stood any chance of escaping.

. . .

We are very sorry that we shall [illegible] forced to appear inattentive to yr. polite attention to us in favouring us both wth yr. company at Caerhaise, by not having return'd yr. visit. – But we have been in [daily] expect'n of having Chaise Horses & have been frequently disappointed. We hope however to do ourselves the pleasure of waiting on you before you leave the County.

Note
  1. See also Rashleigh's letter of 3 November 1791 to the President of the Royal Society.

CRO, Truro, Hawkins Archive: J3/2/214
John Hailstone to John Hawkins
                    Cowes, Isle of Wight, November [?1791]

Your last has afforded me equal pleasure & instruction in the perusal as exclusive of the offers of important asistance [sic], it contains an accurate view of the objects of Mineralogy in general.

The two principal branches are beyond doubt, Oryctognosy & Geognosy (as the Germans form their Greek derivatives; tho' I think it would be more agreeable to the Analogy of the English Language to use the terms Orycto<u>logy</u> & Geo<u>logy</u> in their room). To these two divisions all the rest may be rendered subordinate. Thus in treating of earth species belonging to Oryctology, after the Synonyms & external descriptions I would insert its Analysis & Chemical relations & Properties & then its Native Place History Natural œconomical & Literary ['bestimmter & eingeschränkter' written above]. Thus the article would be extensive enough to embrace every thing known upon the Mineral under consideration.

In describing, Mr. Werner's most admirable method must be adopted & explained. How incomplete are all descriptions but those drawn up after his principles. But in this undertaking what Loads of vague & unmeaning terms are to be removed, the Rubbish with which all smatterers deform the Science they pretend to cultivate. And how nice is the task of inventing new ones which shall convey our present ideas with steadiness & precision. I clearly see as you seem to intimate, that to overcome all these difficulties is nothing less than to translate Werner's little treatise into English. This if performed successfully would answer another useful purpose of bringing our countrymen (at present very uninformed, especially at Cambridge) acquainted with the true object of this science & the most judicious method of pursuing it. Had I sufficient knowledge of the original Language, I should think it my Duty as well as interest to set about this task without delay. The service which you offer in this occasion is of the highest consequence to any translator. I am aware that the French translation is imperfect but a more complete one is promised by M. Struve as I learn from a late No. of Royers Journal. I have nothing material upon the literary History of Mineralogy except what may be gathered from the introductory articles of Werner's treatise before mentioned and R. de L'Isle.

I thoroughly agree with you that the arrangement must be constructed upon the Ingredient whose characteristic properties predominate notwithstanding some difficulties which perhaps a more skilful analysis will obviate.

But what I consider as the most difficult part of my task is contained in the second great division of the subject. Geology is an ocean of Conjecture & Doubt. Whoever pretends to account for the Structure of the Globe by any of the Natural causes which we are at present acquainted with soon finds himself involved in difficulties which nothing but a most determined design of System-building will induce him to encounter. The method you propose of handling this subject is very judicious as it is independent of every Theory. I wish much to introduce a sober & cautious manner of philosophizing upon this subject, confessedly very abstruse as it embraces events which took place before the Annals & even traditions of all Nations & our stock of observations is hitherto very incomplete & unsatisfactory. Within this few years some valuable Mineralogical Travels have been made public abroad from these with the books you mention materials must be drawn.

The examples of Gneiss, Porphry Slate &c which you offer will be of great service to me in fixing my ideas of strata from which they are taken. You may have observed of late that the term Gneiss has become very fashionable with our English mineralogical Tourists whom I suspect affix the same indeterminate ideas to it that they universally do to the word Basaltes which with a certain Dr. of our acquaintance stands for a "large Natural Family" which comprised every thing but Granite & Limestone.

You will be surprized to receive this letter from the Isle of Wight but I have been here three weeks and shall probably stay two longer. Upon my return thro' London I propose paying my respects to you if there. The box that you mention being ready for me I shall be happy to escort to Cambridge. The new cabinet I got fixed & settled before I left that place. It answers perfectly well. It consists of about 30 drawers about 8 of which are occupied by your Volcanic productions. Should you have any commands or news a letter will find me directed under cover to Ld. Belgrave, Cowes, Isle of W.

And this reminds me of thanking you again for your last & apologizing for all the trouble I put you to.

Your Character of B. Born I admire & believe it very just from what I know of his writings. He is a loss to our Cause.[1]

Note
1. This reference to the death of Baron Born indicates the letter was written in November 1791.

Royal Society Library, L & P x 9: 2pp
Philip Rashleigh to The President of the Royal Society
Menabilly, 3 November 1791

Extraordinary showers of Hail & Pieces of Ice have sometimes made Articles of news in the Publick Papers, but I do not recollect to have seen more particulars than the Effect such Showers have had upon Glass & Vegetables, nor did I ever see such a Shower until the 20th of October 1791 about a Quarter after 3 o'Clock in the Afternoon. This was a Cold day with some common showers of Rain in the forenoon – About 3 o'Clock it became very dark and soon after a Shower fell which had the appearance of pieces of Ice, scatter'd very thin upon the Grass joining the House: the Novelty induced me to examine the composition, which I found to be made up of Hail-Stones of the most common size entirely cover'd with Ice; these were of various seizes [sic] & contain'd from two to five Hail-Stones in each piece of Ice; some of the largest measured an Inch & half long, an Inch broad & from half an Inch to ¾ of an Inch thick: This Storm came from the North West & extended no great distance. The Pieces of Ice were very Irregular, & in some places at a little distance they were observed to be longer & narrower than what I measured. The Shower lasted a very few Minutes and was attended with Thunder & Lightening.[1]

From the Hail Stones being entirely cover'd with Ice it is clear the Stones of Hail must have been a considerable height in the Atmosphere & by falling through a Watery Vapor congeel'd [sic] the Water by the Coldness of the Hail & then fell in the shape the Stones are described.

As trivial observations sometimes lead to more material Objects, Publick Societies ought to be the [Bypositories] where different Subjects should be brought for Communication. I therefore trouble You Sir, as President of the Royal Society with this Account, which if it contains only what others have commonly Observed You may commit to the Thames, or if New make such other use of as you may judge proper.

Note
1. See also letter above from Gregor to Rashleigh (27 Oct 1791) in response to his enquiry: Edward King, *Remarks concerning Stones said to have fallen from the Clouds* (1796), 18-19, referred to Rashleigh's account and figured his glass model of the largest hailstone.

CRO, Truro, Rashleigh Papers: DDR/5757/1/67
John Hawkins to Philip Rashleigh   *23 November 1791*

I have no other reason to assign for not having immediately acknowledged the receipt of your preceding letter and of the box of minerals but my intention of announcing at the same time the completion & final remittance of the collection to Vienna. This business is not yet accomplished for I wish to render this suite as perfect as possible and until I have nearly unpacked all my Cornish things cannot do it. There are a few numbers which either on account of their perfection or scarcity would be valuable additions to my own Cabinet such are No. 2, 7, 9, 22, 29. No. 4 & 30 being rather too large I can replace them with specimens equally good but smaller. 32 being stellated Antimony ore is too common at Vienna. No. 40 is not sufficiently interesting & No. 41 a specimen of the new Silver ore appears to be nothing but lead spar & ocher [sic] & at any rate a bad specimen not worth sending. Will you permit me to change the above numbers? I shall transmit a German Catalogue. I have given another hint about the projected exchange to a correspondent of young Jacquin (who is but lately returned to Vienna).

Mr Raspe intends to revisit Cornwall very soon & assures me that he knows a very easy simple mode of smelting the Horn silver ore.[1] Mr Raspe informs me that a specimen of the Tungsten spar was once brought him from a small Tin mine now abandoned at Pengelly nr. Breage, this testimony is corroborated by the description once given me by one of the Cap'ns. of the great work of a white heavy mineral found some years ago in a neighbouring mine, the circumstance made some impression upon me at the time and thus supported would induce me during my next visit to the County to make further enquiries. Some of your freinds [sic] should be directed to keep a good look out at Huel Butson (which is now in fash) after the xtallized Blende & yellow Copper which the inspection of the burrows has taught me to expect there.

I hope that you let none of the Glistening Tin pass by even the rich specimens of the Polgooth Tin are very curious & valuable although of a confused xtallization. This mine may cease to work in a few years & then this needle-like Tin will be sought after as a great rarity.

The process of Amalgamation has been greatly improved since I was in Hungary. I hope to see these improvements next summer at Freyberg & will then give you my opinion how far the process may be applied to our argentiferous Lead Ores in Cornwall. Our Tin Ores can never be amalgamated but Copper may be extracted from its ores by the process indicated by Baron Born & I am much mistaken if we cannot derive some advantage from the partial introduction in the fabrication of the purer Qualities.

I am sorry to inform you of the death of Baron Reden at Clausthal about the beginning of this month. I believe of a putrid fever, by all accounts very suddenly. Our freind Trebra will probably succeed him.

I have just received a very long letter from Claproth at Berlin whose professional occupations have prevented him lately from attending to mineralogical Chemistry. However he gives me the result of one Analysis which he had lately read before the Royal Society. The analysis of the Rothgiltig Erg or Red Vitreous Silver Ore, which serves again to prove how little we can depend upon the Analysis's of mineral bodies hitherto published. Not a trace was discovered of Arsenick which had been considered as the mineralizing matter, but instead of it Sulphur & Antimony. . . . Claproth expressed much commendation of Mr. Wm Gregor's Analysis of the Manachanite.

Mr. Davies Giddy was elected on Thursday last a member of the Royal Society. When you next see Mr. Charles Rashleigh do me the favour of presenting my Compts & of asking him whether the Records of the Dutchy will supply me with the quantity of coin'd Tin for a long series of years. I congratulate you & every Cornish Landholder on the present favourable state of the Mining Interest in consequence of the price of Tin & Copper.

Note
1. In 1791 Raspe published a translation of Born's *New Process of Amalgamation of Gold & Silver Ores*.

CRO, Truro, Hawkins Archive: J3/2/220
Rev. William Gregor to John Hawkins
Caerhayes, 25 November [?1791][1]

I feel myself much indebted to your kindness on many accounts, for your very kind letter, & for what I have since received, a packet of very valuable German Books by wh. I hope to gain instruction both to the matter & the language. – Nor have I forgotten the

Lendes and Keir's paper. But remember, I do not like to employ persons in executing commissions for me, who do not make a statement of what they expend for me. As this wd. most certainly hinder my begging them to execute any thing for me again.

I am much oblig'd to you for the trouble you have been at, in giving me an account of the process for smelting Silver ores; I have communicated it to Mr Hennah, But have heard nothing from him since. The Sale for the ores wh. was advertized, is put off, for what season I know not. This Silver Mine, as it has been called, has made people very industrious in investigating Veins of Metal on the Northern Cliffs. There is a load of Lead ore lately cut in the Parish of St. Minver, wh. is very large, & very near the surface. It is not like common Galena, as it has no Chrystallized appearance; I shd. suspect that it contains Antimony. I have just begun the Analysis of it & I find it to contain rather more than 15 in an hundred of sulphur, further I have not proceeded. But I shall finish the remaining process, as soon as circumstances permit me.

From some experiments, wh. I have made very lately on Menackanite, I begin to think, that this Calx, may by degrees be totally converted to the state of Iron & that therefore it is only Iron in a particular state. – If this be the case it will be a very curious fact in the History of iron & will not be without its use. You will naturally suppose that I am a little awakened by this idea, & intend prosecuting it with diligence. I am collecting a sufficient quantity of it for Experiments & shall let you know the result of them. I exposed 20 grains of it the other day to as intense a fire as a forge cd. raise without any signs of fusion – the heat was contin'd for an hour.

I wait also for some more of the Helstone earth, the last specimens I had, did not agree with the former in all respects, it however contain'd Salited Manganese – I shall make a regular Analysis of it. – But the Veg'ble. extractive Matter is very troublesome – and the Quantity of Salts is but small in a large qty. of earth. – I write in Haste, lest I shd. miss the Post, but I cd. not delay any longer to thank you for yr. accumulated favours.

I have rummaged over the Papers at Trewarthenick concerning the Stannary matters. I found amongst them an exact copy of the same work, the heads of wh. I sent to you. There is a Memorandum in it, that this Manuscript belonged to Sir John Maynard & it came to us by the means of the Colchester family. – I beg that in this or any other matter in wh. I can serve you in this County, that you wd. without reserve shew yr friendship for me, by employing me, & never consider the trouble. I must conclude this Hasty scrawl.

Note
   1. No year given, but the Helstone earth & Silver smelting were mentioned in previous letters sent during 1791.

NHM, Mineral Library, Russell Bequest No. 27/28
Philip Rashleigh to John Hawkins
Menabilly, 30 November 1791

I have no hesitation in permiting [sic] You to take the Specimens you mention from those intended for Miss Raab, as she stands much further removed as the Friend of my Friend, than the Friend himself who I meant to serve. As I sent you a much finer Specimen of No. 7 before I left London & which I had slit on purpose as you prefer'd it large, I did not think this Number would be of any Value to You: I think I can let you have another Specimen of the No. 9 unless it was a piece very bright & not infected with Mundick, as they generally are. No. 29 I believe is not to be had again, I thought this was too small for your Collection. No. 32 was sent as being the produce of Cornwall. No. 40 is exceeding scarce here & they ask a high price for it, I know of none but what I have, & don't know what the Green Crystals are: but suppose Crystal with Shirl or Peach. I look upon No. 41 to be as productive of Silver as any of the Gossan Ore, & have no doubt of its producing $7/100$ of pure Silver, as similar pieces have done.[1] It certainly is not so fine a Specimen as I could have wish'd, but the piece it came from in several trials produced 6,7,8, 10 in 100. [A] great part of this Load yields no Silver, some Yields abundantly more than the above, but [it] is a different Ore. I expected to have purchased some fine Crystallized Pieces at the Sale lately advertised, but that Sale is put off & the Load lost.

I have no great opinion of Mr. Raspe's adroitness in Smelting. These Silver Ores are best reduced with the least trouble; there is a part of the Load would Answer by amalgamation, but I believe the quantity of Ore not sufficient to answer the Expence. I think no production of this County will answer by Amalgamation except the Tin Ore from Streams productive of Gold, & from the experiments I have seen with this. I have every reason to believe it will answer well.

I am sorry for Baron Reden as he was promoter of the Art of Mining & I shall be very glad to hear that Baron Trebra succeeds him.

Mr. Claproth's is a very ingenious Acc't. of the Red Vitreous Silver Ore which I suppose is the Rothgulden, I think it very probable that some Specimens may contain Arsenick & others none, for there seems great variety from the same Mine: That which Decomposes & rots every thing near it, I should suppose contains Mundick with Nitrous Acid: as I think several of our Mundicks do – and should All be Analised by a better Chimist than Raspe.

I never saw Mr. Wm. Gregor's Analysis of the Manacanite: Mr. Benallick has supposed to have found (but I do not believe he has found) Cobalt, Tin, Calx of Wolfram, Manganese & Iron in the new Mineral: Mr. W.G. can find neither Cobalt Tin or Wolfram. I hear Mr. W.G. has discover'd Cobalt in St. Stephens.

My Bro'r. Charles says the Dutchy Office contains the Acc't. of Coind Tin, but he doubts if they will supply You with it: he has the quantity from the Year 1765.

Though the India Company have taken a large quantity of Tin, those who supply them will put nothing in their Pockets by such Sale, further than by the Consequences, which will raise the Price of what remains: considering that the County for some Years past has raised more Tin than the European markets consume it is a great thing to have such a quantity taken off the Smelters hands.

I thank you for reminding Mr. Jacquin of the proposals for an Exchange of Minerals. I only wish to know if it was agreeable or not. The Mine you speak of in Breage produced some – large Grains of Tin Ore in considerable Quantities of a very light Colour, but when I was there I could find no Tungsten, & I believe the Mine stop'd very soon after – I shall make some Enquiry about the produce of Huel Butron. Whenever I meet with uncommon Substances I am very Covetous & endeavour to secure all I can for myself & Friends. I still hope to get some of the new Mexico Silver ores but cannot yet get a good Piece tho' there are many.

. . .

Note

1. Rashleigh's lists of these minerals are preserved in the Mineral Library, N.H.M., London Russell Bequest Nos. 29 -30 – 'Catalogue

for Mlle Raab – small specimens by J. Hawkins Esqr. 1793' and 'Miss Raab's Catalogue alter'd & Renew'd the numbers taken or Rejected by J. Hawkins, Esqr'.

CRO, Truro, Hawkins Archive: J3/2/185
Rev. William Gregor to John Hawkins   *Undated [?1792]*

I always receive great pleasure & Information from yr. letters & I return you my thanks for yr. last favour. All I meant when I objected to not paying you for the lenses wh. you were so good as to send me, was that in performing <u>commissions</u> it was a wrong principle. As from a motive of delicacy, it naturally prevents a further applic'n. to the same person. – I shall be much oblig'd to you for Raspe's Transl'n. –

I have rummaged over all the old Manuscripts I can <u>yet</u> find at Trewarth'ck. But I know that there are some more still under the Books, wh. from a new access'n. from Restormel, are in no small confusion; when my Brother is gone, I shall endeavour to collect all the manuscripts I can find & mark on the outside their contents. I have inclosed all that I can think can be of use to you & these, I fear, will give you no new lights. However, I had rather send you trumpery than withhold what may be of service in yr. present useful investigation. No. (1) is the substance of a petition to a Convoc'n. held in 1660. There are two Letters annex'd. – Then follows an account of a Convoc'n. held 1710. – This is a long paper in the original & is useful as it gives all the [Towns] of a Convocation. If you wish me to be more particular in any of these things I will be more particular, wherever I have copied exactly I have mark'd it by 'commas'. – The letters are exact copies. – I shall continue my search into papers on this subject.

I have been peculiarly unfortunate in any Experimt's on Menachanite, as I have once lost all the qt'y I had procured by the falling of a crucible & another time a vessel containing the sol'n. met w'th the same fate. – I have however begun again & hope soon to give you the Result of my labours. – I told you that I had endeavoured to analyse a Lead Ore from H. Minver. I found some extraordinary qualities in it.

[A lengthy account of all his succession of chemical tests follows]

. . .

[Prescript] I shall procure Bertholet[1] on Dyeing, tho' I believe I have some pages of his on that subject am much oblig'd to you for yr. offer concerning Mr. Tennant's Paper. I dare say we shall have it soon in some periodical work.

Note
1. Comte Claude Bertholet (1748-1822) French chemist who discovered the bleaching properties of chlorine (1789) and the double decomposition of salts (1803).

CRO, Truro, Hawkins Archive: J3/2/190
John Hailstone to John Hawkins
Trinity College, Cambridge, 12 March 1792

I thank you most heartily for your last communication which has convinced me of the hastiness of my censure of Werner's Stile arising from my want of sufficient acquaintance with the Language. The Essay is now nearly written out for the press with your corrections and additions.

I think your hint respecting the geographical arrangement of the British fossils very deserving of being executed. I know enough of the North of <u>England</u> to sketch out the general Outlines of the Mountains but cannot pretend to detail with accuracy all its Mining Districts. If you will be so kind as to send me the West, I will endeavour to annex the North as well as I am able.

Your Descriptions of the Ohain & Leske Collections with the Notices of the principal ones in Europe would I think form a very proper Supplementary Note to the Essay could you spare as much time as is requisite to draw them up. You know with what Difficulty every foreign Work is got into the University. I have not therefore as yet had an opportunity of perusing Werner & Karsten's Catalogues though I expect them every day from our Bookseller. It will be very necessary and acceptable to English Chemists to annex Karsten's Tables to the Syllabus if they arrive in time.

I have not seen Dr. Beddoes' Syllabus nor have I at present any very great wishes for that purpose as probably it would not afford me much asistance [sic] and interfere with my present ideas on the subject of arrangement which is almost as difficult as composition if executed well. My ideas run in the following train

[Numbered list of aspects of Natural history to be studied with an itemised sequence for Mineralogy]

By this means the other branches of Mineralogy are interwoven in the Course at their proper places. It might perhaps be as well to annex a few Synonyms tho' I don't conceive this of much use as the Science is yet in its infancy. The German names would be of much more importance.

I find much confusion in Authors respecting the proportion of the different earths that shall constitute Feldspath as distinct from Schorl. I wish the subjects of the second part of the Lectures Geognosy, were arranged to my hands, they have given me more trouble than the above by a great deal. I have not time to lay my method before you at present, it comprises a good deal of what is sometimes termed Physical Geography.

. . .

I have been trying Lowitz's Experiments with Charcoal lately and find that they will not succeed if access of air be prevented whence it follows I think that this purifying power is to be ascribed to the property which charcoal possesses of attracting oxygen and thereby <u>burning</u> as it were all the feculencies.[1]

. . .

Note
1. Feculencies were the dirty dregs & unwanted substances.

CRO, Truro, Rashleigh Letters: DDR/5757/1/68
John Hawkins to Philip Rashleigh   *undated [10 June 1792]*

My engagements have occasionn'd [sic] some delay in acknowledging the receipt of your favour and in returning you my thanks for your kind attention and endeavours to render my Cornish collection for Miss Raab as compleat as possible. The transparent green ore of Copper in hexagonal Tables which you mention must be the green mica of Werner examined by Bergman or a mention of that muriatic acid with Copper and argillaceous earth at least according to Bergman for we have no compleat analysis of this very rare mineral.

The hexagonal xallization is peculiar to Cornwall for that of Saxony & Bohemia is a square table with a particular truncation at the edges. Certainly I shall be very glad to send Miss Raab such a specimen as you mention but I should be glad at the same time to secure one for myself at least for the purpose of carrying over & shewing to Werner and still more so if you could procure me a small solid piece to have analyzed by Klaproth.

I believe I have not mentioned an alteration of the plan of my tour subservient I think to your departure for town. I shall pass the Autumn & Winter in Germany, the latter at Freyberg with Werner whose late admirable Work <u>A new Theory of the origin & Formation of Lodes</u> I have now in my hands.[1]

[Hawkins here outlined the main points of this theory and then listed three Criteria according to Werner that established the relative Age of such Lodes and the features by which they could be distinguished]

Mrs Powell has been in town. I bought a few things. I still hope that I shall have time to unpack some of my German Fossils & transmit to you some of their contents. Professor Hailstone will meet me in Germany & accompany me to Freyberg.

I wish you would draw up an account of the Moose Deer horns found in the Stream Works for the Royal Society.[2] It is an interesting circumstance in the Physical & mineralogical Geography of the County.

Mr Schmeisser can make nothing of the Manachanite. I know Mr. Wittenbach by reputation very well – he is an ingenious man & few better know the mineralogical curiosities of Switzerland. I have given letters of recommendation to you to Gen'l. Komargewski & Dr. Herschel.

Notes
1. C. Anderson translated Werner's theory in 1809; see P. G. Embrey and R. F. Symes, *Minerals of Cornwall and Devon* (London: British Museum (Natural History), 1987), 9-10, for current terminology of the principal vein systems (lodes) and replacement structures.
2. See also subsequent letters 20 July, 3 and 17 October 1792; Hawkins eventually communicated Rashleigh's account of these stream works, drawn up in 1792 for publication in the *Trans. Roy. Geol. Soc. Cornwall*, 2, 1822: 281-284.

CRO, Truro: Hawkins Archive: J/3/2/196
Philip Rashleigh to John Hawkins

Menabilly, 16 June 1792

I thank You for a letter I received from You very lately without
a Date: In the first place I must execute a Commission from my
Bro'r. Charles & tell You the Business you Writ him upon may be
done in the manner you mention.

I hope to send You Green Crystallized Transparent Copper Ore
before you leave London if you will give me a Fortnight's Notice
before You begin your Journey. I never saw but one Specimen of
this Ore until very lately, & that was at Pendarves; it certainly
contains a great deal of Copper, but in what proportion I cannot
Exactly tell: This Ore does not appear Solid, but is crystallized
in thin Plates in the Hollow parts of the Stone, but having broke
a piece not very Fortunately, I have saved the shatter'd parts for
Experiments: The chief Body of Ore in which these Crysals [sic]
are found is a solid Red Substance intermix'd with Mundick or
some other Mineral substance of the like Appearance: The Red
ore is not the Common Red Copper Ore, it is not so Rich by half:
& I should suppose contains much more Iron.

I think Mr. Werner is right in his Opinion that All True Lodes
are Real Fissures & fill'd with the Mineral substance after the
Fissure has been made, & that the Fissures have been caused
by earthquakes, or the Settlement of the Strata after loosing
[sic] its Softness & Humidity: but I do not think that every
Lode intersecting another Lode is more recent than that which
it intersects, especially such Lodes as carry the same Substances
with each other; but where a Cross lode is composed of different
Matter, then I think it evident that such a Cross Lode must be
more Recent; they could never be form'd at the same time; but
after the main Lode has been form'd, I see no reason why the
Lode itself may not be separated by an Earthquake in a Cross
direction, & then the Fissure fill'd with other matter; but if fill'd
with the same matter; then I think it most probable the Fissures
were caus'd by loosing [sic] the Humidity. If the General Mass by
which the Fissures would be made in different directions, & being
of equal Levels / altitudes would fill at the same time with the
same Matter.

[Hawkins Annotation inserted: 'the impetus in whatever
direction it came would certainly exaust [sic] itself on the fissure

already [sic] open instead of producing any fresh one on the entire rock.']

– I do not see why the Middle of a Lode should be more recent than what is nearer the Walls, for if the whole Lode was in a Fluid State when it came into the Fissure it would find equal Levels, but it is most probable that what recurs in the upper Levels of a lode should be more Recent than what is found in Inferior Levels. I perfectly agree to the 3rd Proposition, nothing can prove it more plain than some of our Fluors.

Before I left London, Mrs. Powell told me she was in daily Expectation of some New Specimens. I shall be very glad to remove any Specimens you may think proper to send me before you go over the Water. I shall be very glad to see Gen. Komartzereskai & Dr. Herschel; the former knows Menabilly, but the Poles will want his Assistance if Russia proceeds with Invading their Country. Our Miners are very eager in Searching for Ore of Tin & Copper, but I hear Nothing New. I suppose you will wait to see the Disturbance in Germany a little abated before you make an Excursion into that Country.

I fear we shall loose Mr William Gregor out of Cornwall, the Bishop having given him a Living in Devonshire worth 250£ a Yr. The Smugler [sic] which beat off the Revenue Cutter with the Assistance of Guns from the Shore, is Taken.

CRO, Truro, Hawkins Archive: J3/2/203
John Hailstone to John Hawkins
Hamburg, 14 September 1792

I received much pleasure from the perusal of your last which arrived on the very day that I had persuaded myself I should hear from you. Your conjecture is well grounded respecting my stay in Hamburg. You will perceive that I have not yet left it. It is not as you seem to imagine a place that furnishes much amusement to a stranger. What has induced me chiefly to prolong my residence here is the great leisure which I find myself possessed of. In a world of mercantile people every one is too much occupied with his own affairs to enquire what his neighbour is about. And this is exactly my case. I live in the middle of the City in an inn surrounded by the <u>Kaufleute</u> yet I attract the observation of none and do just as

I please. My time as you will conclude is all devoted to the study of German Literature and tho' very favourable to so much of my plan as regards the <u>reading</u> of the language yet I add with regret it is too solitary to advance me much in the talent of <u>speaking</u> it. As for a Table d'Hote there is the confusion of Babel rather than any distinct language.

To speak the truth I should have left Hamburg some time ago if I had not met with a few very well informed literary men with whom I sometimes pass a few hours in a very agreeable manner. . . . But however I seriously think of leaving this crowded & dirty place soon, and wish you had been a little more explicit in mentioning the place where you thought it probable our rencontre would happen as that would have helped me to determine my route with precision. Shall you take the Hartz in your way to Freiburg? or do you push on directly for the latter place? From another perusal of your letter which I have just made I think you intend to pass by the Hartz.

That Ramsden[1] is an arrant Schurk as we say in German – I am infinitely indebted to you for your assiduity. The set of queries which you have just distributed is I fancy a new one. I wish you could establish an enlightened correspondent in one of our stratified mining Countries, as Derbyshire for instance, as it is of great importance to compare the phœnomena of the Lodes in different sorts of Countries and would certainly throw much light upon Geognosy.

I am much pleased with Raspe's discovery, as likewise with the alacrity of the Miners of Cornwall. Here is an immense consumption of Copper in Hamburg as no lead whatever is used about their buildings and their enormous church spires are entirely covered with sheets of that metal which the air has calcined and formed a coat of green Malachite over them.

I am sorry Dr. Beddoes has relinquished the translation of Werner's work. Was it owing to his favourite Prejudices that he became disgusted? – I have thought of nothing less than Mineralogy for this last month being occupied with the general Literature of Germany with which I am wonderfully delighted already and see new sources of information & pleasure opening to me. At Freiberg however I shall return with the greater appetite to the leading object of my [page torn with loss] after so long an abstinence.

Here is a terrible report to day which I hope will not be authenticated, that Luckner has engaged the Prussians and been beat with immense slaughter. No one execrates this infernal

League of the Powers of darkness more than myself. Yet I do not think the Jacobines take the best measures for the salvation of their unhappy country.

. . .

Note
  1. Ramsden, had been asked to provide a barometer for use on Hailstone's expedition – (see letters of 1 and 14 July 1792).

CRO, Truro, Hawkins Letters: J3/3/209
Philip Rashleigh to John Hawkins
Menabilly, 17 October 1792

I think Your Friends have shewn their Affection to You by persuading you to defer your Tour for some Months; I think very few places on the Continent are at present in a situation for Searching after Natural objects. A Country should be Quiet & Composed for such Scheems [sic], or you might be taken for a Spy as others of my Acquaintance have been. –

I shall incluse [sic] You a Sketch of the Bull's Horns found at Porth, that is the Pelt without the Horn, for no part of the Horn remains. The other Horns are just the same as the Forest Stags; Bon, Bay, & Tray with three on Top; & one with four on Top. Sir John Call desired some time ago that I would observe the different Alluvial Strata in this Moor, & he would add a Drawing of Carn's Machine for moving the Ground, which he thought would be a proper Subject to Exhibit before the Society of Antiquaries. You think it worthy of observation by the Royal Society of London; & the Editors of the Mining Journal at Freyberg. I do not know that either of the Societies would think it worth Reading, but I have no Objection to its being Communicated to any, of this you are the best Judge.[1]

Lady Falmouth tells me you have had a very great Collection of Minerals sent you from Cornwall, so that I do not wonder you are able to supply Mr. Werner with one so complete from this County.

I very much fear the Letters I writ in last April to Baron Trebra & Mr. Knorre, were not deliver'd to our Post Office, but that the Postage was Pocketed by the letter carrier, & the Letters destroy'd: Mr Knorre knew not of what Vessel to enquire of for the Box; as a good Specimen of the Olive Green Tin Ore was in the Box which your Friend did not see in Mr. Trebra's Cabinet. I should have liked to have known Werner's Scholar's description of the Things I sent Baron Trebra, but being in German I should not understand it. I shall be exceeding glad to see your observations on the mineral Veins of Cornwall, for I really think as much knowledge is to be obtain'd by an Accurate Observer of this Country, as of any in the World. I will endeavour to Collect the Varieties of Elvan Stone for You, but I think they are not Numerous in this Neighbourhood, I don't know what the Fire Stone is, unless you mean a bastard Opal.

I believe there never was so much rain as this Season, & I fear the Corn cut will be Damaged so as to lessen the supply at the Markets; & the Tillage has been delay'd: so that the Export of Wheat, the import of People from France, a Wet Harvest & late Tillage, will be the Cause of Distress.

. . .

P.S. Your Bro'r is Promoteing a Publick Library at Truro. I have no great Idea of the utility of it, except to those either in or near the Town.

Note
1. Eventually, published in 1822 through Hawkins.

CRO, Truro, Hawkins Archive: J3/2/219
Rev. William Gregor to John Hawkins
Coldrinnick, 24 November 1792

I am sorry to say that I can give you no satisfactory cause why I have not answer'd your kind Letter before this Time. Believe me I do not feel the less satisfaction on the acct. of your lengthened residence in England, because I have not expressed it – I wish that you cd. be prevailed upon to fix your root in the soil & benefit your Native Country. – I have little now to say to you but to thank you for your very kind Letter and for your Manuscript on the German language wh. I have received some time & doubt not but that it will be of use to me. When you see Dr. Pearson thank him for me for his ingenious Paper on the Decomposit'n of the Aerial Acid. I hope to write to him before a long time.

From delay in receiving some Glass vessels &c. I have been

prevented from finishing a Chemico-Pneumatical apparatus wh. I think necessary in order to make a fuller investig'n. of Menackanite. I have constructed also a pair of bellows for bending glass Tubes & wh. I find very convenient as it saves your lungs the trouble of puffing & blowing.

[brief comments on various specimens and experiments]

We had a large copper meeting at Truro on the 22nd. My Brother made a long speech to shew that Sir. F. Bassett's proportions were Impolite to us & unjust to the East India Company. We made a motion that they shd. be rescinded & he then brought forward others in their [turn]. I think he did himself credit, Mr Tremayne seconded the motion. Sir F. complained that he had not suff't. notice that he came unprepared, that business of such moment requires the most serious deliberation & he then made some short cavils for this as his mode of answering arguments. – The meeting was at last adjourned to a future day in the beginning of December.

I have not subscribed to the Truro Library, because I do not think it probable to be of such a sort as to answer the ideas of a County Library. As [a] County Library ought to consist of books of Science & books of value w'ch. you do not meet w'th in general in the Country. I am not at all certain (I am sorry to say) that I shall remain in this Neighbourhood. – Can particular papers in the Philos'l. Transactions be procured? If this be the case, I sh'd. with that you wd. procure me John Hunter's paper on Bees with the proviso that you put it down to my account.

CRO, Truro, Hawkins Letters: DDR/5757/1/74
John Hawkins to Philip Rashleigh   *28 November 1792*

I enclose a letter from <u>Baron Trebra</u> received by yesterday's post. In his letter to me he acknowledges the receipt of your minerals (he says not when) in return for which he will send you the few good specimens which he has been able to procure.

I have now your two letters to answer I cannot precisely tell you where Raspe found the aerated Barites. Chevalier Nassion found it two years ago in North Wales. Raspe spot is not far from Minsterly in Shropshire.

Young Pennant who is just arrived in town tells me that his father dares not pronounce on the horns. My opinion of this gentleman's merits as a naturalist nearly coincides with yours. The Clay from Norfolk Island is not the same as that analysed by Mr. Wedgewood. I have deferr'd sending you the box of specimens from inattention but will do it in a few days.

I am surprised at your not knowing Elvan & Frestone, or rather at your knowing them under exchanged names. The first may be called in reference to its utility in building. <u>Frestone</u> but all miners know it under the name of <u>Elvan</u> & mineralogists would call it a <u>Porphiry</u>. The great Cross Course Channel or Quarry at Polgooth is composed of this rock. This course by a singular collision of names is there called Elvan or Elvean. The second is the very hard black rock which you describe & which is so common in the hundred of Penwith & there usually skirts the Granit [sic]. I beleive [sic] it is allso [sic] found at St. Agnes.

I feel myself much obliged by the pains you have taken to search for both substances. I hope my letters have not <u>misslead</u> [sic] you in respect to the names. I might have accidentally written one name for another. When you next go to St. Agnes, or have an opportunity you would oblige me much by procuring me a few plain specimens of <u>Peach.</u> You know that Werner calls it <u>Chlorit</u>.

Have you heard of the great discovery of a new fluid like the electrical, which pervades the nerves of animals & under certain circumstances stimulates their muscles.

The great Works constructed at a vast expence at Freyberg for amalgamating the Silver Ores were accidentally burnt to the ground a few weeks ago. Baron Trebra proceeds with experiments on Lead Smelting with Iron precipitates. My letters from abroad announce symptoms of great political fermentation in Italy. I am informed that from the tin mines lately discovered at Monte Ré in Gallicia 600 Tons (black tin) have been raised.

A very ingenious young Spaniard belonging to the Mining Department at Madrid & a pupil of Werner proposes to pass through Cornwall on his return soon. I shall take the liberty of giving him a letter of introduction to you, but at St. Austell I must abandon him to the risk of being treated as a mining Spy. You may mention to Cap'n. Phillips when you see him that if such a person should make his appearance at Polgooth there will be little occasion to watch him, he can do very little mischief. Perhaps he may pick a bit of Tin out of the halvans or break specimen of Killas, or stare while at the Whims, but I shall counsel him not to enter the Fire Engine house nor to ask a single question.

NHM, Mineral Library, Russell Bequest, Hawkins Letters
No. 33/34
Philip Rashleigh to John Hawkins
Menabilly, 1 December 1792

Your letter inclosing one from Baron de Trebra I received this
Morning & am much Obliged as well as Indebted to You for it.
My German Linguist not being near If you will be kind enough to
read this Letter & inform me of its contents, it will give you trouble
& me Satisfaction of such particulars as I am unacquainted with:
and add further Obligations. I find the Baron likes the Olive Green
Tincroft Ore & the Huel Boys Antimony which I thought would
please him.

You might well be surprised at my not knowing the Elvan Stone,
I always took it for a Fire Stone until lately, & now I am better
inform'd I shall procure it for You. The Channel at Polgooth runs
pretty near through the County, the Stone near Truro is very
similar; with these you shall be supplied: and as the Frestone is in
this Parish & what I have long observed, I shall have no difficulty
in geting [sic] as much as you want, I have already brought a few
Pieces home, & if they should not be the very Thing you want, I
believe they will be equally Valuable, as I know of none like some
of the Stones which have different Colours & Strike fire with Steel.
If they will Polish they would be beautiful. These Stones like those
you mention in Penwith, are but a few Yards from the Moor Stone
in Luxulian. I will endeavour to get you some Specimens of Peach.
I think it the same as the *Terra Vert*, I never saw any Quantity of
the earth, except on the surface of Stones & Crystals of Tin Ore,
I have enquired for it without success before, but will try again. I
suppose this & Tungsten are in the County but the latter totally
unknown to the Miners.

I have heard but a very unsatisfactory Account of the new Fluid
you mention: it may turn out to be of great use.

It gives me much concern to hear of such Fermentations as are
now raising in different Parts of Europe, & more so as some of
the Leven has got into this Country. It astonishes me to think any
People of property can support the Ideas of a Mob, whose only
aim can be Plunder: I have never yet heard two men agree on the
Standard for Equality, or how they would go to bring Property to
a par. There has always been Contest for Governing, those who
do not enjoy the great offices of State wish to Posses [sic] them, but
not to annihilate them. There is no difficulty in Raising a Mob.

The Greatest Scoundrel is the most likely to Collect together his Associates, but generally finds they are not to be Controlled when once Assembled.

I wish your Young Spaniard may come to Menabilly when I am there, I will endeavour to Entertain him the best I can, & shew him such things as he is desirous of seeing. Our Neighbours are very Tenacious of their Arts & perhaps from want of Communication avoid Instruction. The Week after next, from the 9th to the 16th, I shall be absent & therefore hope this Gentleman will come either before or after. If you can guess the time pray inform me.

CRO, Truro, Hawkins Archive: J3/2/224
John Hailstone to John Hawkins
Freyberg en Saxe, 20 December 1792

Can you in the midst of this Season of Plots and Revolutions find time to peruse a few lines from a friend whose mind to be sure has lately been running upon revolutions & catastrophes which have happened on the earth but I humbly presume in times far remote from the present period to come under the meaning of the late circular letters & proclamation.

In the first place let me express my disappointment at not meeting you at Freyberg. I suspected some change in your plan and had left Hamburg to prosecute my tour before your last arrived. I shall not at present attempt of what I have seen in my Progress but just give you a sketch of my Itinerary.

. . .

I likewise staid at Blankenburg a little time and visited some considerable Iron works & the Marble quarries in that neighbourhood. I also descended into Baumanshöhle much inferior to our caverns in Derbyshire or Yorkshire.

Altho' so long at the foot of the Brocken, I never had an opportunity of ascending it. Had I been accompanied by a Friend I have no doubt but I should have overcome all the difficulties. The want of the mutual spiriting up (Aufmunterung) of Friends is the point when I have felt your loss most materially.

I left the Hartz and passed thro' a flat arable tract of Country containing nothing to detain a Mineralogist and came to Leipzig, where I first began to feel a relish for German manners and Society. This indeed is a most delicious spot to live in and a man might then almost forget old England. I increased my stock of books here pretty considerably as you know there is not a book printed in Germany but may be had here. It was just at the close of the fair that I came to the town. The next place of any note I stopped at was Dresden and there I remained for a considerable time chiefly with a view of increasing my stock of German. However my time was not totally engrossed by that. I met here some fine Collections which have considerably augmented my mineralogical Ideas.

I formed an acquaintance too with the possessor of a very magnificent cabinet with whom I find you are also acquainted. You will guess Baron Rachnitz who possesses also no small knowledge of the subject.[1] To mention all the new subjects I found in these Cabinets would exceed the bounds of a letter. Dr. Titius the Inspector of the Electoral Cabinet has shewn me a number of Civilities. He has a Collection to sell of which I send you the prospectus with the assurance that the Cabinet is not by any means inferior to the account given of it. Will you be so kind as to spread the Prospectus among your mineralogical friends as much as you can. I owe the Dr. this good office for many civilities & unreserved communications during my stay at Dresden.

The Leskean Museum has been purchased into Scotland and the Born or Raab Collection is also in England.[2] For neatness and exactness in the choice of the specimens & concinnity in the arrangement nothing can exceed Dr. Titius' Cabinet.[3]

From Dresden I made an Excursion to Holpen to see the Basalt so famous from the days of Agricola in Mineralogical H[ist]ory. As it was the first Columnar Basalt I had ever seen I was infinitely gratified and it formed one of those rare instances when the fact exceeds the description conveyed in Authors. It would only be renewing my vexation were I to mention to you all the cases where I have gone with the idea formed from a fine pompous plate & description in my head to consult Nature upon the spot and found myself duped. This did not happen at Holpen, altho' I have something to say against B. de Trebra upon this score from what I observed at the Hartz.[4]

. . .

Adieu I hope to see in the beginning of March & crack a bottle of Wine with you in Chandos Street.

[Letter closed here with 'Leben Sie wohl' & signature]

[Later continuation] I have resolved to make a packet of this and therefore continue my observations & reflections. I really think you will not be able to put your intended tour in execution as the continent will next Spring be most likely all on fire and I am afraid our own Country involved both in external & internal commotion. Such steps as have been lately taken by the Government warrant the most alarming conjectures concerning the state of affairs at home.

I suppose at present every man suspects his brother of harbouring dangerous designs and all mutual confidence is destroyed. If it be allowed to write any thing in politics at present inform me what cool men think of the present crisis. You may imagine my impatience to see the Speech & the debates upon the opening of Parliament and yet at Freiberg I may not be gratified this month. But foreign correspondence upon Politics is impudent at this juncture & therefore I close the subject.

. . .

Mr Werner's Catalogue of the Pabst Ohain is now complete. Once more adieu. Direct to me a Monsr. Vein, Freyberg en Saxe.

Notes
1. Baron J. F. Racknitz (1744-1818); German Hofmarschal, who built up a beautiful & complete mineral collection that was purchased by the Dresden Museum.
2. Hailstone was wrong – the Leske collection was acquired by the Dublin Museum [see letters from Walter Synnot]; Greville acquired the Born mineral collection (see Wilson, 1994: 75).
3. Carl H. Titius (1744-1813); physician & Inspector of the Royal Saxony Natural History cabinet in Dresden; had extensive mineral collection of his own; his catalogues published in Leipzig 1805, Dresden 1821.
4. This probably refers to Trebra's account in his *Erfahrungen von Innern der Gebirge* (1785).

NHM, Mineral Library, Russell Bequest, Hawkins Letters 7/8

Rev. William Gregor to John Hawkins   *4 May 1793*

I return you many thanks for your kind letter. I am only sorry that it gives me the Intelligence of the time of Yr. Departure from this Kingdom. Tho' this must arise from a degree of selfishness, as there can be no doubt but that you will travel with advantage to yourself & the Public. I shall be exceedingly glad of an account of yr. former expedition, wh. you so kindly promised me. It will on every account be highly Interesting to me ...

I have been some time, & am at present occupied with the idea of changing Residence. I believe I informed you that I was about to exchange one of my Livings for Creed. I shall be forced to repair & alter the House there before we can go to it. As you observe, I shall leave a very agreeable spot & as you kindly remark, one that had the recommend 'of agreeing so well with Mrs. W.G.' But it is my Duty to reside upon one of my Livings & I have therefore no choice ... but I feel truly happy that I shall be enabled to live in Cornwall. I shall add to the House & make it comfortable. Indeed I think the spot may be made pretty. I am happy also to inform you that Mrs W.G.'s Health has been so much amended by Sea Bathing that at present she does not stand in need of it. We shall not, when at Creed, be at a very great Distance from the Sea.

I have had little opportunity to pursue any train of Experiments lately. I have found that I was deceived in one of the conclusions wh. I wrote to you some time since.

[An account of his various experiments follows]

The Science of Chemistry requires great caution before you are entitled to draw conclusions. I am very careful in general of varying the trials lest some unknown circumstance may have contributed towards deception.

The Calcareous Stone I mentioned to you was in very small quantity & therefore I cd. not be certain of its contents. It appear'd, however [to have] some curious phœnomena. I have none of it left, nor have I been able to procure any more or to obtain Information of the place from wh. it was raised – only that it was not a native of this County of Devon. –

. . .

I am exceedingly glad to find that Klaproth is pursuing his highly valuable work on the Analysis of Gen [page torn with loss]

. . .

CRO, Truro, Hawkins Archive: J3/2/231
John Hailstone to John Hawkins   *Cambridge, 4 July 1793*

Dr. Pearce informed me yesterday that it was probable a letter might still reach you before you left England and presuming on this I write to thank you for the Box of Fossils which I found on my arrival at Cambridge and which you had sent down. I have opened some of the specimens and find them very interesting particularly the Porphyries from Patras with the transparent Feldspar Cristals or perhaps Adularia. I have a pretty complete collection of Erzgebirge Rocks on the road & also some from the neighbourhood of Cassel which I took myself from the places and in a year or two I hope my Geognostical Collection will be pretty considerable.

I arrived in England on Friday last & was sorry to find neither Davies or Cautley in College so that my enquiries respecting your Plans were fruitless till I saw Dr. P., who told me he had seen you lately, but that you were on the point of embarking on your grand tour. Your Friends in Freiberg all of whom I left well have given over all expectations of seeing you altho' I gave them all the encouragement in my power by affirming the contrary.

The temper of the University is at present unfavourable to scientific Plans. – it is not at all improbable that I may again be abroad in the Course of a year. I hope during your absence you will favour me with a few lines now & then which will give me great pleasure.

Your Friend Count Gesler has been residing at Freiberg for above a year. He is now at Dresden. Werner is very much occupied for besides his teaching, the Elector has made him a Counsellor of the Mines, which employs him a good deal. . . . The Charpentiers[1] are an excellent family – the Bergrath is occupied with the building of the Amalgamation works which will be the completest in the World when finished. If you go thro' Freiberg inform M. Charp.

. . .

You will hear there of my travels I was in most parts of the Erzgebirge where it was allowed to go and descended into most of their principal mines. The study of the Veins engaged much of my attention but I found the phœnomena of Saxony in general not so favourable to Werner's ideas as I think those of our Country are. To Basalt I paid great attention. The determination of your Vesuvian Fossils will employ me some part of this vacation. I doubt the Volcan[i]city of some of them, having seen similar from Hungary at least, they are not the productions of modern Volcanoes.

I wish you with all my soul a prosperous & easy Journey thro' the Levant neither infested by Pirates or the Plague. . . .

P.S. Where is my Barometer? Pallas is as you informed me the dearest book ever published. Altho' a good Zoologist yet as a Mineralogist I don't set him very high.

Note
  1. J. F. W. T. Charpentier (1728-1805); German mineralogist &
     author; his collection was acquired by Baron von Erlach & later by
     the Natural History Museum in Bern.

RIC, Truro, Rashleigh Archive: RASH/1/66
Rev. William Gregor to Philip Rashleigh
Caerhaise, 27 June [1794]

I received your kind letter. I am glad that you think the Chrystals of
Selenite curious. ... I believe [sic] that they came from Somersetshire.
I send you a sort of Earth which contains a bituminous matter
& shd. think that if it is found in a large quantity it might be
valuable. This is also a Somersetshire production I believe. – The
person who found it, is not willing to declare the spot where it is
[found].
   . . .
   According to your desire I send you my account of the
Menackanite. It was first published in German. The German
Translator has, I find, in some places mistaken my meaning, &
the French Translator of that paper has Committed a still greater
number of blunders. – I cannot expect you to wade thro' the tedious
minutiæ of my experim'ts. As this sand was a new substance, detail
was necessary, I have therefore drawn up a brief general account
of some of the leading properties which mark the Character of the
calx contained in the black sand – I send you also a small quantity
of the Calx itself free from Iron.
   I have seen no account of the Menackanite except a short analysis
by Mr. Schmeisser. He differs from me very considerably with
respect to the proportion of the Calx to the Iron. He affirms that
the Calx does not amount to more than 28 in an hundred – If I had
assigned to great a proportion of this Calx, I have every reason to
think that Mr. Schmeisser has curtailed it [inserted] 'considerably
too much'. I can not yet be persuaded from the Experimts I have
made since, that there is less than 40 parts in an hundred. –
   You may keep the Journal De Phys [page torn with loss] as long
as ever you please, I am in no want of it nor shall be for many
months. – Any other of the Volumes are much at your service. –
   . . .

RIC, Truro, Rashleigh Archive RASH/1/53
Wm. Day to Philip Rashleigh   *York St., 5th July 1794*[1]

Your last favour I received the day after I had wrote to you & as
the contents of yours did not require an immediate answer I have
not ventured to trouble you till now. I agree with you in regard to
Mr. Wätzl's charges of the specimens of Antimony, I think them
exorbitant, but as I did not think myself in a situation to venture
an opinion upon them & his stay in London being so short as
not to admit of their being sent to you & return'd again should
you not approve of them, I thought it best to act as I did. I have
represented to him that the charge is much too high, he says that
it is impossible to charge them lower, but on his return should you
not like to keep them he will receive them back & give you other
minerals in exchange to the full value you paid for them. –

I take the liberty to inform you that I am going in a fortnight's
time a short excursion into North Wales the Mountains of Cader
Idris & Snowdon & the Isle of Anglesea will be the principal
objects of my research both for Mine [page torn with loss] &
Views for drawing – if there are any remarkable things in the
Mineralogical line which you are acquainted with & you think
particularly worthy of attention, I will thank you inform me of
them & if they come within the compass of my Tour I will collect
for both you & myself.

My Friend Mr. Charles Hatchett means to make a mineralogical
Tour into Cornwall this summer,[2] he particularly wishes to be
favoured with a sight of your [collection] if I am not taking too
great a liberty with you, may I request the favour of you to shew
it to him should you be at home when he is in your part of the
County. You will find him a very good mineralogist, & a very
pleasant young man.

Notes
  1. A previous letter from Day (17 June 1794) refers to other
     transactions.
  2. This occurred two years later; Hatchett recorded visiting Charles
     Rashleigh on 9 May, but makes no mention of seeing Philip
     Rashleigh (see *The Hatchett Diary: a tour through the counties
     of England and Scotland in 1796 visiting their mines and
     manufactories*, ed. A. Raistrick (D. Bradford Barton, 1967).)
     However, a 1797 account published by W. G. Maton and the
     letters of Thomas Rackett establish that this trio were at Menabilly
     on 24/25 August – see letter below.

CRO, Truro, Rashleigh Papers: DDR 5764/9
William Day to Philip Rashleigh   *York, 21 July 1794*

I should have taken an earlier opportunity of returning my thanks to you for the obligations you have conferred upon me by your obliging invitation of my Friend Mr. Chas. Hatchett but I waited till [I] had seen him, that I might be able to inform you of the time you may expect him in Cornwall. – this morning I saw him & he informed me that he expected to be able to pay his respects to you about the middle of August & that he would take the liberty in the course of a few days of addressing a few lines to you, when he should be more at a certainty to regard to the route he means to take.

Your information relative to the Calamines & Fluor I am much obliged to you or, but the last time I was in Wales I went many Miles for the sake of both & was much disappointed. The Halkin Mountain in Flintshire is the place where they are all found.[1] The Fluor in one mine only called Moel a Creá but it is many years since they have found any & by what I could learn they never met with any perfect crystals. I got a pick & turned over a good deal of the old rubbish but found nothing but a few fragments very much dis-coloured by exposure to the air.

I have just sufficient to shew that they have both octaedral & cubic crystals of it & some of them most beautifully encrusted with a fine coloured purple. – of the calamine I procured a few returned specimens – green, yellow, & grey in a stalactitical form, but they are not large. The most noted Mines for Calamine on the Halkin are called Pant, Pant y Pwllawr, & Pant y Pwdw. – there is a lead mine the whole produce of which consists of white ore of lead very rich. I looked over near a ton weight of it, but it being very much enveloped in clay & my time very limited, I had not opportunity to make much of it. – They informed me at the mine that at times it produced very large crystals, & I am inclined to believe from some of the specimens I brought away, that there must at times be found very fine specimens. If you have any correspondent in Holywell, Flintshire they might procure some for you. The name of the Mine is Brynsannon. Another Mine on the Halkin called the silver Rake produces a green arsenical lead ore. The above are the only remarkable varieties I had an opportunity of examining when at Holywell. . . .

Mr. Forster returns from Spain in about 4 Months time. I understand that he means to come through Cornwall in his way to town. So I suppose you will have an early opportunity of seeing him. Mrs. F. informs me that he has got some very wonderful specimens particularly crystallized sulphur from Cadiz.

. . .

Note
1. As a result of this letter Rashleigh wrote to Pennant on 21 July 1794 asking whether he could provide specimens from this locality.

RIC, Truro, Courtney Library, Rashleigh Archive: RASH/1/57
Charles Hatchett to Philip Rashleigh   *13 December 1794*

I am glad to find that at least some of the ores were acceptable, and in respect to the Asbestos I can assure you that I brought it myself from Savoy where it was found amongst the Alps not far from the Vale of Chamonni – I am quite of your opinion that the Gold and Silver Ores from Siberia are poor, for I never in my Life saw a rich specimen. The Silver Mines however of Kelyvan pay well for their Working Altho' the Specimens in themselves do not appear productive the Government of Russia possesses but few of the Copper or Iron Mines; but all together taking Mines, Coinage and Duty on Iron at the Forge, it receives about £ 679,182 pr. Annm at an Average, exclusive of the profit on the Coinage of the Gold and Silver which is Imported.

[Hatchett comments on various experiments.]

I shall postpone saying anything more till I have the Pleasure of Seeing You.

CRO, Antony House, Torpoint, Carew Papers: CC/K/25
Philip Rashleigh to R. Pole Carew
Menabilly, 12 April 1795

I set out from London about 9 o'Clock last Thursday Morning, & got to Menabilly on Saturday night about Nine, where I found Mrs Rashleigh much better than I expected. Dr. Gould thought her as well as usual when he came to see her. Mr. Stephens concluded I should leave London from his letter, if nothing very particular prevented me; & Thursday being no Post day from this part of the Country made me not wait for another Day, Mrs Rashleigh and most others have the Cough which has so long been Rife in the Country, but in other respects she is nearly as usual.

A discontent prevails a good deal among the Common People about the Want of Corn more than the High Price, and there seems some Reason for their Complaint, when they see Corn either sent out of the Country, or Converted into Liquor, whilst they apply to those who Possess it for Bread, with Money in their Hands to pay the possessor's own Price.[1] Short Measure has in some places caused Murmerings, but on the whole I think no great Mischief likely to arise Unless by some Wicked Men who endeavour to excite Murmurs, such a Person has been to several of our Mines to endeavour to convince the Tinners that the Land owners are the cause of dearness for all kind of Provisions. They could not succeed in this part of the Country, but I hear (only one) a plausible Fellow is gone West to see what Mischief he can make there.

PS. Will you let us know when the Franking Bill Passes, I should suppose it would be one of the last in the Session.

Note

1. John Stevenson suggests that these food riots were due to the army encamped in the South-west to meet the threat of invasion, which led to a rapid increase in price (around 25%) and that the militia were 'extremely poorly paid': see J. Stevenson, *Popular Disturbances in England 1700–1832*, Longman, (2nd ed., 1992), 121-4. In 1795, Pole Carew, then MP for Lostwithiel, was a member of the Corn Committee; see letter below (24 April 1795) for further comment on prices and provisions.

CRO, Antony House, Torpoint, Carew Papers: CC/K/25
Philip Rashleigh to R. Pole Carew

Menabilly, 24 April 1795

I thank You for a Letter of the 21st.Instant & have the pleasure of telling you Mrs Rashleigh has continued Well for several days, she soon got rid of the Seizure she had when I writ You & she says several years since she had the like Numbedness in her Arm. Notwithstanding she seems so well & I believe is so, yet I can perseive [sic] a little alteration in her Recollection, though very little; yet I attribute it to the Effects of the late Illness, & I think it will soon wear off; but is now scarce so much as many Persons advanced in Years are naturally afflicted with.

The different circumstances of this Country & France are so contradictory that I scarce know what to think of Peace or War: The French seem in a situation they must change by some means or other, & appear inclined to form a Government that may be considered as permanent; & Yet we are increasing our Military Force. Orders are given to add two more Troop Companies to our Horse [Fencibles?][1] & to increase each Troop to 75 men. This does not look like Peace; And Yet I think Ld. St. Helens is not gone to Paris on trifling business.

The Riots in the different parts of England are very Unpleasant, but People must have Provision but they use a very ineffectual means to procure it; Those who have generally supplied the markets will not carry their Goods there to be Insulted, but will prefer selling them by private application in their own Neighbourhood. The Price of Labour should Always keep pace with the Price of Provisions. If the Farmers would consider this, they would find it better to ask a moderate rate for their Commodities than an Exorbitant one. If there was a real Want of Corn owing to a short Crop, the farmer ought to have such a Price as to enable him to cultivate his Ground, but I do not think that was the case of the last harvest in such Extreem [sic]. The Corn in this part of the Kingdom was bought up almost before it was saved, & sent either to the Maltman or Distiller, & that has now caused a Scarcity. The Corn to be sold the 30th Instant at Plymouth will reduce the Price & cause Plenty, for I am told there is as much as the Annual Consumption of the four Western Counties.[2]

I don't think we have any Serious disposition in the People to disturb the Government, but when Riots begin on one Account they proceed to others before they are corrected, & therefore I think where the Offence begins Punishment should ensue, & the first sacrifice will be the least Evil.

I am glad to find your Bror is safe return'd from Sea, I fear he will now be call'd upon another disagreeable Court Martial. I hope your Bror Edward had a good Sale of his Hunters & Hounds last Wednesday, as I think such an Event would make him decline the eagerness he used to follow his Hounds.

PS. I believe there are some Papers in the Vote Office worth having, such as the East India Accounts, & the Bill on Committees for Contested Elections. Will You be kind enough to secure them for me from Mr. Babb.

Notes
1. 'Fencible' was the term used for soldiers limited to service in their home neighbourhood.
2. Riots occurred throughout the country during the 1790s as a result of political & religious matters as well as food shortages; Uglow, *Lunar Men*, 464, recorded that the winter of 1794–95 was the worst for 50 years, experiencing the coldest January to date which followed poor harvests and resulted in these food riots in Cornwall.

CRO, Truro, Rashleigh Archive: DDR/5757/1/80
C. Lippi to Philip Rashleigh[1] 21 *July 1795*

A person as you, who abounds in Minerals of his own County, should not have objections to grant some specimens to a Mineralogist, who travels these ten years in the Mines of Europe, and from whom a reciprocation of many other foreign specimens may be expected.

I want two specimens of Crystallized Antimony from Wheal Boys; two specimens of Tin from Glastinnin; 4 specimens of green Copper; one specimen of transparent green Copper; and perhaps four or six other specimens, of which you have a great quantity.

You shall certainly receive in next Winter good specimens of Apatites, Topases in their matrix of Saxony, and perhaps two specimens of Tungstein. But if you will wait 18 months more, namely untill [sic] my arrival home, you shall receive the largest specimen of Tungstein, that has been seen in Germany, for I have two specimens in my own collection of an uncommon size, and I must observe to you that this fossil, has always been found of the size of a small nut. In short I intend to act with you in a manner of which you will be satisfied; but I want a little time. I shall moreover not fail to send you something uncommon of this Kingdom and of Norway, if in my journey I shall meet with it.

I shall leave this Town next Friday. If you intend to grant me the above mentioned specimens and accept Mr. Daniell or Mr. Fox for my Warranters, I have no objection to bring with me a security of a Hundred pounds, and leave it you, in order you may receive this

money, if I do not send you the specimens for the value of yours.
I expect then a line from you before Friday, that I may have again
the pleasure of seeing you next Saturday in Menabilly, and receive
at same time the specimens in question.

Note
1. Lippi claimed to be in the Service of the King of Naples; Ferdinand
   I (1751–1825) Bourbon King of the Two Sicilies & King of Naples;
   his collection was donated to establish the Royal Mineralogical
   Museum in Naples; it is now in the Institute of Mineralogy, at the
   University of Naples.

CRO, Truro, Rashleigh Papers: DDR/5303/23
Walter Synnot to Philip Rashleigh
                          Mountjoy Square, Dublin 26 May 1796

I have to return you many thanks for a fine specimen of Aurum
Graphicum1 which I received from Dr. Mitchell some time ago,
it is I believe the only one in this kingdom, which makes it more
valuable to me; I should have acknowledged your favor sooner but
waited till I could give you some account of the Leskean collection;
it is perhaps the most interesting one in Europe as it contains
specimens of most of the minerals and fossils that are known; I say
most because it wants some of the articles lately discovered; your
collection Sir (as I have heard from Mr. Higgins and Mr. Blake) is
much more magnificent and abounds in far finer specimens; the
Leskean[2] are extremely well calculated for promoting the Science
but are very deficient in point of beauty; it is a place where a person
may study with every advantage as Mr. Kirwan in his excellent
Mineralogy refers to many of the specimens, and I think it would
take at least a year to be perfectly acquainted with the whole as
there are above 7000 specimens; the Museum built by the Dublin
Society is forty feet long and has a gallery above all round, full of
cases of minerals, they are made like the Glass cases in Jewellers
shops, but many of them double, thus ♠. This arrangement has
not so handsome an effect as when in Glass cases against a wall,
but it answers as well for inspecting the Fossils. Mr. Higgins who
is an excellent Chymist has the care of it, it is open two days in the
week and the members of the Dublin Society have the privilege of
introducing who they please, so there is no difficulty in seeing it.

I have been a Member near thirty years and I introduce every one that asks me.

. . .

Mr. Kirwan told me yesterday that he designed to give his collection of Fossils to our Museum, I have not seen them, he bought most of them from Woolf in London. I fancy they are not very numerous.[3]

I have heard of several Gentlemen that design to come here this Summer from England to see our Museum, Mr. Hatchett is one of them. I am much obliged to you for introducing me to Dr. Mitchell, he has a more extensive knowledge of fossils than any person I ever met with, he has been so obliging as to mark several fossils for me that had been mistaken, and he discovered Topaz in two specimens of Tin ores that you sent me, which he said he never saw in English Tin ore before.

. . . my Fossils which I hope soon to arrange properly as I have purchased a large house in Mountjoy Square where I shall have room for them; I hope Sir hereafter to be able to send you something from this Country as many mines are now opening; I leave Town for the Summer in ten days, so if you favour me with a letter direct to Ballymoyer, Newry.

Notes
1. Aurum graphicum: Sylvanite ($AuAgTe_4$); very fine crystals up to 1cm long have been found with native gold.
2. Leskean Collection: The collection of Nathaniel Gottfried Leske, Professor of Natural History in Marburg, containing over 7,000 specimens of minerals, rock and fossils was purchased by the Dublin natural History Society in 1792 for £1,350; see Hawkins' comments 24 January 1799 (below).
3. Kirwan's collection: The collection of the Irish chemist and mineralogist Richard Kirwan – the author of '*Elements of Mineralogy*' (1784) the first systematic work on the subject in English, was considered to be 'the best collection on earth' by the crystallographer W. H. Miller.

CRO, Antony House, Torpoint, Carew Papers: CC/K/26
Philip Rashleigh to R. Pole Carew   *Undated [?June 1796]*

. . .

If you can learn what business calls the meeting of Parliament at
Midsumer [sic], or so near it, I shall be glad to have a line, as I have
no inclination to fling away £50 in a Journey to add one more to a
majority on an Address. If there is the least hazard of the Speaker,
let me know in time & I will at all Events be in the House on the
Question; but I think nothing but his own Will can prevent his
being Re-chosen.

CRO, Truro, Rashleigh Papers: DDR/5757/1/82
Walter Synnot to Philip Rashleigh
Ballymoyer Lodge, 10 July 1796

Your favor reached me last Monday, be assured it always gives
me pleasure to hear from you. I am sorry you are not acquainted
with Mr. Kirwan as he is not only an excellent Philosopher and
Chemist but a very pleasant Man in conversation; from having a
weak constitution he is singular in many things, he heats his room
to a degree that is disagreeable to most people; he has a difficulty
in swallowing for which reason he always dines alone and his diet
is Ham toasted on a fork with a little milk, sometimes he adds a
little Fish; when he goes to the Royal Academy he retires exactly
at Nine o'Clock and often walks out when a very interesting
paper is reading which gives offence to those that do not know his
Character; he has by no means as great a knowledge of Fossils as
Dr. Mitchell who is better acquainted with them than any person
I ever met with, he has a perfect knowledge of all the forms of
Crystallization, and it was by that and not the colour that he
discovered Topaz in two specimens of Tin ore you sent me.

Mr Higgins studies have hitherto been mostly confined to
Chemistry, but he must soon have a good deal of knowledge of
Minerals as he is obliged to shew the Leskean collection two days
in every week, and he has an opportunity to study them as much
as he pleases ,as he keeps the keys; in talking comparatively of your
Museum with the Leskean, he gives yours for the preference as to
the magnificence of the specimens, and I am certain he was right,

as the Leskean is far more instructive than beautiful, some of the Classes are very poor, for instance the Siliceous in precious stones; the Fluors are very deficient not half the number, variety or beauty even of my own. In gold ores not one rich or beautiful specimen, there is one of Gold mineralogy that is very rare; There are a great number of Silver ores but not one large or beautiful specimens. The Copper ores are pretty extensive but not better than my own. In Lead ores their collection is very inferior to mine. . . .

The Classing of the whole (of which you have a good description in Mr. Kirwan's preface to his Mineralogy) is useful and excellent; you cannot without seeing it, have an idea of its perfection; there you study in a separate division without regard to any Class, the degrees of Transparency, colour, fracture, concretion, specific gravity &c &c. And in the œconom [page torn with loss] part is to be met with every earth or mineral that is [page torn with loss] useful to artists, manufacturers, or improvers of Land, this is quite a new idea and of infinite utility. I wish it was possible to seduce you over to see it next Spring when I am in Dublin, I would constantly attend you there or to any thing worth seeing in our Capital, and have also the pleasure of introducing you to Mr Kirwan; to add to the inducements I think it possible you might see in my collection some things that might be acceptable to you and to which you would be most heartily welcome, when ever I look over my Minerals they remind me how much I am indebted to you.

Mr Kirwan was much pleased with the Cornish Copper ores you were so obliging as to send me, how much more would he be if he was to see those in your Collection, for my part I always lament that it is not in my power to visit it.

I am much obliged to you for the Analysis of the Aureum Graphicum, Mr Kirwan in his second Volume not yet published, calls it the Sylvanite, I did not know that it contained Silver, or so great a proportion of Gold, I should be glad to know in what Country it is found.[1]

Note
  1. Sylvanite is a telluride ($(Au, Ag)Te_2$), formed in hydrothermal vents; its fine crystals occur in lines which has led to the name 'graphic tellurium'; the chief localities are in Western Australia and Colorado, but Transylvania was probably the provenance of the specimens referred to here.

CRO, Truro, Rashleigh Papers: DDR/5304/27
C. Lippi to Philip Rashleigh   *Naples, 12 November 1796*

You will be surprised without doubt of my not having sent you some fossils of Germany. I had my great Collection in Trieste, and passed that way on my coming to Naples, only to open two Boxes, and forward you some Specimens, but this town being in a very great alarm, occasioned by the cursed french, who threatened at that time to enter Friuli, I was obliged to Ship the whole Collection for Naples without having an hour [for] opening and searching into the Boxes. I am now very uneasy, since have no news of the Ship, so much the more that being a Venetian one, am afraid of her being captured by the Algerians, who have entered a war with Venice at the very same time of her sailing from Trieste. Should I have the pleasure of receiving my Collection you will be not forgotten, on the Contrary you will be contented with me. When I left England, my intention was to make an expeditious tour through the Mines of Hungary & Transilvania, and in this Occasion I had surely gotten several specimens which are wanted in your famous collection, but my passage from Yarmouth to Hambro' having been taken by a french frigate and having lost money and everything I had with [me] was thus disadvantaged. Nevertheless I hope next year to pass in Hungary for the second time, and will then absolutely send you some fine Minerals.

Baron Trebra has resigned his services of the Mines of Hartz, and lives in his Estate, about 10 miles from Clausthal. I hope you have received an answer to the letter you was pleased to commit to my care, for I put it into the hands of the director of the Mint of Hambro', an intimate friend of Mr. Trebra, to whom you may direct your Letters should you want to write to the Baron.

The weather is still to [sic] hot as not to permit me to pay a visit to Vesuvius, and begin a Collection of Volcanic productions. I will be very glad to collect for you the finest Specimens would you have them. I beg you will exercise me with your commands, should you find me capable of doing it.

CRO, Truro, Rashleigh Papers: DDR/5757/1/85
Rev'd William Gregor to Philip Rashleigh
Creed, 15 June 1797

[Letter Fragile]
In these Times which minister to every thinking mind much anxiety for present evils to aweful [sic] anticipations of Future ones, it may seem trifling to write a letter upon any other subject than what concerns the public [but as that] is a topic upon which little or no comfort can be extracted, one wishes to cheat care a little by endeavouring to forget ones cares in some favourable amusement. – This letter, therefore I promise You shall be given up to Mineralogical observations, without [the] least alloy of Political ones. – I have not forgotten [my] promise to you concerning the Endellion Antimonial Ores. [I shall] therefore proceed to give you the Results of my enquiry tho' it [illegible]
[The remaining three pages of this letter contain detailed accounts of his experiments]

RIC, Truro, Rashleigh Papers RASH/1/61
Rev'd. William Gregor to Philip Rashleigh
undated [annotated '8 September 1797']

. . .
In my last letter to you [15 June 1797, see above][1] concerning the contents of the Padstow Antimonial ore, the difference, which seem'd to arise from my calculation arose from my estimating the weight in one case from the calces of the metals, and in the other, the weight of the same metals in their State of Regulus; wh. is always inferior to the former. That this Ore contains Lead, Antimony & Copper with Sulphur approximating towards Vitriolic Acid, I am clearly of opinion. As diluted Nitric Acid in the cold completely converted the whole of this Sulphur into that Acid. I have the vitriolated copper now by me in its permanent Chrystalisation. This State of Sulphur has not, I think, been sufficiently attended to by Mineralogists, as a variation of this kind may account for minerals, that are said to consist of the same component parts, assuming different external Characters.

Note
>   1. Rashleigh (1797) figured an Antimony ore from Wheal Boys, in
>   the parish of St. Endellion, nr. Port Isaac on pl. XIX. Although
>   the name 'endellionite' was used for a time, his specimen is now
>   recognised as the first example of bournonite.

RIC, Truro, Rashleigh Papers: RASH/1/63
Robert Hoblyn to Philip Rashleigh   *[?] September 1798*

I thank you cordially for your kind congratulations on account of
the discovery at Herland.[1]

I told Mrs Rashleigh whom I met in my way to the Mine acct.
meeting last week, that I would endeavour to procure some
specimens of the silver Ore both for you and myself, but I am
sorry to say I could procure hardly anything worthy of notice
at that time, & I believe it will be difficult for strangers at any
time to procure specimens for the Adventurers have given orders
that all the Ore shall be broken to pieces as soon as it arrives
on the surface and accordingly two men with sledges, like two
executioners, attend & use their instruments without mercy so the
best specimens I was able to procure I delivered to Mrs. Goode
to transmit to you, which was of the trachites kind having small
capillary filaments of silver very visible in the stone & I also see
some of the soft ore, which from its colour, I suppose to be the
[Goose?d?ing] Ore. But these are specimens rather for the Assay
rather than the Collector & I have [page torn with loss] to the
Capt. Davey to save out some of the best specimens he can procure
& to charge for them according to their intrinsick [sic] value, the
half of which I have destined for your use.

The discovery is certainly a very uncommon one, and I am
convinced contains a variety of uncommon combinations of silver
ore for some of the silver is mineralised with lead, with copper,
with bismuth, with cobalt, with spathose iron & perhaps with
many other combinations & with different proportions of arsenic
& sulphur of course. – If you make any experiments with the
specimens sent I shall be much obliged to you to favour me with
the result of them. As to the state of the Mine itself, I will send you
the particulars of it for I endeavoured to get as near the [illegible
due to fading] as possible. The Silver is contained in a cross
course, chiefly of Lead, which intersects nearly at right angles

that +[page torn with loss] copper course, the load is very rich [in] silver near the main course, but gets poorer as it recedes from it, and it continues only for about eight feet: beyond that it seems to contain little or no silver; the general sample of the ore when properly mixed produces about 1/33 of silver; but the Samplers who have tried particular specimens only have a produce some of one per cent, whilst others from richer specimens gain twenty five; this probably has given rise to so many various reports. It is first discovered at a level 107 fathom under the Adit, where four men are now working on it, & the same number also work on it at the next deep level, & as many more at the deepest level, & it is rather richer at the bottom of the [illegible] than at the top. If you would like to visit the spot, I shall have business that will call me to Redruth on Monday the 8th of Octr. and again on Tuesday or Wedy. the 12 & 13 of Novr. that will call me to Gwinnear to hold a court, & I shall be very happy to accompany you on either of the times above mentioned.

Your great Collection of Minerals tho' at first begun perhaps for the sake of particular amusement is now become a collection for the promoting of general science and in either point of view I shall at all times be very happy to give it my aid.

Note
1. For Herland Mine (previously 'Manor Mine'), see Rashleigh's letter to Hawkins 1 November 1798; now listed as Wheal Herland, Gwinnear.

CRO, Truro, Rashleigh Papers: DDR/5304/37
John Hawkins to Philip Rashleigh
Sunbury, Middlesex, 28 October [1798]

I beg leave to announce to you my return to England after a residence of five years and two months on the continent of Europe and chiefly in Greece.[1] My long and desultory ramble thro' the Levant have deprived me of the means of hearing from most of my friends in this country at least as often as I could wish and I have much to learn respecting their health and their occupations. Permit me therefore to renew my claim on your correspondence and to express a wish to hear from you soon.

I have but little to communicate on this subject of Mineralogy. My long removal from polished Europe has made my very ignorant of the progress of the Arts & Science and I have to learn from you and others their history for the last five years. In respect to the objects of my researches they have been as various as you can well conceive for in a country like Greece every thing has a more than common interests. I have been very active and have made great collections the most portable of which I have brought safely to England. In the pursuit of these objects I have encountered great difficulties and dangers. I cannot reflect upon them without shuddering. I hope to hear of your intention of visiting London this winter which will put it in my power to see you and perhaps to shew you some very curious antiquities & drawings.

Note
1. Hawkins left on this second journey in August 1793; he reached Freyburg on 23 September 1793 and eventually arrived back in England at Hull on 6 October 1798. See H. W. Lack, *The Flora Graeca Story: Sibthorp, Bauer and Hawkins in the Levant* (Oxford: Oxford University Press, 1999) for a full account.

CRO, Truro, Hawkins Archive: J3/15/1717
Rev'd. William Gregor to John Hawkins
undated [? November 1798][1]

I take up my pen to offer you a few words of congratulation on your safe arrival upon English ground after a long absence in distant countries amidst the Dangers & difficulties inseparable from such an Expedition. Now that you are once again with us, I hope that you will remain so. You have certainly done your part in the way of foreign research & you shd leave [rights] & enterprize to others. . . . All that remains for you to do at present is to make the advantages you have gained by yr. labours truly your own by communicating them under due forms of arrangement to your Countrymen –

During your Absence we have not been even in this country at our ease, but have partaken of the tumultuous & unsettled State of the World; & for what we have not really suffered, we have made up by anxiety for what might happen & the busy anticipation of Evil. I must however at present think we see the Bottom of the

Cloud, that we shall ensure ourselves & the rest of the world from the Tyranny of French Liberty,

I hope that we shall have the Benefit of your labours in [those] Historical & Philosophical Observations wh. you have made in that portion of Europe wh. is so imperfectly known to us. You will, I hear, have yr. hands full of Botany, nor will Mineralogy be neglected I hope.

I have done but little in the way of Chemical Experiment for little or nothing new has occur'd to me.

. . .

Note

1. The reference to Hawkins' absence refers to his returning from the Levant, which he did in both 1789 and 1798; 'hands full of Botany' indicates the latter, as do the subjects of Silver Ore & Strontian (also mentioned in this letter) which also occur in letters to Rashleigh in 1798.

CRO, Truro, Hawkins Papers: J3/15/1678
Philip Rashleigh to John Hawkins   *1 November 1798*

The sight of your handwriting gave me very great pleasure the last Post. I was much rejoiced to hear of your being once more on English Ground, and I very heartily congratulate you on escaping the many Dangers & Troubles you have encountered. You must have met with great entertainment in the course of your Travels to have detain'd you so many years from your native Soil, & I have no doubts of your communicating some part of your labours at least, to the publick, as they must be interesting to all Classes. This Country since You left it has been threatened with many Troubles, but by the Providence of God we seem in a way to overcome them all, & I hope to Live to see a General and a lasting peace restor'd to Europe. Your Friends have long wished for your return, & I believe your late companion's Affairs, Dr. Sipthorp [sic] have stood much in need of your assistance of the Learned as well as the Artist.

Minerallogy in this Country has wonderfully increased since you left it, both in Collectors & Fossils; we have not only discover'd Silver Lodes, but a great variety of Interesting Substances in this county; some are lost again as a Lode that produced Horn Silver & some others in Herland Mine (Late the Manor),[1] a cross Lode containing native & other Silver Ore has been found & this seems likely to have a continuance; as yet I have seen no fine specimens from it, but am promised all the varieties. Tincroft has produced some Curious Copper Ore, & other Mines different varieties. I hear you have collected by your Agent a greater Quantity of Wood-like Tin Ore than all the World besides.

I have Published a few Prints of some of my most particular specimens of English Minerals & I have one of these little Books at your Service. I had often a desire to have some of these things drawn, but could not find any body to undertake it for some years & never any who had any Practice in such objects; at last I succeeded in one or two who undertook the business tho' new to them. I suppose in the course of your Botanical work you will want both engravers & colourers in abundance.

I intend being in London against Parliament meet after Xmas, as I conclude little more will be done (so late in the Year) than calling for papers & Official Documents for proceeding after the recess. It will give me a great pleasure to see you again in London or Cornwall. Some of your Friends have paid me a Visit in your absence & among them the Dean of Christchurch & the Warden of Wadham. When I rec'd your letter last night my Sister Charles was here & had your Compliment, she now returns them with every good wish.

PS. By a fall yesterday I hurt one Arm so much, as at present to have no use of it.

Note
1. Herland Mine (Late the Manor); this rich pocket yielded 115 tons of silver ore c. 1799–1800: see Embrey and Symes, *Minerals of Cornwall and Devon*, 40.

CRO, Truro, Rashleigh Papers: DDR/5757/1/88
J.Tobin to Philip Rashleigh   *Bristol 20 November 1798*

. . .

Having already acquainted you that all the different varieties I furnished you with as Ponderous Spar are now considered as <u>Sulphate</u> of <u>Stronthian</u>, I shall now only add, that no less than three scientific Gentlemen of my acquaintance are at present employed, in still more compleatly analyzing this Mineral, viz. Mr. Hatchett of Hammersmith whom you will know, Mr. Clayfield of this City, and my Brother-in-Law Mr. Webb at Falmouth: and I have reason to conclude that two of the three, at least, intend to favour the public with the result of their investigations – This new substance has so much attracted the notice of Mineralogists, that the vein at the Old Passage has lately been ransacked by two parties, with the assistance of Miners, Quarrymen, and Blasters, till it is nearly exhausted, as several hundred-weight has been carried away – Yet I am informed by a friend, who attended both these researches, that no specimens have been found, which are better than those I sent you – Nor can I learn that, after all the pains which have been taken, a single <u>perfectly</u> <u>regular</u> Chrystal has been met with – The pits near this City which afforded the first samples of this Mineral which you had from me, have also been lately filled up, and the ground converted into gardens.

. . .

Sincerely wishing this may find you perfectly recovered from your late accident.

CRO, Truro, Rashleigh Papers: DDR 5757/1/89
Charles Hatchett to Philip Rashleigh
Hammersmith, 10 December 1798

Some family affairs having induced me to remove from my Father's House at Hammersmith into another of my own, I find that I shall not have room to arrange my Collection of Minerals, and have therefore determined to part with it. I have two parties in treaty for it, one is the British Museum and the other is the Count of Portugal. – I should get more for it from the latter, but as in that case I shall in all probability never see it again, I prefer the former, and only require to be reimbursed what I have actually expended viz. £700 – without reckoning the presents of Minerals which I have received and which in fact, much increase the <u>Value</u>. The part of my Collection which you have seen amounts to 4000 specimens, besides which, there are nearly if not quite 3000 more so that including the Systematical Collection of Rocks and Volcanic Products, the total number amounts to about 7000 specimens.

Dr. Gray informed me last night that the Trustees of the BM have requested Sir J. Banks, yourself, Mr. Greville and him to view the part which is arranged and report the State of it. – now although from your last letter I doubt if you will be in Town by the time appointed, yet as you have seen this part and probably remember many of the most Valuable specimens, such as the Rubellite of Siberia, the mass of Elastic Bitumen which weighs 14 pounds, the series of Apatite, and many of the Tin and Copper Ores, I am sure that it would give great satisfaction to the Trustees, as it certainly would to myself, if you would write to Dr. Gray your opinion as far as what you can recollect of that part of the collection will enable you to do. I have explained to the Trustees the impossibility of unpacking and arranging the other part in the House where it now is, and I have no doubt but they give me credit for what I have said of it.

If my Collection should go into the British Museum, the whole of that part of the Museum is to be arranged under my direction, and I hope will no longer be the disgrace to it and to the nation which it is at present.

CRO, Truro, Rashleigh Papers: DDR 5757/1/91
Charles Hatchett to Philip Rashleigh

Hammersmith, 17 December 1798

I have received your very kind letter, but as it is not my part to fix the day for inspecting that part of the collection which is arranged, I must beg leave to refer you to Dr. Gray at the British Museum & he will settle matters with Sir Joseph Banks and Mr. Greville. Whenever the time is appointed I will not fail to attend you.

P.S. I assure you it gives me the greatest pleasure that my Collection is likely to remain in so honourable place as the B.M.

Note

> Hatchett's mineral collection was purchased by the British Museum for £700 in 1799; Charles Greville together with Banks joined Rashleigh in assessing its value on behalf of the B.M. Incidentally, at the same period Rashleigh, Greville and William Babington assessed the state of the Museum's own Mineral collections.

CRO, Truro, Rashleigh Papers: DDR/5757/1/92
John Hawkins to Philip Rashleigh

Sunbury, 9 January 1799

I lose no time in answering you obliging letter I would have written before had I not expected to see you so soon in town. I fear however that this pleasure will be protected a few weeks longer. My long stay at Sunbury is partly due to filial regard, partly to my health which altho' not impaired, yet required repose of mind and body after the very harrassing [sic] tour which I have accomplished.

Your former letter conveyed much curious information respecting new mineralogical discoveries in Cornwall.

I hope to hear that your Cabinet has been proportionally enriched and I thank you for offer of a copy of your work. I am glad to hear that a favourite study has obtained a new votary in the person of St. John St. Aubyn. Indeed I apprehend that it is become now much more popular than it was, which may tend to the benefit of this kingdom in general.

I passed so hastily thro' Germany that I had not time to learn all the advances made in this Science, or in mining in the course of the last five years, but I have brought with me all the new publications among which the two volumes of Analyses of Fossil bodies by Klaproth of Berlin is by far the most valuable. It is this work which has laid the basis of all natural arrangement of Minerals. Every classification of mineral bodies published before the appearance of this work, was premature. I need only refer to the statement of the constituent parts of the precious stones by Bergman & Achard which is now found to be wholly fallacious.

You know perhaps that the Manaccanite has been found in great abundance in various parts of Germany and Hungary. The red shirl of the Carpathian Mountains is discovered to be the same substance. Most of the cabinets abroad are for sale. Trebra disposed of his by Auction five years ago. There are 50 Cabinets of Minerals in Vienna alone, 10 in Dresden & 5 or 6 in Berlin.

I lament much that Werner is now so much diverted from mineralogical pursuits by his attention to the general administrations of the Saxon Mines. He has promised me however to publish soon a new edition of his Classification of the <u>Saxa.</u>

I fear that Sir John St. Aubyn's collection will be much injured by the sulfureous air of London for I found it to produce a great effect on my specimens. Several very large Steam Engines on Bolton's principle have been lately built in Silesia for the use of the coal mines which are now worked on an extended plan which does much honour to the zeal & abilities of Count Reden.

The Great Adit is now nearly brought home to the mines at Clausthal on the Harz, but without having cut a single lode and much doubt is entertained of the continuam[sic] of the ore at so great a depth. The Mines in Saxony flourish. Those of Hungary have declined in silver & gold but have been more productive than usually of copper. Baron Born's process of Amalgamation has been abolished in Hungary but still maintains its ground in Saxony where the alarming decrease of wood fuel renders it more and more beneficial.

. . .

CRO, Cornwall, Truro, Rashleigh Papers: DDR/5757/1/94
J. Hawkins to Philip Rashleigh   *Sunbury, 24 January 1799*

You are very good to devote any portion of your short leisure to my instruction and entertainment for every thing which you chuse [sic] – the Levant has at least the charm of novelty. My attention has not been much engaged as you suppose on botanical subjects nor do I possess more than a smattering of that amusing science.

I have never had time or proper opportunities for pursuing it as I could wish. I had so many objects to attend to in my late tour and Botany as well as Zoology were so well followed up by my fellow traveller Dr. John Sibthorpe, that I devoted my time and my labour to objects more within my competency such were, for instance, a general view of the mineralogical Geography of the countries over which I passed, a trigonometrical Survey of Greece, the knowledge of its climate, its soil, the state of its Agriculture, its Manufacture of Commerce, its Population, the character of its inhabitants, and its government with many other things of less moment.

I have made no very material additions to my former mineralogical observations on the Levant except the discovery of two extinguished Volcanos the productions of which have enabled me to ascertain the volcanic origin of several islands of the Archipelago. I collected a number of very curious marbles which together with my specimens of <u>Saxa</u> &c were left behind. The most valuable perhaps of all my acquisitions in this tour is a fine collection of the earliest Greek <u>autonome</u> medals[1] and this I have had the good fortune to bring safe to England. It is a pleasing thing to have so many memorials of the ancient history of Greece and to be able to trace so distinctly the progress of the arts of design in that country.

I am sorry that we have as yet no translation of Klaproth's celebrated work, you would find therein many of our Cornish Fossils. He had not yet analysed the Green Copper of Tincroft but meant to take it in hand without farther delay. The material, if you recollect, were furnished by you and should you possess any thing which requires examination in the humid way you can commit the trust to no one who will fullfill it so well as my freind Mr. Klaproth. I saw the Leskean Museum many years ago at Leipzig and thought the specimens in general very paltry. I think Mr. Kirwan would have done better to purchase the collection of Pabst von Ohain which is truly superb and in the productions of Saxony compleat. It is still unsold.[2] Karsten was a very young man when he drew up the catalogue of the Leskean Cabinet and there are many inaccuracies in the description as well as the arrangement. I doubt much whether Dr. Mitchell was capacitated for such a translation before he had studied the language of Mineralogy in the Wernerian School at Freyberg. With regard to the triple arrangement adopted by Karsten, I own I think it just because it is founded on the different doctrines of Mineralogy and the division of Science, like that of labour, facilitates it.

I know not whether Tregoning has reserved for me the beautifull [sic] specimen of copper which you describe but I will write about it. I understand from Mr. Chilcott that he has many things in reserve for me. I am rather surprized [sic] to hear that Mr. Hatchett, who is a man of fortune as well as Science, should wish to disposes of his collection. Baron Trebra's collection was certainly disposed of by auction four or five years ago previous to his retirement from the superintendance [sic] of the mines on the Harz forest.

. . .

The Mail has brought us less news than I expected. Nothing can equal the pusillanimity of the court of Vienna, or the temerity of that of Naples, which every thing is to be feared from the activity and decision the ambition and the perfidy of this new military republick.

Notes

1. Earliest Greek autonome medals: following the practice of stamping white gold ingots begun in Asia Minor, c.700 BC, the rulers of kingdoms, or the autonomous states and cities preserved

their authority by marking coins and medals. Eight periods are recognised as occurring throughout the Roman and Greek empires between 700 BC and AD 270 and these are distinguished by the quality and nature of the artistic designs portrayed – see British Museum, *A Guide to the Principal Coins of the Greeks based on the work of Barclay V. Head* (1965).
2. This collection was sold to Portugal and sent to the University in Rio de Janeiro: see Wilson, 'The history of mineral collecting', 186.

CRO, Truro, Rashleigh Papers: DDR/5304/41
John Hawkins to Philip Rashleigh
Sunbury, 4 February [misdated January] 1799[1]

Since my last I have received very unpleasing accounts of the health of my freind Mr. Klaproth which induce me to think that he will not live long enough to finish the several analysis which he has in hand. He has examined a considerable number of mineral substances at my suggestion and expence. No contract was made, he is much too liberal & disinterested, but I occasionally presented him with a gratuity for his trouble.

Germany has just lost another of its principal Chemists Professor Grün of Halle. An untimely death I think has been the fate of most of the eminent men in this line and I am inclined to think the occupations of a laboratory if followed up with much spirit generaly [sic] fatal to health.

I rejoice for the sake of my country at the high price of Tin & Copper. Your fears are groundless respecting the competition to be expected from the Mines of Armenia. I have long been in possession of pretty exact information respecting their produce & its price. About ten years ago much of this copper found its way to England but it proved of such an inferior quality as to be unfit for most purposes before it was refined. Its price nevertheless was so low as to make good this extra expense. Fortunately for us such impediments have since been laid by the Turkish government on its exportation that this branch of trade has totally ceased.

I have just heard some particulars respecting the silver mine in Gwinnear which convince me that we are not to expect great riches from it. The lode which produces the silver is a common lead lode running N. & S. and crossing the main Standard lode without much diss-arrangement to either. At this point of intersection not a particle of silver has been found, but immediately after, the lead lode becomes rich in particles of native silver and continues so for about six feet after which it becomes too poor to pay for working and even the rich mass of ore yields only on an average from 3 to 4 parts in an hundred of silver and more than 50 per Cent of Bismuth.

My neighbour here Mr. Krawshay who has taken up the Beeralston mine informs me that he has already expended thereon about £5000. He seems very confident of a speedy reimbursement and indeed it appears not to have been the fault of the mine that some freinds of mine a few years ago lost so much money by her.

As the frost has set in with so much severity on the continent it is probable we shall have a long winter. I shall not go to town before the middle of this month and not then if this hard weather continues.

Note
1. Although Hawkins dated this 4 January, both its post marks and Rashleigh's annotation indicate it was written on 4 February 1799.

CRO, Truro, Rashleigh Papers: RS/12/8
Philip Rashleigh to Messrs. G. C. Fox of Falmouth
London, 26 March 1799

I wish I could send you a better report of the Bill depending in Parliament on the Copper business, I fear we shall scarce be able to get any relaxation of the Ministers proposals, & if not I think all the Copper Mines except 3 or 4 must be ruin'd, & those now going to work, be stop'd in the outset. I suppose the Gentlemen concerned in these Mines will send some Person fully inform'd of the Articles of Expence, & advantages arising to Government as at present establish'd. I have already told them the Income Tax alone would produce them full 20 Pr. Ct, for there will be 10 Pr Ct on the Ore, 10 Pr. Ct on the Copper, & 10 Pr Ct on the Proffit on the Materials, beside the Duties &c.

The particulars of which I am not sufficiently inform'd of. Lord de Dunstanville & Sir Wm. Lemon being Principals in this concern will I conclude be very attentive to the Progress of this Bill.

. . .

CRO, Truro, Rashleigh Papers: RS/12/2
Philip Rashleigh letters to Messrs. G. C. Fox, Falmouth
11 June 1799

I have just left Mr. Pitt who was attended by Mr. Gregor, Mr. J. Vivian & one or two more on the Copper Business.[1] I am sorry he persists in his endeavours to lower the Standard of Copper by some means, or other, either by preventing the East India Company from exporting above a certain quantity, or limiting the Standard; but he has defer'd giving a desided [sic] opinion for a day or two; but his inclination is plane [sic] & I therefore fear will be prejudicial to the Copper Mines. Mr. Vivian, if he has time, will write You more fully than I can at present.

Note
1. R. G. Thorne, *The House of Commons 1790–1820* (1986), 83 recorded Francis Gregor's opposition to the government's regulations on the price of copper.

RIC, Courtney Library, Truro, Rashleigh Papers:
RASH/4/43
William Day to Philip Rashleigh   *London, 3 July 1799*[1]

In answer to your favour of the 26th Ult. I have not again seen Mr. Kirwan, & have no expectation of it as I leave London for Hastings in Sussex next Monday & if I am not summoned back again by Business shall stop there 2 Months.

At present I do not see any probability of disposing of my cabinet of Minerals & indeed am not very anxious about it for I must confess, however prudence may dictate the propriety of it. Yet my love for the Science of mineralogy will make me regret the parting with it & as I am now come to the positive resolution of not expending more money to increase it there will be no danger of its injuring my Family. My intention in respect to my Collection is to arrange it in open cases or tables & have covers for to keep the dust off or some other contrivance that will be of little expence, & save me the trouble of a long attendance when I have to shew it to strangers. I have a spare room in my house excellently adapted for the purpose, in this case, my present Cabinet will not be of any further use to me, but am afraid you will want it sooner than I shall be able to empty it which I cannot do till my return to Town, but if that time will suit you, & you do not think 12 Guineas too high a price, it is at your service, & shall be delivered to any place you may direct, but if it is to be packed up to send to Cornwall the expence of packing & porterage to be at your cost. The duplicates of my Cabinet being now all dispersed of, & as I do not make any excursions into mineral country I find my supply of new articles almost stopped – & as I mean to increase my collection, as long as I retain it, but at the least possible expence,

I think the following plan may suit those Gentlemen who can procure duplicates of new substances or crystallizations, not before known. If they will supply me with a good specimen for my own Cabinet, in return I will make them a correct drawing of it. To many gentlemen I know this will be an acceptable exchange, & as you have already been at the expence of having a good many drawings of your British minerals done for you, if you choose to accept of my service in that line, it may be a mutual accommodation to us both. I do not pretend to the neatness of finishing equal to Mr. Underwood,[2] but from having some knowledge of the science of mineralogy, joined to a moderate skill in drawing, I presume my drawings will have the merit at least of being characteristic.

. . .

Notes

1. Letter annotated: 'Mr. Day respecting the sale of his cabinet of Minerals 1799'; Embrey and Symes, *Minerals of Cornwall and Devon*, 74, listed Day 'but of whom nothing is known'.
2. Thomas Underwood, was one of the artists Rashleigh used to illustrate his specimens in 1797.

CRO, Truro, Rashleigh Papers: DDR/5757/1/97
J. Tobin to Philip Rashleigh   *Bristol, 20 September 1799*[1]

Three or four days ago I had the pleasure to receive your Box with the Copper Ores, &c. for which fresh mark of your politiness [sic] I beg you will accept my best acknowledgments – Most of them are new to me, and will make a very acceptable addition to my little cabinet –

. . .

I observe what you say of having seen 'some <u>very fine</u> Crystals of Strontian from the Bristol Quarry, in the possession of Sir John St. Aubyn' – I have taken, I believe, as much pains as any body to procure good specims. of this Mineral – And while it was plenty, I have broken up many of the largest Masses I could meet with on the spot, without finding what can properly be called a <u>perfectly regular</u> Crystal – The forms which the Crystals mostly affect are, Bevelled Tables, Rhombs, and Cubes; but these are never compleat on all the Surfaces – There are also some pieces which are scaly, and a few which are fibrous. Three or four Months ago I sent some good samples of this Stone, both to Mohr the German and to Browne & Co. of Tavistock Street. If Sir John St. Aubyn was supplied by either of these Dealers, I am pretty certain they could not furnish him with any pieces so good as those which I formerly sent to you: and of one variety (the very white scaly kind) I don't recollect that I had any to spare, as the pit which yielded it, has been long filled up, and ploughed over. There was indeed a Russian Collector down here (named I think Driarbon,[2] or something like it) who in conjunction with some Gentlemen from your part of England, carried off a large quantity of this substance. – They may perhaps have been more fortunate on examining their acquisition: and Sr. John may have procured the crystals you mention through <u>that</u> channel. I should like to know this: and also whether the crystals in Sr. John's possession are <u>truly regular</u> and compleat as to form: what shape they assume: and what size they are of: and whether they are single <u>detached</u> crystals; or attached to a Mass, and only exhibit one, or two regular Faces –

The veins at the Old passage have been almost entirely ransacked, and exhausted. I was there about two Months ago, and could only find three or four large Lumps, which I brought away with me; any of these I will send to you just as I procured them, if you think they are worth your attention, that you may break them up yourself: or I will split them here, and try if they produce, on fracture any better Crystals than those I have already seen –

A new vein of this Substance was lately discovered in the Burying ground of a Chapel in the Suburbs of this City – It runs through, and is mixed with a Stratum of a yellow ochrous Earth: the Crystals are scaly and confused: but as it forms another variety you may perhaps have no objection to see some Specimens of it – I beg therefore you will use no kind of ceremony in giving me your Commissions in this Line; which I shall always execute, with great pleasure, to the utmost of my abilities – Indeed whenever I open my Drawers, I feel fresh reason to consider myself as, Dr. Sir Your much obliged Humb Servt.

Notes
1. There are other letters from Tobin dated 27 January, 22 February 1797, 11 November 1798; a catalogue of 79 specimens was received from Tobin 1797 (DDR 5758/5/5).
2. Deraebin (fl. late 1700s to 1818) became Director of the St. Petersburg Mining Institute; Rashleigh is said to have acquired specimens from him.

CRO, Truro, Rashleigh Papers: DDR/5757/1/93
William Day to Philip Rashleigh   *5 November 1799*

According to your desire in your favour of 29th Ult. I send you an Acct.. of the charges I have been at in respect to the Cabinet. The Cabinet = £ 12. 12. 0 – Cases & Packing = £ 2. 1. 0. Total = £14. 13. 0. to which will be to add the expences [sic] of delivering on board the vessel, but I cannot at present procure the account from our Wharfinger. . . .

. . . The Mathematical professor you mention,[1] I venture to guess was a Scotchman, ever since Dr. Hutton published his theory of the present appearance of the Globe being produced by fire all the literati of Scotland have embraced the idea. I am informed that in the University of Edinburgh/I do not mean [illegible]/ the Dr. is looked on as a man, who has done as much honour to it by [this] discovery, as Newton has done to England by the discovery of the powers of Gravity.

I have had a letter concerning the purchase of my collection from a Mr. Binns of Dublin, but from the manner of his writing do not expect him to become a purchaser, neither will I let him have it until Mr Greville has seen it. The Count de Bournon has mentioned to Mr. G[reville] yr [saying.] my Cabinet would be a very desirable acquisition for any person of Fortune who wished to form a cabinet of English Minerals/to begin with/he is to see it as soon as I can get it properly laid out, & he will then mention it to the Dutchess of Devonshire. I shall not now offer it to any person untill [sic] Mr. G. has determined about it.[2]

I am very glad to find you was pleased with what I mentioned concerning Crystallization. The primitive form, I perfectly agree with you, is very difficult to determine. Supposing there is such a thing, my two masters Bournon & Hauy seem to differ concerning the point. Bournon does not admit the central nucleus in all crystals, but I confess I am a little at a loss to understand all he says on the subject, from my deficiency in the language & his rapidity of speech. If I had his theory in writing I could speak more certainly to it. Hauy's doctrine is, that in all crystals there is a central nucleus of a determinate form, round which the secondary forms may be supposed to be accumulated, not that it is his opinion that all crystals are formed by the process of having a nucleus first & their lamina accumulating on the faces because the most minute & the largest crystals of the same group are found of the same form. But that those crystals he has found large enough to distinguish easily the facets & the striae marked on them in some direction (which is always constant in the same species) & that are not too hard to prevent him from separating the lamina in those crystals by following the direction in which the lamina would divide off easily, he always found the center a regular solid that would yield to no further regular division. He could only break it. This he calls the primitive & by determining the [manner] in which the lamina accumulated on the faces of it diminish either on their sides or angles, he determines the law of diminution they are subject to. The central nucleus of Calcareous spar is a Rhomb of certain determinate angles. By one mode of accumulations the dog tooth spar is formed. By another mode the hexagon prism with flat ends & so on to an infinite variety, & out of upwards of 500 different forms of calcareous spar, whose forms have all been determined & angles all measured, not one but what can be derived from this rhomb & has that as a nucleus, inside of it. The Heavy spars the same, so Quartz & indeed every class of crystallization which has yet been examined.

This is a constancy in the work of Creation truly wonderful & I think fully sufficient to vindicate those who pay a little attention to it, from any unjust reflections thrown on them by an ignorant person. Crystals are the only forms which the Almighty has subjected to Geometrical shapes. Many of them possess powers of attraction & repulsion which appear to [page torn with loss] to the form they appear under a thorough investigation as to the causes & effects of crystallization may very probably lead to such discoveries as at present we can form but little idea of. – I beg your excuse for the slovenly manner of writing but I am at present much hurried & have not time to transcribe it again.

Notes

1. This refers to John Playfair (1748-1819); mathematician and geologist; Professor of Mathematics at University of Edinburgh 1785–1805; became Professor of Natural Philosophy there, 1805.

2. In a later letter from Rashleigh to Sowerby (21 March 1807) there is a reference to Day's collection having been offered to him; Wilson, 'The history of mineral collecting 1530–1799', 167, stated that it was acquired by Sowerby, who figured many of Day's minerals between 1804 and 1808 (see also R. J. Cleevely, 'Discovery of the 'Barnstaple Zeolite' – a minor geological controversy of the early 1800s', *Transactions of the Devonshire Association*, 2007 [2008], 133-67, fn. 53).

CRO, Truro, Rashleigh Papers: DDR/5305/7
John Hawkins to Philip Rashleigh

Sunbury, 19 December 1800

I ought not to have suffered your kind letter to remain so long unanswered, but in truth my whole attention has been directed since my return here, to some literary investigations which had been too long neglected by me and you well know how easily the mind becomes absorbed in some favourite pursuit so as with difficulty to be disengaged from it. I would not have you think that I am arranging any papers for the press; No! I am gradually compleating what Information I have collected on my tour thro' Greece by the addition & collation of ancient authorities and this is an undertaking so vast that I have no prospects of getting thro' it for some years, but it is a great amusement to me in reading Pliny & other ancient writers to find such a coincidence between the facts which they mention & those which I myself observed. My respect for these gentlemen, of course, increases much with this progress of my reading and I am not a little vain at times of the support which they lend me. With reluctance I broke off these lucabrations on occasion of my late excursion to Derbyshire and with a pleasure proportionate to that reluctance I resumed them. But it was necessary that I should not omit so fair an opportunity of taking up pursuits long relinquished previous to the opening of a new mineralogical campaign in Cornwall and in this way I consider the time spent in that excursion [was] not ill employed.

[three paragraphs describing the geology and minerals of Flintshire follow]

The produce of the Flintshire mines has decreased in the same proportion of late years as that of the Derbyshire for which the reasons assigned are the exhausted state of these mines and the low price of lead. The bad system, however, of mining which has been hitherto pursued in that country leads me to suppose that much ore is still left behind in the old works and that if several of these were united in one set of Adventure & worked upon a large scale, the economy would be so great as to make it answer, and in fact this is the idea which is now pursuing in regard to these mines near Holywell in which my freind Mr. Pennant is concerned. Lately the Price of lead Ore & of Calamine have risen much. The Miners are all Welsh, but the Managers are mostly the descendants of Derbyshire Emigrants. Two Emigrants from Cornwall have lately planted themselves there and I fear are not qualified to do us much honour, the one is Mr. Prout, who has established a Ropery. The other is a Mr. Langworthy who is since dead. Further details respecting these mines I shall beg leave to postpone untill I have an opportunity of communicating them viva voce.

On my return here I received a letter from Mr. Klaproth acquainting me with the continuation of his laborious Analysis. He has compleated that of the green Copper Ores of our Cornish Mines including those of Tin Croft and has found them to be all mineralized by the arsenical acid. ... Mr Klaproth mentions also that Mr Gruber is translating his Works into English.

A paper is now preparing for the Royal Society on a very curious subject that of stones which have fallen out of the air, & the fact is sufficiently well attended, and the substances are now analyzing. There is reason to suspect that the famous mass of native Iron discovered in Siberia has been generated in this way. I have been lately drawing up, an historical account of the like accidents which I suppose will now no longer be disbelieved.

[short paragraph reporting availability of some minerals brought from Vienna for sale in London follows]

I shall be obliged to you, if you would take an opportunity while you remain in the country of ascertaining how much bread a given quantity of wheat will produce. The Wheat this year is allowed to be of a superior quality. Suppose you ascertain the weight of a certain measure by several trials. Then take a certain weight of this Wheat and see what weight of Flour it produces & lastly take a certain weight of this flour and see how much bread it will produce. The loaves to be weighed while warm & after they are grown cold. Excuse me for wishing to give you so much trouble but my object is to have grounds of comparison between the English and the Levant wheat.

A friend of mine who sowed a little of the foreign bearded Wheat last year in Cheshire had an astonishing crop. What Think you has been the rise in the price of Cheese in Cheshire since the year '81? It has more than doubled. Some very considerable enclosures are now taking place in this neighbourhood which will certainly increase the produce & improve the appearance of the country, but the poor complain grievously that their interests have been overlooked in respect to the compensation which are allowed them.

. . .

You enquire about the ores of Tellurium I believe this substance is found only in the Magyacher Gold Ores & in the so named Aurum graphicum.[1]

Note

1. In a letter to Rashleigh (20 October 1800) Gregor referred to Klaproth's analysis of these Hungarian ores; see also reference in Synnott's letters, 1796.

CRO, Truro, Rashleigh Papers: DDR/5757/2/8
Rev. William Gregor to Philip Rashleigh
Creed, 10 May 1801[1]

[Letter opens with acknowledgment of Rashleigh's response to Gregor's water sample analysis and then continues with an a/c of an Ore of Titanium]

I come now to the principal object of this letter, which is the inside passenger of it & which will speak for itself. – I wish much to have your opinion & the opinion of any mineralogical friend that you may shew [page torn with loss] concerning it – A vein of this black substance was discovered lately [word erased] in sinking a well near the new building of Kea Church. The vein is about six or seven fathoms depth & runs east & west. I was sanguine enough on my sight & first examination to conjecture that it was [illegible] for of Coal – It is evidently [illegible] penetrated by some black substance. [Gregor then records his various tests]

– Perhaps you may be acquainted with friends used to coal countries. I shd. esteem it a favour if you will shew the small specimen to some of them – A discovery of coal in Cornwall wd. be a discovery indeed! – The man who worked in the Well complained of the bad air in it.

This circumstance looks well on every side of the Question. Coal is certainly a new substance in the County. But there is a wide interval between <u>improbability</u> & <u>impossibility</u>. The Down in which this substance has been found, has never been tried in the mining way.

. . .

I cannot close this letter without congratulating you upon the late great change produced in [a short] time in our national affairs. By the Blessing of God, the Sun has broken thro' the gloom of our political horizon. I trust, that we shall have [hole in letter with loss] a peace on honourable terms, which can be the only [case] that can be a lasting one.[2]

Notes

1. Letter sent to Norfolk Street, Strand.
2. The reason for Gregor's comment is uncertain, it could relate to the naval victory at the Battle of Copenhagen (2 April 1801) that halted the renewal of the League of 'armed neutrality'; or refer to the Union of Great Britain with Ireland earlier that year; or Addington succeeding Pitt as Prime Minister to pursue his own policy of peace and retrenchment, that led to the Treaty of Amiens in 1802 – a truce that ended the first phase of the war with France.

CRO, Truro, Hawkins Archive: J3/3/267
Rev. William Gregor to John Hawkins

Creed, 3 September 1801

Believe me, I was one amongst the many of your friends, who were sincerely rejoiced at hearing of the late change in you situation & future prospects. I was rejoiced because I was persuaded that it wd. materially tend to increase your happiness & comforts. Love, they say, is blind: But I give you full credit for being able to see through the slight [illegible] bandage, which may have been thrown over your eyes, and I doubt not but that your lady will contrive to appear the same to you as a Husband as she first appeared to you as a Lover. – –

I have had ten years experience of the married state, and I can safely say, that those ten years have been far the most happy of my life. The <u>comforts of Home</u> are amongst the chief blessings of life, and an amiable wife is the <u>formex of Home</u>. It is she, that fixes a man and becomes the centre of his domestic Happiness. You have had enough of Travelling and have laid up a sufficient stock of ideas & information collected from other countries. –

I trust that you have travelled abroad so as to relish your own country better, and to become more useful to it.

I had, I assure you, anticipated a very lively pleasure in seeing you, this Summer. I had planned many little Schemes and mineralogical investigations. I had predetermined to obtain from you a great deal of information. But I shd. be miserably selfish, if I were not rejoiced that you 'cannot come'. I hope however, that you will bring your Lady into this County next year, and that you will do us the pleasure of introducing her to us. I will not trespass upon you longer. . . .

CRO, Truro, Hawkins Letters: J3/3/268
Philip Rashleigh to John Hawkins
Menabilly, 3 September 1801

The Great disappointment I have in being deprived of seeing you this Year at Menabilly is in a great degree recompenced [sic] by the cause, as it must be the means of your future Happiness; for though a happy – disposition never wants amusement, yet there are none to be compared to that you have now chosen, the most solid, the most Chearful [sic], & I hope the most permanent this World can produce. You and your lady have my hearty Congratulations on meeting together; & wishes for a long enjoyment of every consolation a married state can produce. I shall be very glad of an Introduction to the Lady, knowing your choice must make a new Acquaintance desirable. Had I known your address, I should not have remain'd so long without giving you Joy on this occasion; I expected to have heard tomorrow where you was to be found, as I am to partake of some Venison at your Brothers.

I am not acquainted with Col. Sibthorpe, for by some uncommon misfortune I know very few members though I have been so long in Parliament; my memory was always bad, & the advance in Life makes it much more trecherous [sic]; From your connection I shall find him out.

It is a happy circumstance that your choice has fallen upon a Lady whose amusements are similar [to] your own, as when when [sic] the entertainments of two persons who live together are similar, the pleasure is increased & succeeds best. Hymen seems this Year to have hit many a mark with his Arrows, my Bror. Thomas had lately Six Settlements at one time in his Office, some of which are consummated & others advanced towards it.

Since I have returned to Menabilly, I have procured several good Minerals, as the Mines are going down very fast, we cannot expect abundance of Cabinet specimens; Tregoning made a good hand of his Fluors, such as he offer'd you & others, he had several pieces which he got at one time. These things are now sold at such extravagant Prices as to prevent those of moderate fortune from engaging in Minerallogical pursuits.

. . .

CRO, Truro, Rashleigh Archive: R/5757/2/3
Rev. William Gregor to Philip Rashleigh
Creed, 15 October 1801

[Page torn with loss through damp] received about a fortnight ago from Mr. Michell of Calenick smelting House, a tin slag wh. was produced at St. Austell smelting House which he told me contained Cobalt. I have examined and found that metal existing in it in a notable proportion. In round numbers 70 Tin to 24 of Cobalt on the hundred parts, what is very remarkable a very small quantity of iron cd. be detected & no Arsenic. – Mr Michell told me that the ore from which that slag was eliquated , was raised at Polgooth & that he had seen Tin Ore wh. had been raised at the Mine which evidently contained Cobalt. This being the fact shd. think that it would be worth while for the Miners to keep a good look out upon the ore raised, in order to discover the peach blossom efflorescence which indicates the presence of that valuable metal. From what Mr Michell informed me, I should not be surprized if Cobalt Ore has been often mixed with Tin Ore in this Mine. The Cobalt Ore of the Wherry mine was really a Tin Ore mechanically mixed with Cobalt ore [page torn with loss] troubling you [page torn with loss] As [page torn with loss] mineralogical inter [page torn with loss] is acceptable.

I heard lately from my friend Mr. Tennant, he told me that he shd.

send you the curious specimen of Ruby Tin mixed with Copper, which he had discovered, after that he had broken off sufficient for Analysis. But I have very great doubts as to its containing any <u>Tin</u>; I have every reason to believe that it is the Ruby Copper Ore wh. generally crystallizes in octoedrons [sic], the regular crystallization of which has by some means or other been impeded. I picked up a specimen at Truro exactly resembling it & I found my conjectures verified. Mr. Tennant will write to me the result of his further investigations of this fossil.

Just off tomorrow for Devonshire and hope to return in about ten days. I trust that you bear the foggy dripping weather well. I shd. fear that it was unhealthy yet, I do not hear that any epidemical diseases prevail. We are I [page torn with loss] [page torn with loss] ,well in this house

CRO, Truro, Rashleigh Papers: DDR/5305/16
John Stackhouse to Philip Rashleigh
Paris, 18 September 1802[1]

You will like to hear some thing of the Travellers if you have not been in the neighbourhood of Trehane, or have not chanced to see Dr. Wynne. Our Journey to this Place has been attended with every satisfaction that could be expected. Good Inns, excellent Roads, & the greatest degree of Civility & Attention. We are very commodiously lodged in a very large Hotel in the centre of the City, and as I think it a reasonable rate at three Guineas & half English per week. My Table including Breakfast, Tea as to the Cream Bread & Butter &c. as we buy our own tea for ourselves & servts. – eight in number – amount to about £1.13.4. Wine is not included in this & our Carriage is about a guinea a day; a French Servt. who finds himself costs 3s / 4d per day.

I shall entertain you with the National Museum & Garden des Plantes, as you may hear from others of the Statues & Pictures which are open twice a week <u>gratis</u> to all Visitors, & Amateurs may spend as much time as they please, & they are accommodated with benches. The Museum is a very elegant Building facing the Jardin des Pl[antes] the Botanic Garden. The Apartments are very extensive, each floor being a single Room divided by Arches without any Doors. On the First Floor as you enter, the Minerals present themselves. I wish I was able to enter into the subject scientifically.

The Arrangement pleased me very much. The Glass cases in which they are placed are very shallow that the Specimens may be near the Eye, & both the Glass & the Specimens are without a particle of Dust, or any stain to hinder their being seen to the greatest possible advantages. Each Specimen is fixed on a wooden Pedestal in the front of wh. is placed in print the name, & the different mineral substances which combine in that Mineral as for instance, arsenical Copper &c. &c. Each Metal is kept to itself, as are the Quartzs, the Selenites and as far as to the earths: nothing seems omitted.

The arrangement is said to be most masterly. It is the work of Abbè Hauy, a name I never heard of but he is said to be superior to Fourcroy & Lavoisier. All the names & references are in French, as being a National Treasure. It occupies a great length of cases & is rich in exotic Specimens. The fossils succeed, & are extremely numerous particularly in the Fishes. To them succeed Shells among which is a Patella, an unique wh. [Deutucasteaux] brought home as the last specimen collected by La Perouse. The insects & Reptiles in Spirits occupy the remdr. of the 1st floor. In the upper the Butterflies in the highest Preservation & far exceeding in brilliancy any thing I had a conception of are first seen: all the Moths, Beetles, spiders &c. which are preserved dry follow them: then the Beast arranged from Linnaeus, among which is a Hippopotamus, Cameleopard in high preservation. All the Attitudes are finely preserved & from the artificial Eyes & the red colour about the mouth they appear to be living. The Birds which follow pleased me, as being something of an Ornithologist above all the rest. They are in the most perfect Arrangement. All the Cuckoos, all the Jays (a most numerous order), all the Hawks, of every Quarter of the Globe, are placed side by side, & form a very interesting study to observe, wherever they resemble in what they disagree. The Botanic garden is a very busy piece of Ground extending to the River Seine. It has a wide walk planted with shady Trees for its whole length & the plants are arranged systematically, with stakes descriptive of their names. A Menagerie with Lions, Bears &c. adjoins the Gardens, open to every person gratis; & they are making separate Enclosures with proper stands for the harmless kinds to take the Air occasionally. The largest Elephant I ever saw has a grass Plot to himself. With the united Regards of this party to you & Mss M.R.

I have been presented to the President of the National Institute & attended their sitting, I have presented my work to them.

Every Moment seems occupied but I think to leave this Place in a Fortnight.

Note

1. Postmarks on this letter indicate that it was transmitted from Paris through the Foreign Office. Addington, the Prime Minister, had succeeded in his policy of peace and retrenchment with the signing of the Treaty of Amiens in March 1802, which had brought a period of peace (which in the event lasted nine months) in the conflict between France and Britain. The treaty triggered a spate of trips to the continent by scientists and upper-class citizens. Probably the most significant was that of the astronomer William Herschel, who was anxious to discuss his observations with his French contemporaries and correspondents.

NHM, London, Mineral Library, Russell Bequest, John Hawkins Letters: No. 37/38
Philip Rashleigh to John Hawkins

Menabilly, 13 November 1802

As I can converse with you just now free of Expence,[1] I acknowledge the receipt of a kind Letter I received from you last night immediately.

The Errand which engaged – 'you in Somersetshire' has been attended with more success than I expected. You could not think to find a House ready built so much to your satisfaction, as from a Plan of your own. By your Account of that you have seen alteration might easily be made for better accommodation to your own Family & Visitors. . . . The Objections you make seem so easily removed. You will scarce find a House ready built with fewer Inconveniences. I do not remember the Place.

The other part of your Letter is to me of much more consequence, as it forbodes your Banishing yourself from this County, a Circumstance many of your Friends will Lament; The short time I can expect to enjoy the Company of any Neighbours or distant Acquaintance, make their residence less regreted [sic]; but you are likely to live long and enjoy Society for many Years, & that you may do so is my sincere wish.

The second part of my Mineral Prints I believe was left at your late house in Baker Street: at all events I can supply you with another when we meet. It is an Unfortunate thing for the Lovers of Natural History that you have been deprived of giving them your observations on Mineralogy of this County, which I think is more Interesting than any I have heard of, and never properly attended to. So your Account would not only be accurate, but New. Even the Change you propose of turning your thoughts from Minerallogy to Foreign objects, I much lament; for the attendance you have given to Mines & their productions, must have made you better informed on such subjects than most Englishmen; few have had the opportunity, & fewer the ability of retaining the Lessons they have heard & the Practice they have seen. The use of such information as you could give, would be attended with great benefit to those who are concerned in the Mines of Cornwall; for I think daily observation shews the want of Ability in our Mines & Assayers, except in Assaying Copper Ores, in which I think they excel.

Dolcoath Mine has long been known to have a good Lode of Cobalt Ore, but so mixed & Minerallized with Iron as to render it useless: don't you think some means might be found of separating these Ores by heating them with Sulphur when reduced to powder, with a careful fire ? Some proposals have been made for reducing this Ore, but I have heard of no success that followed or the means used.

By your introducing Mrs. Hawkins to collect, you have probably not been so attentive to your own, as thinking one in a family pursuing the same object is more likely obtain perfection, than if divided. The Expence of procureing [sic] Specimens has increased to such extravegance [sic] that if my Collection was not considerable at present, I should not have begun now.[2]

I shall hope Mr Klaproth's 3rd Volume will soon be Translated, as the author of the last Translation promised. How much such a Chemist is wanted in this Country? Mr. Chenevix is I believe a very good one, I have not so good an Opinion of Count de Bournon.

Notes
1. This suggests that it was possible to send the letter from Menabilly to Trewithen by hand.
2. Quoted by Russell, 'Philip Rashleigh of Menabilly', 7-8.

CRO, Truro, Rashleigh Papers: DDR/5757/2/25
Rev. William Gregor to Philip Rashleigh

Creed, 17 November 1802

On my return from an excursion in the Neighbourhood of Falmouth your second Publication of 'Specimens' was put into my hands, which I consider in every point of view to be a most valuable present and for which I return you my warmest acknowledgements. Your work will be a lasting monument of your liberal encouragement of the Science of Mineralogy & of the arts; and in addition to its intrinsic value, I shall prize it still more as a proof of your kind attention & friendship.

I delayed thanking you for yr. new work, in the hope that I shd. have been able to send you my Analysis of the Adamantine Spar from Thibet.[1] But salts are sometimes very capricious & will not crystallize so speedily, as we might wish them. At present the Argillaceous part of the Stone is not sufficiently dry for ignition to be previously applied to the weighing of it. . . .

I have lately met with the Titanium in a fossil which if further examination proved it to be a <u>native of this County</u> will be an interesting discovery. It is a species of Basaltes, which I found in the Hedges upon the high grounds next to the Sea on the Estate of Place in the parish of St. Anthony. I was upon a visit at Admiral Spry's, and in my walks these black stones attracted my notice. There are two different sorts. The one is a large <u>pebble</u> & has evidently been taken from the sea shore, the other is not so black nor so full of the Crysolith, but both are porous, and both contain Titanium mixed with the Iron, & I believe Kalc. The circumstance of a basalt containing Titanium is new, and if I can trace the vein of it, it will be a very curious discovery. The Tide was up and I could not get below. But as soon as Season & Tide permit I shall visit the coast. – Mr. Hawkins is much interested about it. – I have kept a specimen of each sort for you. It is <u>possible</u> that these stones may have been brought as Ballast, but not very <u>probable</u> every circumstance being considered. There being no cove or landing shore near.

We were very much disappointed to hear that Mr. Wm. Rashleigh has been so good as to call at Creed, in <u>our absence</u>: remember us if you please kindly to him. He gave me some time since a specimen of an ore, wh. he took to be white Iron ore. The figure of the Crystals struck me as extraordinary for that species of ore, and a slight Analysis proved that it contained more Silex than belongs to it. On shewing it to Mr. Hawkins, he pronounced it to be Thumerstein which I wonder I did not discover before. It was found at Restormel. So that we have another place in the County where Thumerstone is discovered.

Immediately as I have a little time to spare, I shall undertake the Analysis of the China-stone, which has, I find has the Honour of a place amongst your 'specimens'

. . .

Mr. Hawkins has lent me the third Vol. of Klaproth's Beytrage – it contains many curious Articles. There is an Analysis of our Arseniate of Copper. He agrees nearly with Chevenix. There is also an Analysis of the Gadoline but Mr. Vauquelin differs from him as to proportions of its constituent parts & concerning one of them & I think that Vauquelin is probably in the right, as far as the publications of each enable me to Judge.

I expected that Mr. & Mrs. Hawkins would have dined with us to day, but the weather proved so unfavourable that none of the Trewarthennick party came. I am much obliged to you for your kind Invitation, to come to you, when Mr. & Mrs Hawkins are with you, and I shall gladly accept of it.

Note
1. Gregor's paper 'on a variety of Corundum' from Tibet – see *Nicholson's Journal*, Vol. 4, April 1803: 209-14.

CRO, Truro, Rashleigh Papers: DDR/5757/2/26
William Gregor to Philip Rashleigh

Creed, 17 March 1803

Many thanks to you for your kind letter. I have not the least doubt but that, whatever Analysis M. Chenevoix takes in hand, it will be performed with accuracy – The results wh. he has drawn from his examination of the Adamantine Spar, may be relied on. But I cannot believe that the particular sort, wh. I analysed, has fallen under his notice.

. . .

The fellow Traveller of these East Indians, is a Native of our own County, but he is a Native which claims our respect & attention, & one with whom I think that you will wish to be better acquainted. – Unless I am very much mistaken, the red particles

& crystallizations in this stone are <u>Rubies</u> – and if they really turn out to be so, I shall think it an important discovery. – I thought that they might be Garnets. But many circumstances convince me, that they are Rubies. The form of the Crystallization is, I think, a double four-sided pyramid. The Garnet is duodeca[h]edron: – The particles of this red stone adhere together but slightly, but they possess great hardness in themselves – a bit of the pounded stone tinges Borax an elegant green. This is a property of the Ruby – And an Analysis wh. I have begun confirms my opinion & betrays already traces of the oxide of Chrome, to which it is known that the Ruby owes its colour – Where it was discovered I know not, but I have used every means to get more specimens & I shall make a point of setting the best I pick up for you. The rubies, if they are such, are inbedded in a friable pyritous stone. – If it is known that this stone contains rubies, in a very short time there will not be a specimen left. I shall therefore at present keep my own counsel and I shd. be obliged to you to say nothing about it as yet – till I procure further information respecting the mine where they are raised. &c. &c.

. . .

I do not know what mineral is designated by the term Thalite, wh. you mention. There are so many Mushroom names that spring up in a short time, that it is almost impossible to keep pace with them.

. . .

CRO, Truro, Rashleigh Papers: DDR/5757/1/102
John Hawkins to Philip Rashleigh
Trewithen, 1 October [?1803]

I had the pleasure of receiving your letter of the 24th on my return here last Tuesday and this moment your letter of this morning has been put into my hands. We shall be very happy to wait upon you on the fourteenth that is two days after the departure of Mr. Jonathan Rashleigh and we feel much obliged by the precautions you mean to take to guard our infants against the hooping cough upon which subject you will not find me unnecessarily fearfull [sic].[1] We shall be with you at dinner on the 14th and I earnestly wish a continuance of the present fine weather that the beauties of your situation may be seen to the best advantage; we have a resource however in the worst weather within doors which will afford unceasing amusement of the most instructive kind.

. . .

We are now at leisure to attend to our freinds who I trust will not take it amiss that we have neglected them. I have not yet had the pleasure of viewing Mr. Williams famed collection nor shall I have an opportunity before I go to spend a few days with Mr. Chilcott near Truro when I shall be within a short ride of Scorrier. I have added scarcely any thing worth mentioning to my own collection for to own this truth, my finances now as a married man are not equal to it. The prices in fact of all valuable specimens are become enormous and as I have now so many new calls for my money they are fairly out of my reach. I am sorry to have missed falling in with Mr. Greville. I remember to have heard of Mr. Sheffield in Derbyshire and he was spoken of I think as an Assay master.

Note
  1. The reference to 'our infants' is confusing suggesting that this letter could not have been written before 1804 when his second child Mary Anne was born. Yet letters from Gregor (17 November 1804) and Rashleigh (27 July 1804, 25 November 1804) make no mention of a visit that year. But surviving letters from this period Rashleigh (13 November 1802) and Gregor (12 November 1803) indicate that Hawkins was in Cornwall. Many years later Hawkins commented that he had not visited Cornwall for some 25 years, which would be consistent with this.

CRO, Truro, Hawkins Archive: J3/2/290
Rev. William Gregor to John Hawkins[1]
  Creed, 12 October 1803 [altered to Grampound, 14 October]

I take up my Pen to make enquiries about you & yours in this season of anxiety & alarm.[2] I hear that you are soon to quit Dawlish, & thank you intend to reside in London during the winter. Have you a house in view which you have destined for your future abode? I shall be glad to hear, that you have succeeded in this important object. I trust that as our County is thrown out of your plan, you will succeed in meeting with a seat in Devonshire. It has certainly many advantages in point of scenery &c. over Cornwall but with me, the *natale solum* & the constant habits of my life are placed in the opposite scale. We are fortunately so framed, that we are the Creatures of habit, and where we have been long used to live. We cleave, as it were, to the soil and feel for a time a sort of transplantation, if we are forced to quit it.

. . .

Mr. Nicholson has also inserted in his Journal a letter of mine on the existence of sulphat of Manganesia in coal Ashes[3] – which probably arises from the decomposition of Pyrites & Schistes. At least, I obtained Sulphat of Magnesia, by heating Mundic & Steatite together in a common fire, and what is something extraordinary, it was not contaminated with either the sulphate of Iron, or Alumina.

I shall say little of public Affairs, which at present engage so much of our thoughts and conversation. For it is a disagreeable subject. It appears to me, that we possess much physical strength in the Country, but very little talent to wield & direct it. Wavering councils & discordant plans suit not with the present crisis. At all events, much misery & bloodshed will ensue from an Invasion – and if the enemy shd. not attempt it, he will protract our expenses, & continue to hold us in the situation of alarm & apprehension & consequent armament & see wherever in future, it suits his cause. – In short *Vicenia damns est* – we are in a bad neighbourhood. – We do not seem to be under any great apprehensions in this County. We trust rather to our insignificance than to any military protection, which is by me no means great, a few Thousand of French men would do us infinite mischief. – We have Meetings & we talk about it & about it. – but I cannot say, that our system of defence is organised as yet, – It will be favorable for the whole Nation, if the threatened descent is deferred for a few Months longer.

. . .

Notes
1. This letter is addressed to: John Hawkins, Esq., Dawlish, Exeter who annotated it: 'Answ'd. Novr. 12'
2. Gregor's concern at this time reflects the resumption of hostilities with France.
3. See *Nicholson's Journal*, Vol. 5, 1803: 225-227

NHM, London, Mineral Library, Russell Bequest, Hawkins
Letters: No. 39/40
Philip Rashleigh to John Hawkins

Menabilly, 19 December 1803

It is now some time since I received a very kind letter from you
before you left Dawlish & by this time I hope you & your family
are safe arrived in your Lodgings at London where I wish you all
a Merry Christmas & many happy Years after.

. . .

I thank you for enquiring after my Health which continues
without being much affected by the variety of weather we have
had, which tries many constitutions. I am however pretty nearly
confined to my house though without much pain.

Gentlemen in this County will be more affected by the Property
Tax than in most others, because they let their Estates more on
Fines, & few persons more than myself having Let many estates
on Fines soon after I came into Possession, in order to pay my
Brothers & Sisters Fortunes and my Mothers Jointure. By this
Means I raised large Sums by Selling about half the Value of those
Estates, which I considered as Principal, & so applied the produce;
and now I am called upon to pay a Pr. Centage from those Leases
I have been granting for near forty Years on Fines, more or Less in
number & Value annually, to be all subject to the tax in one Year,
to be paid by the tenant & deducted out of his Rent. I see this Tax
in a tremendous light, by being thus levied on property; I likewise
think it lays a foundation for other taxes which will soon reduce
both Peers & Gentlemen to a level with Plebeians, which I think
most of the European nations have been destroyed by.

The Mines are in a florishing [sic] state, but doubtful if they can
spare the number of Men called for to attend Bonaparte when he
arrives. Two of my Nephews, Mr. Wm. & Mr. Colman Rashleigh
are engaged as Captains in the 'Stannary' Royal Cornwall Artillery
with Mr. Tyrwhittl – Colonel; Mr. Trelawney & Mr. John Vivian
– Lieu^t. Cols.; Mr. Gwatkin & Mr. John Tremayne – Majors, with
several other Officers, & 1000 men. The present & late Fogs have
been temptations for Bonaparte to set out in hopes of escaping,
nothing could be so favorable for him or disadvantagious [sic] for
our Fleets.

. . .

I have added very little to my Minerals since you saw them,
being out of the way of meeting with any except from the County

I am in; but I have procured a few, if I live to shew them to you it
will be pleasant. I should like to know if Forster who used to live
in the Piazza, Covent Garden, is returned from Russia; though
I believe you seldom deal with him; his Wife changed her house
and lived near the West end of Gerrard Street if I mistake not;
He must have procured everything Russia or Siberia affords
during his long absence: Mawe I believe intends to rival him in
business. Our late Possessions I think must produce new subjects
for our cabinets. From the destruction we are threatened with,
there is no encouragement to improve our situations or increase
our collections, but the sanguine hopes of making our Enemies
repent of Invasion should they Land on any part of the United
Kingdom.

When you was at the Wherry Mine do you recollect seeing
stones there with small white Cubic forms about – of an Inch, or
in Lozenge shapes in Chlorite with small Crystals of lead ore? this
Mine you know is now level with the rest of the Beach. Stenna
Gwinn likewise has produced some small Stellate Crystals of a
white colour, perhaps Zeolites, with a few very small six sided
Xtals of a grass green colour, but so small & so few as scarce
to get enough for proving what they contain, they are most like
Copper Ore, but I could not perceive any on polished iron when
dissolved in an Acid. I had some of the White Zeolites before but
doubt their being of that Genius [sic]; some of these stones contain
more solid pieces tending to form cubic forms of a milk white
colour. I do not hear of more Apatite being found.

University of Bristol Library, Special Collections: Joan Eyles
Collection (DM1186)
Philip Rashleigh to James Sowerby
Menabilly, 17 January 1804

Among the Books I lately received from Messrs. Nicol I found
your very Polite Letter of an old date, for which I thank you, &
am much obliged for the Compliments you pay both to me & my
Minerals: I am too far advanced in Life to take much more trouble
to Collect, or to get them represented to the Publick. I should be
sorry to let them be Transported into our enemies Land & trust
that Providence which has so long Protected us, will continue to
keep us out of the Power of such an Enemy as threatens us with

Total destruction. I look upon the Minerals of this County more productive of Cabinet Specimens than any part of the World, though some few Foreign Collections are very Numerous & Superb. At present we have very few Fossils raising worth notice, some things from the Mines of Manganese in Devonshire are different to any I have seen from other places, but they are more valuable for Collectors than Manufactories, & therefore not likely to be long worked.

. . .

Perhaps you have Count de Bournon to assist you in drawing your Crystals; he is the first Man in this Country who understands it. This is a part of knowledge I do not begin with, & am now too far advanced in Life to undertake such a laborious study. All parts of Mineralogy has been so much improved within these few years, that the Old Books & Old Masters neither Teach or learn any thing worth knowing, on this subject: The little variation which modern Chymists find on critical examination, & give new names to makes a new Edition of a Nomenclature frequently wanted.

I think we want a good Lapidary & an able Chymist in this County, for except for examining Tin & Copper ores, our Miners look for nothing else. The few Silver Ores which have been discovered have been found by mere chance, & some Cobalt ores likewise, we have scarce any of either of these valuable Ores found at present.

. . .

Such a quantity of Minerals of this County have been sent to London, that they are become cheaper there than here, where the price is enormous. Should you want any particular Substance the produce in this County, let me know it, & it shall be endeavoured to be procured.

NHM, Mineral Library, Russell Bequest, Hawkins Letters: 1/2
Rev'd. William Gregor to John Hawkins
Creed, 14 February 1804

. . .

I thank you for your last kind favour It was out of <u>respect</u> to the Royal Society & Sr J.Banks that I did not obtrude my paper on a variety of Corundum on them. Nothing but what is perfectly new & remarkable shd., I think, be inserted in the Transactions of that learned Body. There are many facts & observations wh. are worthy of being preserved, but not worthy of a place in so good company. Every reptile is not worthy of being preserved in proof spirits.[1]

My attention has lately been drawn by two mineral substances, which I think may be new, & curious, If my ideas of them shd be confirmed by future experiments I shd. not scruple to lay them before the Royal Society and I wish to consult you concerning them. They are both natives of Stenna Gwinn. – The first has been considered as a Zeolite.

. . . My Experiments prove that this Mineral is not Zeolite [a detailed account of his experiments follows].

CRO, Truro, Rashleigh Papers: DDR/5757/2/28
Rev'd. William Gregor to Philip Rashleigh
Creed, 14 February 1804

Whenever I have any Mineralogical intelligence to communicate, I never scruple to trouble you with a letter. I have been lately examining two curious productions of Stenna Gwin [sic]. The supposed Zeolite and two other substances which often accompany it.

[A very detailed account of his analysis follows]
I am now come to an end of my paper & I fear of your patience – I walked up to Stenna Gwin on Thursday last & was a long time there searching for these minerals but I was not very successful.

University of Bristol Library, Special Collections: Joan Eyles Collection (DM1186)
Philip Rashleigh to James Sowerby
Menabilly near Fowey, 3 March 1804

[Paragraph discussing minerals sent to Sowerby]
There is a small box in the large one which are not represented in my Book & have never been drawn; as you are so kind as to promise to execute this business, I send them for that purpose

depending on your returning of them safe to Menabilly. I believe there is a ticket with each of these as well as with the others; but least [sic] there should not, I will mention those in the little box in some part of this Letter.

. . .

My Infirmities which have deprived me of the Honor of Attending Parliament, will likewise prevent me from Traveling [sic] to London & seeing your Museum.

In the little box of choice Specimens I would desire You to unpack them with care, by taking out the small pieces first. . . .

[Continues with two further paragraphs describing the material sent]

I beg you will send back the four Specimens I wish to have drawn as soon as you can; so many of my Friends have lately died suddenly, makes Life very precarious.

Our Miners are Jelous [sic] of having the Mines known from whence Specimens come.

NHM, General Library, Sowerby Archive: Rashleigh 47/10
Philip Rashleigh to James Sowerby

Menabilly, 5 May 1804

. . .

I do not collect myself samples of Rocks, I know some who do, but I think they extend those Collections beyond the seize [sic] of a moderate House. Such as are useful for Manufactures or Ornaments may be worth attending to, & if I was able to move about as I was formerly, I might be able to get you some of these articles. . . . When I was Stout[1] & able to get about the Country, I was ready & willing to Assist my Friends in collecting Fossils, more than I ever shall again; I must now be contented with the chance of meeting with such as accidentally fall in my way. Notwithstanding such unreasonable quantities of Minerals have been sent from this County, the Prices for anything gaudy keeps up unreasonably, & the Travelers [sic] give anything that is asked, whether Curious or not.

. . .

[PS] Franks are so scarce you need not give yourself the trouble of seeking for them as I do not mind Postage.

[Various figures of costs/prices were appended by Sowerby at the foot of this letter]

Note
1. 'Stout' used in the sense of being 'sturdy'.

CRO, Truro, Rashleigh Papers: DDR/5757/2/30
Rev. William Gregor to Philip Rashleigh
Creed, 14 May 1804

I received sometime since through your means Mr. Charles Hatchett's paper on Huel Boys Antimony Ore together with the Count de Bournon's accompaniment. I am particularly pleased with the former, as it compleatly [sic] established what I long ago asserted respecting the constituent parts of this mineral – If you recollect I have frequently told you that Lead not Antimony was the predominating ingredient – There is too much excursion into the Region of Theory in the Count's paper to please me entirely. What he asserts respecting molecules &. aggregations & Crystalixt'ns may be plausible 'till it be pushed aside by some more captivating speculation' – He certainly has a keen eye for a Crystal & can see deep into it. I am much obliged to you for yr. kind attention in so speedily forwarding to me these interesting memoires and for yr. very kind letter.

. . .

I believe now that I am authorized by experiment to say, that the small acicular Crystals from Stenna Gwinn diverging from a center, & wh. have been deemed Zeolites are clay in a pure crystallized state. The water of Crystallizn. amounts to upwards of 26 pr cent. This, then, is a new & a curious mineral – The other substance wh. is found in parallelopipedon plates with angles cut off [small diagram] of a green colour & those of a yellow waxen colour of square scales adhering to each other contain a mineral, wh. I have not been able to examine with sufficient minuteness in order to ascertain its nature. It resembles in some points the oxide of Uranium but in others it differs from it. I am in doubt whether it is that substance or Molybdonated Iron – it is a very curious substance & exceedingly scarce – and now that this mine so bountiful in curiosities is stopped, we shall have no more of

[it] or any thing else – I was there not many days since – But there were no men at work and I picked up but a very few scales of the above mentioned substance –

Of Politicks we may say that we have 'Confusion & [are] more confounded' alas! alas! If Bonaparte does not come soon & makes us more at unity with ourselves, we are making rapid advances towards ruin!!

NHM, Mineral Library, Russell Bequest, Hawkins Letters: 3/4
Rev. William Gregor to John Hawkins
Creed, 20 May 1804

I wrote a long letter to you a considerable time ago: . . . I infer from your silence, that the letter never reached your hands. . . . In the letter, . . . I consulted you upon some Mineralogical questions and I enclosed little bits of specimens, of which I entertained doubts. In order not to Tax you for my queries, I took the liberty of enclosing it under cover to Col. Sibthorpe, Cavendish Square.

I have subjected the acicular Crystals, which diverge from a Center [sic] and are found adhering to Quartz in Stenna Gwinn – mine, to Analysis. – They are sometimes found in a more compact assemblage resembling Zeolite: and for which substance this mineral has been taken. The result of my analysis is that they are Crystals of pure clay.[1] . . .

Let me hear from you soon in answer to my impertinences [sic]. I hear that you have at last obtained a House. Where is it and how do you like it? . . .

PS Mr. Charles Hatchett very politely sent me his paper: very ingenious & satisfactory analysis of the Huel Boys Antimonial ore. – I was particularly pleased with it as some experiments I made on it some years ago led me to the same conclusions of it.

Note
1. Sir A. Russell, 'The Rev. William Gregor (1761–1817), discoverer of titanium', *The Mineralogical Magazine*, 30, 229 (1955), 617-624, referred (at 618-9) to this letter and noted that 'Gregor was the first to examine chemically and describe the species wavellite . . . from specimens he had collected . . . at the end of 1803'. Later both Humphry Davy and William Babington described this Devonshire

mineral; the former calling it Hydrargillite, the latter as Wavellite after Dr. Wavell of Barnstaple, who had supplied them with the material. Both Davy and Gregor had considered this mineral to be a hydrate of alumina, although only Gregor had also detected the presence of phosphoric acid and fluorine – see his own account of his experiments and also the descriptions given by Sowerby, *British Mineralogy*, 1805, Vol. 2 Pl. CXLII & (1807) Vol. 3, Pl. CCXLIII. Other experiments mentioned in this letter were on torbernite and autunite.

University of Bristol Library, Special Collections: Joan Eyles Collection (DM1186)
Philip Rashleigh to James Sowerby

Menabilly, 13 June 1804

Your letter of the 6th Instant has given me much pleasure on several accounts; one that the things I sent you for figuring having been of some use to you, & of their being on the road back, which I never doubted: As old acquaintance I shall like to see them again. As these have not been very difficult to represent, I shall in my next remittance trouble you with one or two which will require much more skill & judgment in drawing; but if they should require more time than you can spare to represent them, I beg you will return them without attempting to figure them; as they are both scarce & difficult; but by what I have seen of your execution, I believe nothing is beyond your performance: I mention this chiefly that you may allot some time without much hinderance [sic] to your Publication. I shall probably send you a parcel from hence about the middle of next Week, but things are a long time traveling [sic] between London & Cornwall & back again, I shall observe what you particularly wish for, though I may not at present be able to supply you.

I am very glad to hear of my Friend Mr. Hawkins, by you, as it is the first I have heard of him since he got to London: I look upon him as the best Mineralogist in this Country; & believe he possesses more Wood-like Tin Ore in <u>quantity</u>, than all Europe besides. As I have never seen his Collection, & now have no chance of that gratification; I can say nothing of it; but though his quantity of Wood-like Tin Ore is great, I do not know they excel in Curiosity. He has employ'd a gentleman for many years to procure <u>all</u> that could be had; except two Italian Rogues who came into this County & to the man who was employ'd by Mr. Hawkins, & by telling him he was Dead, obtain'd several pieces; but I believe none were worth much: Mr. Hawkins knows my Collection very well, & has seen all the varieties I have, except a very few I have procur'd by chance since he was at Menabilly. The Mines that produced the most Valuable Cabinet Specimens, are all out of Work; and such a quantity has been carried away from one Mine as to make the Captains look out to prevent such from being carried away, without the owner's consent.

I find many things I thought curious when first I began Collecting, or which have given place to better; are become of no value in laying by, especially where they were affected with Mundick, the worst Weed that can get into a cabinet; these are like the White Ant in America, which destroys every thing they come at. I will look over my Strontian pieces, & send you some of the Duplicates; I do not think I have any duplicate of the Quilted Tin Ore as I call'd it, without proper attention, at least with the varieties that piece contained, I sent you & now expected back.

I thank you for the relief you propose to my Infirmities, & find the reviewing my Cabinet produces some.

These kind of Collections are never at an End, so long as Mines continue, new things are produced, & give some entertainment to those who are Collectors.

. . .

Within your own nice box, I shall put a common Chip box containing some of my most curious pieces:

No. 1022 of Arseniate Copper Ore; . . . from one of the Mines near Gwennap.

No. 1029 Grey Copper Ore covered with . . . bright shining fibrous lines of a Grass green colour, . . . from Do.

No. 869 Copper Ore of an Indigo colour in a kind of spiral crystals in semicircular forms . . . the Mine – uncertain.

These three Curious pieces I shall be glad to have drawn, & a plate of each colour'd; I think they will do Credit to the Number of your Work where they are exhibited; but if you have any kind of objection or find them too difficult to represent, I desire they may be returned to me as soon as you can, but at all events so soon as you have figured them; as I value them much.[1]

. . .

[PS] There has been such a plunder of Specimens for sale from some of the Mines that the Propritors [sic] are much displeased

& threaten prosecution to those who have no right or priviledge [sic] from the owners it therefore should make you cautious about them. When the box arrives I shall be obliged if you would let Mr. Francillon know there is a triffling [sic] parcel for him.

Note
  1. Sowerby figured several of Rashleigh's copper ores in his *British Mineralogy* (1804–1813).

CRO, Truro, Hawkins Letters: J3/3/296
Philip Rashleigh to John Hawkins
Menabilly, 27 July 1804

As I do not mean to retalliate [sic] in keeping time of Correspondence, I think I may now wish you pleasure in having occupation of Twelve Months abode in one situation, which if not the most pleasant, may give you time for looking for a Place more comfortable for as large a Family as you may ever have, though you are likely to be at a distance as much out of my reach as one of the Indies. Yet, I shall hope to hear from you sometimes,[1] especially as you are no more likely to engage in arranging Your Minerals, than you was ten years since. I must now give up all expectations of seeing this Collection, which I have long been desirous of, expecting to see a variety which no other cabinet is likely to exhibit; as few people have had such an opportunity of Collecting, and none with such Judgment. I have added but a few things to my Collection since you saw it, and as the productive Mine for Curiosities Stenna Gwinn's is abandoned, we have no chance of much more from thence

A Terrible circumstance has lately happen'd at Polgooth, by Ld Arundel refusing to confirm a new Grant made by a Person who acted as his Steward some years since & the Proprietors were ignorant of his being dismissed until another claimed the Right. Should this succeed the Loss to the Adventurers will be immense, as well as to the Town of St. Austell. His Lordship has however no Right to the Bounds, which are granted to the present occupiers.
  . . .
  I am sorry for the declining state of health you mention Mr. Greville to be in, & am not very glad his new Museum is to be arranged by Count de Bournon, though I have no chance of seeing

it. The Country is given so much to Crystalliography, that unless to Young Men who have made that Study their particular attention, it becomes more tedious than amusing; for it is a labourious [sic] Study & not very entertaining to the generality of People. Professors of Crystalliography seems as necessary to Minerallogists as any other Phylosophy, & if I had a Vote for one, I would give it Count de Bournon, though he is a Frenchman.

I am glad to find the Collection of Minerals in the British Museum is likely to become a National object worthy of the situation, for it was lately a Miserable one for Publick inspection. Mr Tyssen's addition was Capital, though small, in number, & bought it at an enormous expence; but I see Humphrey had the Collecting of them.

The repeated loss of Friends has been almost too much for me; but it may be providential to make the Pleasures of the Life less desirous, by loosing [sic] our Friends gradually. The hearing of those we respect, diminishes in some degree the Loss of their desertion, & self-Retirement.

Note
1. Hawkins' annotation 'Answered Nov. 25th' indicates that it was several months before he replied.

University of Bristol Library, Special Collections: Joan Eyles Collection (DM1186)
Philip Rashleigh to James Sowerby
Menabilly, 7 August 1804

Though I have very little to trouble you with I cannot longer delay to thank you for the small sample of the Muriate of copper that you sent me in your letter of the 17th July which was a long time on the Road & but lately come to my hands; I know it is a very curious Specimen, and I believe only possessed by Sir Jos. Banks whose liberality has distributed it to some of his Friends, among whom I reckon myself; this is a fresh instance of your willingness to contribute to my Cabinet, & I thank you much for your attention.

. . .

I have many times been disappointed in seeing any piece of Stones that are said to have fallen from the Clouds in many Kingdoms,

& I regret it the more, as I believe a similar thing happened in this County last Winter, from a very small piece I had given me a few Weeks since; by which I endeavoured to make further enquiries by a very good man, but he is such an unbeliever of these matters & laughs so much at those who credit this extraordinary circumstance, that I got only a vauge [sic] account of it.

CRO, Truro, Rashleigh Papers: DDR/5757/1/101
Rev. William Gregor to Philip Rashleigh

Creed, 26 August [1804][1]

. . .

I think that there is strong ground for believing that you are possessed of a fragment of a stone similar to the Thunder stones,[2] if we wished to give them a hard name of Greek derivation we might call them Ceraunobolithoi – The specimen of Chromat of Iron is curious. If this stone had been discovered in this County, it would have been set down as a Copper Ore from the green oxide which pervades it.

I have been of late employed in the minute analysis of the supposed Zeolite of Stenna Gwinn: and wh. I have discovered to be a crystalized Clay. The scarcity of this mineral confines my analysis to a small quantity. And as it adheres to Quartz it is almost an impossibility to obtain it without some fragments of that substance adhering to it. – I am at a loss also to determine the figure of its crystallization, altho' I have borrowed for the purpose of poring with all my might, a very powerful microscope. – If you can contribute any help to me either relating to its crystals or in any other respect I shd. be obliged to you – As this Mineral is a non-descript & curious from its nature, I think that its existence shd be recorded & I shall therefore If I succeed communicate it, probably to the Royal Society. – By way of adjunct to my Paper I intend to make mention and record some experiments on the crystallized plates both green & yellow which are frequently attached to this said mineral.

. . .

Notes
1. Dated 26 August but without a year; other correspondence with Hawkins in February and May 1804 deals with the same subjects.

2. James Sowerby also described 'Thunderstones' (meteorites) in his
publications during that year.

CRO, Truro: Rashleigh Papers: DDR/5757/2/37
James Sowerby to Philip Rashleigh
Lambeth, 29 October 1804

I thank you for your last kind letter by frank but do not desire you
to be fear full if my paying for your kind letters as I shall never
grudge it. I am glad when I find you have any thing I desire you to
possess ['Diamonds &c.' – inserted] and only feel glad if any thing
may be wanting when I have the power to supply you, as I wish
you every possible enjoyment in this life:

I have got the Sky fallen stone from Yorkshire at my home, and
anxiously wish to compare yours with it, and it would be doing
me a great favor to send it at any expence by the first coach or
other carriage you find convenient it were well perhaps to make
it more of a parcel by adding any thing to it of any sort if only
paper or wax. Pray do you know of the rest of the stone yours was
broken from? If so I shall be glad of the information. Do not mind
Laughers or Quizers it was well for them the Yorkshire Stone of 56
lb weight did not interrupt their belief by breaking their pates.

I am glad you like the figures of the last specimens you sent, as
it appeared you did not think they could be represented at all. It
is the more pleasant & satisfactory to you. Do you know whether
your Black diamond is softer than the Whiter ones? Tell me if
you can and the form of the crystal if so. Not a cut one if it is
naturally crystallized and [should] you dare venture it I should like
to examine it when the sky fallen stone comes. I had rather say you
lent me one than anybody else.

CRO, Truro, Rashleigh Archive: DDR/5757/1/108
Rev. William Gregor to Philip Rashleigh
Creed, Thursday Morning [?November 1804][1]

I have been waiting since my arrival from London for an
opportunity of sending a little packet to you. The little Box includes
the specimen of the Molybdinat of lead, which you were so kind as

to send, and which I was unwilling to spoil as a specimen, being concerned that the yellow crystals wh. I was examining did not belong to that species. I return it therefore with many thanks for your kindness & consideration. The Specimen of the Barnstaple Zeolite, I have returned for reasons which I will inform you of in sequel.

. . .

Amongst the dear rarities in Mineralogy, nothing seems now to be more earnestly called for, than specimens of Stones fallen from the Clouds – They sell for very high prices – and the demand for these has risen. The price of the Siberian Iron wh. is supposed to have some sort of relationship to the former – I saw a thin piece of this last at Mrs. Forster's, about an Inch and half in breadth for wh. she asked twelve guineas! – I have a small piece of the Stones, wh. if I cd. put my hand upon it, I wd. send to you to compare wth. yr. Saltash specimen but I have put it away safe – I hope, however in the course of the Summer to bring it with me. Really, if we exclude loss of life & limb and conflagrations, it wd. be a very profitable windfall, for any person to have a shower of these stones in his neighbourhood, during a Thunder Storm —

Mr Davy has submitted his paper on the Barnstaple Zeolite to the Ryl. Scy. I have not seen it — He asked me if I had observed any peculiar smell in the water wh comes over in the [? receiver] by exposing my Stenna Gwinn Crystals in a retort to heat. I told him that I had, but that I had attributed this circumstance to an accident. I had supposed that a bit of the Feather by wh. I had driven the powder into the retort had remained behind & caused the empyreamatic smell — He told me that the effect was constant on trials on the Barnstaple specimens; & that the water was acidulous. This fact also I had observed, but had attributed it to the same cause – I asked him whether he had observed any white sublimate in small quantities adhering to the retort on these occasions – He told me that he had not – For this was a fact wh I had observed.

On my return, I thought it right to examine the volatile parts of this curious substance (I mean the Stenna Gwinn Aluminate) and I obtained this empyreumatic liquor, and the sublimate in small white scales – This substance is soluble in water and consists of an earth combined to an acid: The earth agrees with none of the earths whose properties have been described: It forms a regular salt with Sulphuric – Nitric – and Marine acids, the latter salt resembles muriat of Lead. It is not precipitable by Ammonia, but it is by carbonate of Ammonia & is not re-dissolved thereby. It is not soluble; I think in Potash – Its volatility is also a very discriminating property. – What the Acid is, I cannot discover? I suspected the Fluoric and Phosphoric –

But my experiments have not hitherto confirmed my Suspicions – As I could only procure small quantities of this new substance from the Stenna Gwinn Aluminate. I made a trial of some of the Barnstaple Zeolite in the same way & found the same result – So that this earth will have a fair chance of having its nature & properties developed – I attribute Mr. Davy's not having observed it, to his distillery with too low a heat – This circumstance will account for my having broken up the excellent specimen, wh you gave me of this mineral – This new discovery of mine will probably alter all our conclusions respecting the nature of these minerals – And I am not sorry now, for my delay in publishing my account – I shall send my paper next week to the Ryl. Scy with all I know respecting this new earth, or new combin'n. with a sort of engagement of continuing my investig'n.

Dr. Wavell has promised to send me a good quantity of the Barnstaple Mineral. I shall select the best Specimen for you in return for yours.

Note
1. Although this letter is not dated, the subject matter of meteorites and the Barnstaple Zeolite indicate 1804; while the reference to Davy's paper suggests November (see Gregor 28 November 1804).

CRO, Truro, Hawkins Archive: J3/3/298
Rev. William Gregor to John Hawkins
17 November 1804

I was glad to receive so good an account of you & yours in your last kind letter, I trust that this will find you in the same happy state. You taste much fully the comforts of domestic life and as a furtherance of these, I sh'd have rejoiced to have heard, that you were fixed to a spot and in a house of your choice. –

. . .

My Brother has had a very violent fit of the gout, this constitutional malady was excited and exasperated by two falls.

He is now recovering but you might discover in his looks & gait the traces of what he has suffered. – . . .

Whitaker is still amidst the ruins of antiquity & writing at one & the same time persevering a laborious investigation to the lively sallies of a vivid imagination is preparing to publish the History of London.[1] He was in London some time since and promised before he set out, that he would traverse a large space & see with his own eyes a great deal of this antient [sic] City. Alas! he forgot that he had passed his seventieth year. – He never got further than Snow Hill on his own legs and London Air so far deranged his Constitution that he would probably have died, had he stayed in it much longer. – At present he is as well as usual, and derives constant amusement from his literary labours.

You were so kind as to promise me long since that if I shd. make an Analysis of any Minerals that I wished to publish you would introduce the Paper to Sr. Joseph Banks, that it might be inserted in the Phil. Transactions. Now I have an Analysis upon the stocks of a Mineral wh. I think has never been before noticed – and wh. is curious. – If I succeed to the end of my labours, I shd. wish to publish my paper in this way. – The mineral is one, of wh. I spoke to you before. It is a native of Stenna Gwinn – and has been taken for Zeolite. I think th't it is not of that species, but consist of a larger proportion of Clay, when compared to the other fixed ingredients, than any substance hitherto known. The small portion of silica wh. I have detected I attribute to accidental intrusion. I always found it diminished constantly in proportion to the purity of the selected specimen. In a fortnight or three weeks, I will send you my paper.[2]

. . .

Postscript: My Brother has written something on the Cover of this.

Notes
1. John Whitaker (1735–1808); historian, antiquarian, religious writer and Rector at Ruan Lanihorne, Cornwall; Fellow of the Society of Antiquaries, 1771; published *The History of Manchester* (2 vols., 1771-5); also wrote about Mary Queen of Scots.
2. The results of Gregor's various experiments on specimens he had obtained from the Stenna Gwynn mine, including the supposed zeolite, were published the following year (1805) in the *Philosophical Transactions of the Royal Society*, Vol. 95, 331-346; this paper was reprinted in *Nicholson's Journal*, in 1806, Ser. 2, Vol. 14, p. 247. See Russell, 'The Rev. William Gregor', 619 and 622.

CRO, Truro, Rashleigh Papers: DDR/5757/2/39
John Hawkins to Philip Rashleigh
              Dallington near Northampton, 25 November 1804

I perceive by the date of your last letter that I am really become
a very negligent correspondent and no ways deserving the very
freindly letters which you favour me with. But as it is now high time
to enquire after your health I hope to prevail upon you to overlook
what is passed and to gratify me with a few lines in the usual
freindly strain. I cannot help expressing the satisfaction we both
felt on hearing a favourable account of you some time ago from
the Gregors. It is not improbable that your long stay in the country
may have tended materially the preservation of your health which
the late dinner and evening parties in London had you been there
last winter, might have in an equal degree damaged [sic] impaired.
That much I may venture to say by way of consolation for the loss
of the society of the metropolis. As for any other resources which
it affords you do not want them.

   You will be glad to hear that our residence here is in every
respect a pleasant & comfortable one. We have made it as retired
as we could wish by declining the society around us which has
afforded me much leisure for domestic pursuits. I should rather
have said studies. I am sorry to say that Mineralogy is not one
of these. It is impossible to follow it up without a Cabinet of well
arranged specimens. You express your regret at this privation
as well as myself, but I fear you entertain too favourable idea of
my collection. It is true I have had the advantage of forming it in
various countries but it is equally true that these things are not
always to be met with in the countries which produce them & for
the past twenty years, the taste for collecting has been so prevalent
abroad that nothing was to be had cheap. The consequences of
which has been that a man in my circumstances could not procure
choice specimens which have found their way to the best market.
You would find therefore my collection very inferior perhaps to
the notion you have formed of it. My Cornish specimens constitute
by far the most valuable portion of it, and for some of the best of
these I am indebted to you.

   I believe I mentioned to you my having seen the Minl. Collection
at the British Museum. It is spoiling fast for nothing can protect
it from the <u>smuak</u> of London. Count de Bournon undertook the
arrangement of its some time ago, but soon relinquished it. I hear

that the difference between the Polgooth Adventurers & Lord Arundel has been adjusted.

You well know that the Rust or Mildew has been very prevalent among the corn this year & has done a great deal of damage. In our attempts to discover a remedy for such an evil our attention ought first to be directed to the investigation of the cause. The cause of the Rust or Mildew I am happy to inform you, has just been ascertained. It is a minute species of Fungus the seeds of which[,] being blown about in the season of the year when Wheat is in a fit state to retain & nourish them[,] insert themselves in the gland of the epidermis of the stalk which in a particular stage of its growth are open to receive them. A particular account of this important discovery is now preparing for publication under the auspices of Sir Joseph Banks. The reason why early sown wheat is less subject to the Rust is that the glands of the epidermis are too closed to admit the seeds of the Fungus at the season when they are dispersed.

. . .

CRO, Truro, Rashleigh Archive: DDR/5305/20
Rev. Wiliam Gregor to Philip Rashleigh
Creed, 28 November 1804

I enclose you a description of the Aluminate for your aid & opinion. It is the result of my observation of many specimens of this curious mineral. From a letter I have just received from Mr. Hawkins I am informed that Mr. Davy has discovered a substance, hitherto taken for Zeolite, of the same nature as that, wh. I have been examining. I shd not wonder if many Zeolites were, unzeolited and found to be of this species. – In my Analysis, I have met with some Chemical Anomalies wh. have retarded me. A small qty of calcareous earth, so small as not to [be] separated in the usual way, has given me trouble. I cannot account for this. It is so small, as I hesitate in my opinion whether or no, it is essential to the Aluminate or no and yet I have espied some traces of it in several experiments. –

The compact sort, wh you kindly gave me is the same species, and purer, I think than the former. The water of Crystallzn. amounts to upwards of 30 pr. cent: and the Alumina, or pure Clay to 50 or more. – The Quartz varies according to the purity of the specimen. The Mineral, you were so kind as to give me, consisted chiefly of Oxide of Iron. I could obtain no uranium from it I have not as yet been able to procure you any of the Bismuth ore.

CRO, Truro, Hawkins Letters: J3/3/299
Philip Rashleigh to John Hawkins
undated [29 November 1804]

As I am unwilling to loose [sic] a Correspondent I much respect, I shall no delay to acknowledge your letter of 25th Novr. for a similar time to yours, because every circumstance from a Friend gives me great satisfaction in this situation. You have a very good Correspondent in either of the Gregors, & as Mr Williams attends most to Mineralogy that you once was amused with, You may receive from him whatever arises new on that subject; I may yet say something upon it, though all my knowledge of Chimestry is as antiquated as to be a total blank among modern Amateurs:

Mr Davy of the Royal Institution has discovered the substance found near Barnstaple, hitherto called Zeolite, to consist of pure Alumina 3 parts, combined with one part of Water of Crystallization: this to me is very unexpected as I thought from its outward app[ea]rance there was no doubt of its being Zeolite. I am sorry for the state you find the Minerals of the British Museum to be in, because I thought they were in progress of being very Respectable, unless the similar undertaking of the Royal Institution should interfere. The same cause of destruction by situation will affect both these Collections. I understand Mr. Hatchett had set the British Museum in Scientific order – which I should much prefer to Count de Bournon's elaborate Crystallliography. As you are in a part of the Country where neither Chymists or Minerals abound I do not wonder that your attention to them should be suspended.

I should certainly be very glad to hear your present situation a pleasant & a Comfortable one, if it was not the cause likely to prevent your looking out for one with another Qualification, a Durable one. Neither London or its Amusements ever agreed with my Health, or pleasure in comparison with the Country; & now I have Menabilly so much to my satisfaction for the short time I am likely to enjoy it, I have no inclination to move from it.

I am very glad to hear the important discovery of the Rust Mildew in Wheat; I have long understood it was a kind of Fungus, but could never discover it by high Magnifiers, to my satisfaction; I hope not only the Cause but the Prevention is likewise discovered & to be Published.

The difference between the Lord of Polgooth Mine & the adventurers is I believe near settled & likely to be wholy [sic] so; It was a sad oversight & likely to be of considerable Consequence. The dispute of Truro is likewise nearly settled, Mr. Danbuz & Mr. Buckingham are chosen Aldermen, but I do not find they have as yet Chosen a Mayor, & as the Charter day & the Statute days are past, I do not see how they can now proceed though they have a Command from the King's Bench.

I have lately had a very pleasant Gentlemen with me for some days Mr. De Cort, the best draughtsman I believe in England or Europe, he not only makes the best Sketches but chuses [sic] the best spots they can be taken from, I think he has made 15 of St. Michael's Mount. I carried him to Roach Rock in a very Cold day, such as prevented me from geting [sic] out of the Carriage. He took another of my Grotto; but the most extraordinary was one of Carglaize Mine, a large open work on St. Austell down, the most difficult to Show on Paper that can be imagined.

There have been some Riots in this Neighbourhood about buying up Corn for Plymouth, both at Fowy & Mevagissey, but no great mischief ensued. The Army & Navy you know must be supplied to protect the Poor as well as the Rich, but this is the worst County the Contractors could come to, having only one part of it that joins with any other, being surrounded with Sea by all the other parts of the county where no Corn grows.

. . .

I am rather better than I was a fortnight since but rather weaker which must be daily expected.

CRO, Truro, Rashleigh Archive: DDR/5757/2/40
James Sowerby to Philip Rashleigh
Lambeth, 5 January 1805

I had the pleasure of receiving your letter saying the box so long delayed had arrived, Altho' it would be a great pleasure to me to send you specimens worthy of you, I yet feel gratified that you so deserving have got above wanting any Corundums and are so rich in them as Mr Warburton[1] says you are; whatever is worthy your acceptance you will pleasure me by keeping. Any thing not worth your trouble may be returned, if quite at your convenience. . . . I am afraid of your sending boxes by sea and I should be much hurt to lose any thing you shall send. Mr. Warburton bragged of the fine specimens you have of stalactical calcedony and Pyrites &c. Indeed he was quite charmed in speaking of your politeness and collection.

I rec'd. your other letter this day am glad to find you pleased with my work on British Fungi altho you are not a Botanist you have much natural discernment. The blue from the oak seem very naturally to have coloured the Fungus, as you observe. The Prusic alkali will extract the blue from oak, and the oak colours the iron of a nail or a saw blade. . . . I thank you for you publick spirit in encouraging my works. The greatest necessity for using Latin and Greek names is, that in some things they went before us, and gave appropriate names.

[Postscript] I hope to send you a bit of the true Metioric [sic] stone. They all have the same ingredients whether from the East Indies, Hungary, Italy, Germany Yorkshire or Scotland.

Note
1. Mr Warburton – probably Henry Warburton (1784–1858), timber merchant; Fellow of the Royal Society, 1809; Secretary of the Geological Society 1814–16; member of the Political Economy Club from 1821; MP for Bridport (Dorset), 1826–41, and Kendal 1843–7.

NHM, General Library, Sowerby Archive: Rashleigh: 47/13
Philip Rashleigh to James Sowerby

Menabilly, 25 March 1805

By your visit to Mrs. Forster I have added a few rare specimens of Siberian & Swedish Ores to my Collection, but at Extravagant Prices; but as it is the only thing I am Extravagant in, there is some indulgence to be allowed; as these neither Eat, Drink or Pay Taxes: and I consider that it would cost me more to Travel for them either by myself or any other person. I thank you for the calling upon

Mrs. Forster & hope you was pleased with what you saw at her House.

...

My Relations and particular Friends have so much exhausted my duplicates of the Ores, and no new acquisitions coming in, that I can scarce supply you for your Northern Friend as I do not recollect having received a Single Specimen fit for a Cabinet within these two years. Nor do I hear of any Tin Mines that have produced any worth preserving. I have met with a few pieces of Copper Ore, but Mr. Phillips (who I find you know) picked up a hat full in walking through Redruth, & by his Account all of the most curious Crystals I ever saw.

CRO, Truro, Rashleigh Archive: DDR/5757/2/70
Rev. William Gregor to Philip Rashleigh   *26 March 1805*

I ought to have thanked you for your kind letter and the little packet immediately upon my receiving them. As I put it in contemplation to pay a visit to Stenna Gwinn I deferred performing this my bounden duty 'till I had been there, in the hope that I might be able to give you some information respecting this extraordinary mine. – I found a few men working there. They are driving an adit with a new [illegible] of-cutting the lode supposed to run thro' a place called tradi[tio]nally the brass pan. They have indeed cut thro' a seam of what they call copper ore, but I believe it to be of the same sort as they formerly found in the same mine Viz. sulphuret of Tin, Copper & Iron. This vein is not very rich but the ore is sparingly scatter'd amidst the mica and quartz of the stones – I was glad to see Captain Philips as the manager. The adventurers therefore, have this advantage of exchanging a wretched for a good administration – I wish them success with all my heart – I met with nothing curious.

I am particularly obliged to you for the specimen of the Barnstaple Zeolite. It is a very curious one. I am perfectly convinced from the Inspection of it, that it is of the same species with the harder & more compact species of Aluminite found in Stenna Gwinn. My object therefore is answered. And as it is a striking specimen, I sh'd be very sorry to destroy it – I will therefore return it to you, with many thanks, the first time I have any thing to send to you. I have not as yet received any Bismuth altho' I have been promised some specimens, as soon as they can be procured. –

With great difficulty I procured some of the harder species of the Stenna Gwinn Aluminate – I find it to be of the same nature as the softer & more delicate specimens. I believe I have mentioned to you how singularly tedious & protracted the total Crystallization of the Alum is from the clay of this mineral. Month after month, after having done all that is usually done towards promoting the Crystallization I have waited upon it without success – At last I have discovered a very extraordinary circumstance from wh. my difficulties have arisen: a very minute portion of selenite, a little [silica] also, and probably a little of the potash (wh. is a constituent part of Alum) unite with the Clay in the solution & prevent its crystallizing. – I believe that a small portion of calcareous earth not amounting to 1/100 part is an effective ingredient in the aluminate. I think also that a small quantity of silica is a constituent part of it because I have uniformly discovered these in every trial that I have made. So that it is a curious circumstance that this Mineral wh. resembles a Zeolite, has the ingredients belonging to Zeolite but the proportion of them utterly different & reversed. –

. . .

CRO, Truro, Rashleigh Papers: DDR/5305/29
Elizabeth Forster to Philip Rashleigh
London, No. 26, Gerrard Street, Soho 8 April 1805

Your letters came duly to hand, and on Saturday evening I received the box with the Minerals all safe, also the Sum of £22.11s .0d in Bills and cash for the specimens that you selected, for which I am much obliged and thank you, and will take the two chip boxes and letter as directed tomorrow.

I thank you for the kind inquiries Sir concerning my Husbands welfare, he is still in Petersburg, money matters there go on very slowly, he has at last received some of his first payments, and is now endeavouring to get his whole Sum if possible at once, by giving a Collection for the use of the Miners School there, having quantity of Minerals by him, which I have sent him at different times, if he succeeds he intends leaving Russia this Year; I heartily wish he may, as he tells me he feels old Age and infirmities come fast upon him; indeed at our time of life his own home would be the most proper; But if please God we should live, I have no hopes to see him till next Year, as he intends going to Paris first to try to get what property he has there away, in particular some very valuable Minerals belonging to his Collection, and a Collection he bought the last time he was there for £500 of the Intendant of Dauphiny, which he says are very fine indeed.

We have not received a single specimen from our Nephews in S. America and have only heard four times from them, owing to my Husband telling them he had bought a House in Spring Gardens (a very small one just before he left England which we left) they concluded he was to live in it and directed all there [sic] letters there, a great number never receiving any answers concluded we were dead, till they saw in the Madrid Gazette sent to a Gentlemen at Bones Ayres [sic] that there [sic] Uncle had sold his Collection to the Emperor of Russia, they then wrote to Spring Garden, and I accidentally got it owing to the Post man calling in the Strand and saying he had a packet of letters from Madrid that came to 10.6d and could not find the person &c. they said there was a person of that name in Covent Garden he had better ask there, by which means I got them, they have been extremely successful in their pursuits, and have sent an amazing quantity of choice Minerals to Spain particularly Coppers of every cristalization, and every other sort that Country produces and have given the greatest satisfaction, are in good health and I lately hear have presented a Memorial to stay longer in America; there [sic] youngest Brother who went to Russia with my Husband, left his Uncle two Years ago, and travels for a House in Petersburg to collect precious stones &c.

He is now in Madrid, was at Lisbon first, and intends to come there this Summer and then to come here chiefly for the purpose of purchasing Gems, as he will come by Falmouth home. [I] shall take the liberty to send him your address, and if you will have the goodness to let him see your Collection, I should esteem it a particular favor, as I know how highly he would be gratified by the sight of it, as he is a good Judge of and very fond of minerals, and understands them well, I have desired him to try to bring any rare minerals he may meet with from S. America or Spain, which if he does will certainly let you see some of them, I beg your pardon for the length of my letter.

The Collection now offerred [sic] for Sale was the property of Mr. Atkinson[1] he was a Bullion Merchant and lived in Lothbury, went frequently to Holland purchased very fine specimens of Gold and Silver there, has had a number of specimens from my Brother and one, he was always so hurried with business that he had not time to shew me the whole of the Collection, have only seen the Gold and Silvers which are very fine, the Collection consists of upwards of 3000 specimens, they ask 800£s for it which I think is reasonable, I hear it has been offerred to the Royal Institute who have refused it, and that if they meet with no purchase it will be sold by Auction in about three weeks, I intend seeing them this week, I dare say there is hardly anything among them but what you have, but to any one beginning to form a Collection it certainly would be very desirable.

Note
1. Rashleigh mentioned that this sale raised £550 in a letter to Sowerby (28 June 1805) and enquired whether a dealer had bought the collection.

CRO, Truro, Rashleigh Archive: DDR/5757/2/71
Rev'd. William Gregor to Philip Rashleigh
Creed, 25 April 1805

I may appear ungrateful to you for your many kind attentions to me, by not acknowleging [sic] sooner the receipt of your letter packet containing the Molybdenat of Lead & some specimens of Bismuth. I beg leave to assure you that this [is] not the case: I feel your kindness to me very sensibly.

The object, which I had in mind it completely answered by my inspection of that very curious & rare fossil. I am convinced that the yellow crystalline lamina from Stenna Gwinn do not belong to this species. As therefore I am very unwilling to rob your valuable collection of so curious a specimen, I will return it with the Barnstaple Zeolite, the first favourable opportunity that occurs, with many thanks to you for the Opportunity you have given me of becoming better acquainted with this mineral – I am at a loss, what to say of the yellow Crystals of Stenna Gwinn – This much I can affirm, that it is a species of fossil, that has never been accurately described – If it contains Uranium, it contains also some substance very different from that substance, wh. has marked properties; it also contains Lime, & Silica: and I found in one trial lead: Though in other trials it has eluded me – The green crystals are of the same Nature as the yellow except in their being stained by copper, they contain lime as the others do. – As that substance is so complex, you will not wonder at my being bewildered and hesitating upon my decisions on so small quantities. –

I am going to set out for London tomorrow where I hope to stay about a fortnight: I shall have opportunity there of making enquiries of the learned in Mineralogy. – I shall also enquire of Mr. Davy whether he found a minute portion of lime in his Zeolite. I have always found some in my Aluminate much to my annoyance –

. . .

NHM, General Library, Sowerby Archive: Rashleigh: 47/14
Philip Rashleigh to James Sowerby
Menabilly, 26 May 1805

. . .

Another of your favors was very kindly Received Yesterday with a fragment of the Meteor from Yorkshire, for which I am much obliged: It is quite New to me as I never had a sight of any one of these Stones before, & as you observe it is quite different to anything I have.

. . . When I can procure a few Specimens which I think you may like, I will send them . . . but as I am nearly confined to my own House & neighbourhood, I have but few opportunities of seeing any new Minerals, except from a few friends who are so kind as to remember me.

I wish I knew what Specimens you want, as I might have an opportunity of seeing such as would be most agreeable to you; but the dealers have increased their prices so much from the demands which are made, as to prevent moderate people from Purchasing. There is an ore which the Miners call Wood Copper Ore, which I believe is found in no other Country. If you have none of that let me know it, & I will endeavour to send you a Specimen or two. There are many varieties in this County which I have not seen from others, but good Specimens are scarce & the dealers make the most of them. I believe the Workmen now save everything they think new, from some common things they have lately sent me. I have nothing particular to add but my best wishes & thanks for many rarities you have sent me.

CRO, Truro, Rashleigh Papers: DDR/5757/2/41
James Sowerby to Philip Rashleigh

Lambeth, 29 May 1805

I rec'd your letter of kindness this day and it gives me great satisfaction that I had it in my power to give you of the Meteor Stone and the more as it [is] of the rarest being a British stone. When the Phœnomen of their production will be understood I do not know.

The ore which you observe the Miners call Wood Copper must be very acceptable if you can procure them without extraordinary inconvenience, or anything of Cornwall that is at all new to you.

I think you mentioned in a late letter a Zeolite as it used to be call'd from Barnstaple. The same thing is found in some part of Cornwall. I should be glad to see some Cornwall specimens. It is now the <u>Hydrargillite</u> or Wavellite.

University of Bristol Library, Special Collections: Joan Eyles Collection (DM1186)
Philip Rashleigh to James Sowerby

Menabilly, 16 June 1805

The piece of the Yorkshire Stone that fell from the Atmosphere is so totally different from every Mineral of Fossil that has come to my view that it is a great Acquisition; & very extraordinary for those which have fallen in various places & in different Kingdoms should be so similar in their appearance & contents. Some various Ideas of Attraction & Cohesion will one time or other give more Philosophical accounts of these – Stones, & by that introduce a variety of reasoning for other Mineral subjects. For I must consider this subs[t]ance as a Fossil generated in the Air, though all other known Rocks & Stones are formed in the Earth. Such a novelty will set many Philosophers to study the cause of such a substance in the Atmosphere, & apply similar reasoning to many things under the earth. One part of this fragment seems to affect the magnet more than the other, & particularly all the black side which I conclude is Iron, though scarce so strong as one part of the other.

Your Tab CXII seems very like some Stones found near Bristol,

& very different to any production of this County that I have seen. The black parts of mine seem either Animal or Vegitable [sic] Petrefactions, but I know of neither to compare then with; If they are so, they do not belong to this County, as we have no Petrefact'ns that I know of in it, & very little calcareous Earth, which is the general matrix of Petrefactions. There are some Ores which when in Melting will be very refractory on Water falling on them when in a Liquid State, & make it very dangerous to be within reach of the fragments that are sent about it like Shot. May not these Meteors when heated by Lightning [sic] or any Atmospherical influence, fall through a moist vapour, and hiss & crack about like those of copper &c.?

There have been a few Specimens found in Stenna Gwinn Mine, which from their resemblance to Zeolites have obtained that name, but they have some mineral difference, not to be found in Zeolite; the only gentleman in this County who takes any pains to investigate such subjects is my Friend the Rev'd. William Gregor, & you will probably soon see his experiments in Print; but all the rare things from this Mine are so scarce as it becomes difficult to procure sufficient for Trial.

The Mine is again in working & we expect will produce Cabinet Specimens, if but little profit to the Adventurers: & I stand a pretty good chance of having some of them. Next week I expect some of my relations for the change of Air to spend some time with me; I will let you know when & where I send any thing which I think will be worth your Acceptance. In looking over some Minerals that have been put aside, I find some that I can not recollect the Mine that produced them, and therefore will be of little use to you. By an accident of some Woodwork in my Grotto being decay'd, I am engaged in repairing of it; which has obliged me to overhall [sic] my refuse stock which were put away unmarked; where I find duplicates of those in my Cabinet, if any which are worth sending, you shall have part

Just as I had got that far my Invalid Friends arriv'd. & have engaged my whole time ever since. Your Letter of the 10th Inst. is delivered to me, & what is already said will shew you how difficult it is to procure the Specimens you apply for. Mr. Wm. Gregor has found great difficulty in procuring sufficient for making his Analysis, even with what I have been able to assist him with: He always supplies me with duplicates of such things as he knows I want . . .

I conclude you have some of the Barnstaple old fashion Zeolite,

I have just [given] Mr. Wm. Gregor a particular piece of it for his Experiments, which he will either return or send another he is promised.

CRO, Truro, Rashleigh Papers: DDR/5757/2/72
Rev. William Gregor to Philip Rashleigh

Creed, 25 July 1805

I have lately received a letter from Mr. Hatchett, wherein he informs me that my Paper on the fossil, wh. I had called Aluminate had been read before the Ry. Society. I also at the same time received one from Dr. Wollaston thanking me for the same & announcing the publication of it in the next Vol. of the Transactions: so that I hope to be able soon to send you a Copy – I am entirely indebted to you for the most curious parts of the said paper, as I was enabled, thro' your kind present of some of the Barnstaple Fossil, to extend my experiments on the peculiar acid which both it & the Stenna Gwinn Fossil contain. I am therefore of opinion that Mr. Davy's name Hydrargillite will not stand. As an acid is an essential ingredient of both minerals & probably an undescribed acid of vegetable origin. –

I have received a letter from Mr. Sowerby, upon the subject, wh. you mentioned to me: and I have consented to send him a specimen, wh. I think will suit his purpose very well, on condition of his returning it to me safe & sound. He informed me, that he had received specimens from you on the same terms.

He has published an account & an engraving of Mr. Davy's Hydrargillite, the Cornish mineral will, I think excell the Devonian in point of beauty – Mr Davy considers the Hydrargillite as containing 70 of Clay & 30 of water in an hundred – He found also a minute portion of lime and traces of some acid in the water – The lime & the acid he thinks accidental – The clay in the Cornish Fossil does not amount to 70, I always found some silica & a minute quantity of lime, and traces of an acid of peculiar qualities, and as every specimen, wh. I examined agreed in containing these, I can scarcely think them to be accidental ingredients – If we take into consideration the coincidence wh. exists between the Barnstaple Fossil & the Cornish one, accident must I think, be excluded –

. . .

RIC, Courtney Library, Truro: RASH/1/71
Rev'd Wm Gregor to Philip Rashleigh

Creed, 22 September 1805

. . .

I am glad that you are pleased with my [?Paper][1] . . . The Cornish Mineral is no doubt the same with the Barnstaple. And it consist of Clay (or Aluminas) combined with water and a peculiar acid which has remarkable qualities with a small quantity of Silica & a minute portion of lime. This Acid will no doubt attract the attention of Chemists & Mineralogists. The Uranglimmer, which is found imbedded in this mineral is not a new name: it is Werner's name for that which used to be denominated green glimmer, or – which is found to contain Oxide of Uranium.

. . .

A letter from Dr. Wavell announced some specimens of the Barnstaple Hydrargillite, alias Wavellite as being set aside for me: I shall send you a specimen of the best sort when I receive it in return for that very good one, you were so kind as to send me.

. . .

In answer to your kind enquiries I beg leave to say, that we effected all our objects prosperously and arrived at Creed safe & well at the Time we designated at our setting out, Highly gratified with our expedition & grateful for your attention & Hospitality.

I am much flattered with the approbation you kindly express concerning my sermon. On these occasions, discourses shd. be practical not Theoretical and we are bound, I think, to speak plainly and without reserve, if that freedom of speech be tempered with becoming Modesty.[2]

. . .

Notes
  1. Refers to Gregor's paper 'Experiments on a mineral substance formerly supposed to be Zeolite . . .' published in the *Philosophical Transactions of the Royal Society*, London, 95, 1805:331-348.
  2. Reference to a Sermon Gregor gave for the visitation of the Bishop of Exeter to Truro on 17 July 1805 that discussed the qualities and behaviour of Anglican ministers – see R. J. Cleevely and C. M. Bristow, 'Rev. William Gregor (1761–1817): the contributions of a Cornish cleric and analytical chemist', *Journal of the Royal Institution of Cornwall*, 2003, 97.

RIC, Courtney Library, Truro, Rashleigh Papers:
RASH/1/72
Rev. Wm Gregor to Philip Rashleigh
Creed, 26 November 1805

. . .

I have done nothing in the Chemical Way for some time.
Nothing new has occurred. I picked up a stone not long since, that
I thought might be the new Swedish Mineral called the Gadolinite:
My experiments hitherto do not enable me to say what it is: the
presence of Iron is a great bar to speaking quickly or decidedly as
it masks other ingredients. I think, however, that it is a curious
fossil. I shall reserve some of it for you, and write to you again
when I have ascertained its nature.

I heartily congratulate you on the late glorious Victory un-
parallel'd I believe in the glorious [Anniversary] of our navy –
dearly indeed it was bought by the Death of Nelson![1] It gives us
however new hopes & prospects and will I trust be one of the
means under providence of setting some bounds to the Ambition
& Cruelty of the Emperor Napoleon.

Note
1. This refers to the significant naval engagement between the
   combined French and Spanish fleets and the British fleet off
   Cape Trafalgar on 21 October 1805. In her *Recollections* (1853:
   CRO/G/1952) his niece, Loveday Sarah Gregor, recalled that as a
   young man Gregor's 'dream was to be a sailor' and that 'he was
   ever a devoted admirer of the British Navy . . . & his features were
   illuminated with a flash of the eye . . . on naval triumphs.'

NHM, General Library, Sowerby Archive: Rashleigh: 47/18
Philip Rashleigh to James Sowerby
Menabilly, 12 December 1805

. . .

Your letter of the 9th I rec'd last night the whole contents of
which I am much interested in & shall endeavour to tell you why.
In the first place the little box was so long since it was sent away I
begun to think it lost, another was to know what was become of
some late Nos. of B. Mineralogy, as there must be many since the

last received. . . . I have expected them from Messrs. Nicol & shall write him again on that subject.

My state of health has affected me so much as to go any where beyond a Dining visit, & entirely from working after Minerals, that I know of two or three things I want, & no one near me who has both Judgement and Inclination to procure them for me, & this will probably be the cause for preventing me from sending you some more Specimens of the Stellated Quartz which you desire, though I expect to see Mr. John Williams soon at Menabilly & the large stone of this sort is in his Father's Land. I did not much admire the pieces he sent me. . . .

I shall very readily pay for any drawing under your inspection; I had so much difficulty in procuring any person who would undertake this business, that I wonder you have succeeded so much better. I was particularly desirous of having one of my Specimens drawn, as the Crystals seemed unlike any I had seen, & I am very glad you have acquired one to represent in your work. I hope you will make no scruple in charging any reasonable Sum for doing anything for me in the way of your business, as I shall be perfectly pleased with paying for it.

I have scarce had anything worth preserving from the English or other British Mines, lately. Many Mines are stopt that formerly produced good things for Cabinets, though we have some which yield the owners great proffit [sic]: but 9 Mines out of Ten only bring losses.

. . .

Whenever you send me any package, pray let it come by a Waggon which though much longer on the Roads, yet conveys things more secure than Coaches; & direct <u>all Parcels or Boxes</u> to me near St. Austell, Cornwall.

CRO, Truro, Rashleigh Archive: DDR/5757/2/73
Rev. William Gregor to Philip Rashleigh
Creed, Thursday evening 19 December 1805

Your little boxes arrived at this place during my absence for a few days visit at Trewarthennick: I beg leave to thank you for their contents, which are amply sufficient for me to gratify my curiosity on the investigation of what I deem to be a very singular production. It may be perhaps a new substance – And if that sh'd be the case, I sh'd be obliged to you for any further communication concerning the origin. That Mine, I think, you informed me was a Copper mine, when it was raised & the substance is marked Steatite – The first step I have taken is to endeavour to bring this salt to regular Crystalliz'n. Bur this I have not yet been able to effect – It is very easily soluble in Water – I shall then examine whether the substance in wh. the salt is embedded be of the same nature as the metallic basis of the salt itself – I have no reason yet to alter my opinion, that this saline matter is sulphiat of Zinc, but it was founded on too few facts to rise above a probable conjecture. I have an Ore of Zinc wh. has saline efflorescences on it of Sulphat of Zinc, but they resemble in no degree those extraordinary <u>protrusions</u> of Salt wh. mark yr. Specimen. – Immediately as I have sufficiently informed myself of the nature of this substance, I will trouble you with a letter. My curiosity is much excited. –

Huel Rock Mine is again, I find working at a deeper level than that in wh. the Sulphuret of Tin was formerly found. I have seen some small pieces of the same ore, that has been raised at this deeper level & I doubt not but that it will be discovered by & by in larger quantities. The Stone, wh. I mentioned to you as one, wh. I suspected to belong to the Gadolinite Class, turns out (as far as my experiments authorize me to conclude) to be a species of compact Schoerl. I have reserved a piece for you. –

NHM, General Library, Sowerby Archive: Rashleigh: 47/19
Philip Rashleigh to James Sowerby

Menabilly, 3 April 1806

. . .

It being now above five Months since I sent you a few things for your own work, with some you proposed drawing for your H'ble Servant for the price you charge, to which I made not the least objection; but so much time has elapsed since, I scarce expected my life would then have continued so long; I must now beg to make enquiry about them as in the beginning of last December you thought they would be finished & returned in a few Weeks.

. . .

I have often lamented the want of Artists and Chymists in this County where we have such variety of Mineral subjects; & scarce any one who knows how to analise any thing.

CRO, Truro, Rashleigh Papers: DDR/5757/2/74
Rev. William Gregor to Philip Rashleigh
Creed 14 April 1806

I very lately received some Specimens of the Barnstaple Hydrargillite from Dr. Wavell. I sent a few of them to Heligan to wait any opportunity wh. might occur of forwarding them to you – I wish that they were equivalent for the fine specimen wh. you were so good as to give me – One thing to be remarked in the Devonshire & Cornish Hydrargillites is the difference of what mineralogists call the gangue or matrix – The Devonshire consists of argillaceous Schistus, whilst our Stenna Gwinn Fossil is found adhering to Quartz – In my paper on the latter fossil, I asserted that I had discovered an Acid in both the Devonshire & Cornish fossils. But the smallness of its quantity prevented me from ascertaining its nature. I have lately had a letter from Mr. Davy, in wh. he says, that he has repeated my experiments & proved the Acid to be the Fluoric.

Now that a small quantity of Fluoric-Acid should be <u>accidentally</u> found in his minerals of the same species, at such a distance as Stenna Gwinn and Barnstaple, is not I think, probable – Mr Davy thinks that this Acid from the smallness of its quantity, is united to the lime or silica. This is not improbable – And I think that lime, silica & fluoric acid, (all in small quantities relatively to the alumina) are essential ingredients of the Hydrargillite, as I before stated in my paper. . . .

University of Bristol Library, Special Collections: Joan Eyles Collection (DM1186)
Philip Rashleigh to James Sowerby
Menabilly, 15 April 1806

As this is a day when we receive no News Paper from London & having no person with me, I shall
begin a few lines to you, though I may not send them immediately. In looking over some of your numbers I generally find some amusement, & though you have delineated a great number of Articles, there are a great many more not yet noticed of British Minerals, so I conclude you must have a stock in reserve

for several more numbers & Plates. I see you have an excellent Cristalliographer in Count De Bournon, a pleasant Study for a New School, but he is so deliberate & particular in his descriptions, that he fatigues his readers who are but novices in that particular branch of the science, before they are got halfway t[h]rough his Paper or Lecture. He is an excellent Scholar after Roman de Lisle, but very few of the moderns have attended to that kinds of Arithmatick. It is almost necessary for a Mineralogist, & as that Study is so much the fashion, it ought to be more cultivated.

Had your British Mineralogy included more of Mr Chenevixes Analyses or other Eminent Chymists it would have been the first book in Print on that subject, for though it only includes British Subjects it would shew more interesting articles than the rest of the world together. I often lament that I had not the pleasure of knowing you when I had a call to London for several Months a year for near Forty years.

I hope you received my letter that contained my readiness to pay you & your Artists for what You undertook to do for me in the way of your business, I shall never pay money with more pleasure: When I can get a few more things, which I am promised, to make a little parcel, they shall be sent to you. You are now convinced of the delay in sending things between London & Cornwall, but I hope soon to hear the piece of Lead Ore you are so kind to give me, & which I shall set a great value upon, will soon begin its travels, with the Specimens I sent from hence the 21st Octr, 1805 to be returned after your operation. The Collection you bought of Mr. Wm. Day being so well arranged, made it much more valuable as it was then very easily kept in order, by adding every specimen as it came in, to the Class it belonged to. As my Collection was made at various times in many Years, & my Chimical Masters all of the Old School, they were soon out of date; & knowing but little of the present practice, they could give but little information. Such are our Tradesman here, who learn from Father to Son from Generation to Generation & therefore never add to their Arts.

I am in daily expectation of receiving the last things you sent by Messrs. Nicol. I should suppose some of the Gentlemen you employ in your Work would soon be good Artists, & in time continue a similar Plan in Foreign Min'ls. England is so productive as probably to last a long time & supply new subjects: & will enable You to print another Volumn [sic] or two.[1] Count de Bournon would find in my Cabinet many varieties to those he has seen at Mr. Greville's & Sr. Jo. St. Aubyn's, each of whom pays him handsomely; but I believe the latter gentleman has withdrawn some of his bounty, as Sr. John has removed his Collection from London. The dealers had a valuable Traffick with him. Have you seen Mrs. Powell's Collection? I trouble you with this chiefly to keep in your mind the things you promise.

Note

1. Rashleigh's prediction proved to be right for five volumes of the *British Mineralogy* were published between 1802 and 1817, and two volumes of the Sowerbys' *Exotic Mineralogy* that featured foreign specimens were published in parts between 1811 and 1820; see L. H. Conklin, 'James Sowerby: his publications and collections', *Mineralogical Record*, 26 (4) 1995, 85-105.

CRO, Antony House, Torpoint, Carew Papers: CC/L/39
Philip Rashleigh to R. Pole Carew
Menabilly, 16 June 1806

. . .

Mr Brown sent me a Copy of your letter about the Fish Curer being admitted to import Salt for curing Pilchards from France Duty Free, for which they received a fair answer; Yet I find the Stock of English Salt they have on Hand, & the little chance of Selling their Fish, has not yet induced many seins to be put to Sea: & the great loss sustained by the general Fishery last season, with several thousand Hogsheads of Fish now remaining unsold at St. Ives, discourages the adventurers from hazarding the Expense of another Season. I think my Cellars will produce me something more than my Expences, unless I include repairs which the Storms has done the Quay.

. . .

I must refer to a Letter of the 9th Inst. and for which I thank you on the enquiries you made on

Mr. Parkinson's Auction.[1] The piece of Native Tin Ore did not sell for anything like the Sum he expected & therefore I conclude was nothing more than I suspected but which I believe the Royal Society has formerly called Native Tin Ore in their Transactions for 1766. This piece I bought in Soper's Sale. Parkinson will make a good price of his Aventurin Stone, if he gets 400 for it after cutting off two slices at £100 each. I think he gave 200 guineas for it. I bought a few stones of it several years since at 1s./6d each, & might have had many more at the same price per Stone; but that of Parkinson's is much finer & had the Credit of belonging to one of the Roman Emperors. The Sardenix is a valuable Stone, & may cut up into a number of pretty Specimens. Sir Ashton was fortunate in his purchase of it, if he gave no more than two Guineas for it. Are the times so much changed as to cause such a difference; or Mineralogy so much advanced? It has certainly improved to knowing & in proving its contents in an extraordinary degree.

I fear Mr. P. will make but little of the Birds, Beasts & Insects, as few people who know the difficulty of keeping them, will be offerers for such cumbersome things. He has purchased several good Minerals which will sell well, as there was never such a rage for them as at present.

Note
1. This letter is significant in that it provided contemporary evidence of this auction sale. James Parkinson, a dental surgeon, who won the collection of Sir Ashton Lever (that contained many minerals) by a lottery in 1784, auctioned it in several parts between May and July 1806. He has been confused with his namesake, the famous surgeon and palaeontologist who published *Organic Remains of a Former World* (1804-11), the first general British work on fossils based on his own significant collection: see J. C. Thackray, 'James Parkinson's *Organic Remains of a Former World* (1804–11)', *Journal of the Society for the Bibliography of Natural History*, 7 (4) (1976), 451-66, at 465, and the *Oxford Dictionary of National Biography*.

CRO, Truro, Rashleigh Papers: DDR/5757/2/51
Leopold Fichtel to Philip Rashleigh
           London, No. 5 Arundel Street, Strand, 17 June 1806

It was with the greatest Pleasure I have been informed at Sir Joseph Banks that You continue as zealous for natural History, particularly Mineralogy as when present in London. This intelligence prompts me to trouble You with these few lines, which I hope you will not take amiss.

Having brought with me from Copenhagen an entire Collection and several Duplicates of the new substances recently discovered in Norway, which existed previous to my last Year's importation in London in no Cabinet at all. I conclude that You do not possess them, except they came into Your possession from the aforesaid importation of last Year. As I think them very interesting to a Collector I take the liberty to offer You as complete a Set of them as my stock will allow; adnexed is the Price Catalogue out of which You may choose any specimen, or specimens You please which I will package and forward to You by the waggon, as soon as I shall receive Your Orders concerning them. As I intend to procede from here to Lisbonne by the Way of Falmouth, I should request the favour of You to keep the specimens, which you will not approve of by You, till I come to Cornwall, which will be about the 20th of next Month, and as the distance I pass by You is only as I am informed eight or ten Miles out of my road to Falmouth, I intend with your kind permission, to do myself the honour of fetching them away myself. The sight of these specimens will be no expense whatever to You having intended them originally for Lisbonne, I should have been obliged to pay the freight for them to Falmouth at any rate, therefore I beg You will note the amount of freight and other charges, which I will reimburse to you or by allowing for the Somme in the Bill or by Cash in case you should approve of no Specimen at all.

These new substances are the more interesting, as almost all of them have been analysed by chemists of the first Rank, as Klaproth and Vaucquelin, of course they are new not only according external appearance but likewise by chemical Analysis. Kryolit and Cerit are two extremely rare articles and my last specimens; accidents excepted I am not able to procure them again.

The few Zeolites I have the honour to offer You are exquisitely beautiful or quite new; Nobody can get them except through my hands. A mineralogical friend of mine has visited last year the Faeroe Islands and discovered the perfect rectangular Prismes of Zeolite. I have bought of him the whole produce of his Voyage, very few specimens excepted, which he had disposed of previous to my arrival at Copenhagen to some Collectors in that City; how long it may be till another scientific man undertakes a similar Voyage is quite uncertain, perhaps never! He is now gone to Greenland for three Years after the expiration of which time I hope to get all he will find. Even to Mr Greville and Count Bournon the Zeolite in complete rectangular prismes has been quite new, the same case it was last Year with the Norway Minerals contained in the adnexed List.

CRO, Truro, Rashleigh Papers: DDR/5757/2/551
Leopold Fichtel to Philip Rashleigh   *London, 7 July 1806*

I had the pleasure of receiving Your esteemed letter of the 4 instant and am sorry You had by that time not yet received the Box with Minerals, but hope it came safe to hands before these lines will reach you. Your intention of keeping the Box unopened till I reach Cornwall is entirely contrary to my wishes. I should prefer and request You herewith to open the Box and to examine the specimens at your leasure [sic]. It will not only give You an opportunity of fixing on the specimens You may think sufficient interest to keep but it will also save me time as I do not think it possible to stay longer with You than one Morning, the unpacking and examining the specimens could hardly be accomplished in so short a space of time. Having now begonnen [sic] to pack up my Natural History articles I purchased at the Leverian Sale, I am afraid I shall not be able to leave London before the 25th instant, I shall do myself the honour of acquainting You of the exact day I may reach Menabilly

RIC, Truro, Rashleigh Papers: RASH/1/75
John Gould Jr. to Philip Rashleigh   *Penryn 8 August 1806*

I went yesterday to Godolphin where I left my horse and not finding Mr. John Williams arrived and the Tungstate of Lime being nearby four Miles distant, I procured a Pickax [sic] and a Pilot of the ores were acceptable, and in respect to the [sic], and found the Spot without difficulty. It lies in a valley between the South West side of Clarvance Park and Pengelly in a monstrous Lode not unlike that of Maudlin being every possible variety of Actinolite from the most intensely hard and massive Stone to a light stellated Substance resembling the stellated Zeolites. In this mass is embedded rich Galena, Blende Copper in very small Quantity, Iron, Manganese and Tungstate of Lime in great Variety. I brought home some small Pieces in my pocket and [of] Iron. As I receive the larger Pieces will forward them to St. Austle [sic]. Independent of the Substance to which my Researches were directed, I think the matrix are of the most singular I have ever seen.

Not far from the Spot was discovered another substance new to me as a Production of Cornwall, the Pitchstone in many specimens curiously mixed with a sort of fibrous & radiated Asbestos. In some Specimens very much resembling the white Schaerl or Tremolite of the Tyrol. You will receive I hope very soon a pretty numerous Collection of all bits from this Place that you may select what you please for your own cabinet and give some to your Friends, and knowing the Spot I can now at any Time procure You more.

I shall be very glad to hear of the safe Arrival of the Specimens from Mr. Forster[1] and that you are pleased with them. I shall be also very happy to hear of the good Folks from Lambs Conduit Street being safe under your Roof. Lord Dunstanville's Friends are very busy at Penryn, and I should think the baronet, if he persists in supporting all his friends, will find sufficient Employment.

Note
1. Possibly from 'Col. Yearns Sale': see Rashleigh's annotation.

CRO, Truro, Hawkins Letters: J3/3/315
Philip Rashleigh to John Hawkins
Menabilly, 21 August 1806

On hearing My Dear Sir that you had left your habitation near Northampton & not knowing in what part of this Country you had taken up your Residence; I really began to think our Correspondence was at an End; and through by Your letter of the 7th Instant I find the great loss of Seeing You and Your Lady will deprive me of much pleasure. Yet, I hope the short time I have to expect Life, I shall have the pleasure, next to our personal meeting that I shall be sometimes favoured with a few lines to hear of your welfare.

. . .

I have lately very much increased my Collection of Minerals both Foreign and British, but I suppose we shall never enjoy the viewing of them together; nor shall I ever see yours, which I have for so many Years been desirous of. The triffling [sic] Stones Mrs Hawkins left me on the Table in my hobby not being worth carriage will now be destined to mend the Roads.

Tomorrow I expect a German of whom I have bought many things formerly & within a few days, who has purchased many Lots of Mr. Parkinson's, late Leverian Museum to send to Vienna;

I suppose to supply in some degree what Bonaparte has Plundered from the Emperor. He is now going to Spain & Portugal.

. . .

My German Friend has been here & says the principal things in the Vienna Cabinet were sent away before Bonaparte enter'd the City; & being deprived of the best, he would have nothing to do with the Relicks [sic]. The few New Mines have produced some things different to the Old ones; as Common Opal, variety of Horn Blend; Six-sided plates of Blend covered with a coat of White Iron Ore; Actinolite, Tungstate of Lime analysed by Klaproth, &c &c: I do not know that any of these substances are very Curious, but they are varieties.

. . .

CRO, Truro, Rashleigh Papers: DDR/5305/35
Elizabeth Forster to Philip Rashleigh
London, No. 26, Gerrard Street, Soho 8 September 1806

Your favor of the 24th August came duly to hand, and the account of the fine Specimens of Lead being so much damaged in the carriage has given me much uneasiness and I cannot conceive how it could have happened, as I took the utmost care in packing it, and certainly put the Crested parts of the Specimen uppermost. [I] am afraid as the Box was so long on the Road that some person has had the curiousity [sic] to open it and know not how to put the specimen safe in again. [I] cannot account for it otherwise, and regret exceedingly that the accident has arrived to the Specimen, which was the finest piece that I had received from Russia; my old servant took it carefully to the Inn, saw it Booked, desired they would take care of it, and that it might be sent of[f] as soon as possible, and was told it wouldn't go the next morning; But by the time it was received it must have laid in the Warehouse of the Inn for some time which was a great neglect. If I had another specimen in anyway to compare I would willingly send it at as low a price as possible, as it certainly must be a great disappointment for you to receive a specimen of that value in such a state. –

I wrote a few lines at the bottom of the bill which I put in your box stating the loss I had sustained by the Death of my dear Husband which happened very suddenly while he was upon a visit to a friend by an Aplopeptic [sic] fit which took him of[f] in an instant; it is a severe stroke upon me indeed, as I fully expected him this Year at home, But it has pleased God that I should never see him more in this World, therefore I endeavor [sic] to submit to the Will of heaven. I regret very much that he had no relation by him at the time of his death, a good friend a Merchant in Petersburg, who sent me the melancholy tidings has taken the precaution to have all the property there (which is considerable) sealed up by the proper Officers and has placed a servant, that was with my late Husband six years, with two other men to take care of every thing till I should send a proper person with full power to take possession of the whole, as he always understood that I know my Husband's Will and how he has disposed of his affects, if he died in Russia &c. Now all the Will that I have was wrote in two Letters in the year 1800, and in a Letter that I received last April wherein he made an alteration in respect to his large Collection ordering it to be sold altogether and money arriving from the Sale thereof to be divided equally between his Brother and youngest nephew Henry Heuland, all these Letters were mixed with a great variety of matters quite foreign to the subject, and for some time it was doubtful if I should be permitted to administer but now all is settled, I am made the sole Executrix and am afraid I shall have some trouble as the Will is wrote in a confused manner, but I must do the best I can.

I have a little competency left me which with œconomy I hope will serve me, and as the Stock in trade of Minerals [&] Shells here are to be disposed of as soon as I can of which I am to have the half of what they produce and my Brother-in-Law Henry Forster the other half, which I think will enable me to do without business, as I don't covet great things. [I] suppose when all is settled that I may have about 150£ a Year, and at my death can leave it to whom I choose which is a great satisfaction to me as my Brothers have numerous families – so I don't complain; Mr. Henry Forster and Henry Heuland are to have all the property in Russia and Paris divided equally between them, my late Husband's nephew Christian is to have the fine small Collection. He is still in South America, has lost his Brother that went with him by an unfortunate accident which happened near 4 years since; he and two slaves that accompanied him were suffocated in going into a Sulphur Mine.

Our nephew Henry Heuland[1] is now at Madrid, I wished him to go to Petersburg, but on account of business [he] says he cannot go directly, intends to come to England first by the way of Lisbon;

my Brother Henry Forster is in such an infirm state of health, that he can undertake no Journey; I am much perplexed about it being afraid their property may suffer, tho' in Russia I know all will be safe but there will be great expenses incurred.

My Nephew H. Heuland wrote me while at Lisbon that the House he is engaged in at Petersburg has sent him some Superb Red lead, shall I desire him as he will some thro' Cornwall, if he has a capital piece or two to bring these with him and let you see them, or any other very curious thing; Excuse the length of my letter as you had the goodness Sir to mention my little affairs, I took the liberty to mention a few particulars.

Note

1. Henry Heuland (1778–1856); nephew of Jacob Forster; mineral dealer; came to England in 1806 and owing to the enthusiasm of British collectors was able to maintain a successful business as a mineral dealer and auctioneer in London for several years. There are some 60 letters in the Rashleigh archive at the CRO written between April 1807 and May 1809 that indicate that he was the principal source at that time for additions to the collection. These have all been fully transcribed, annotated and commented on by Michael P. Cooper in 1997 (a copy is available in the CRO). See also Heuland's letters below, dated 16 June and 7 September 1807 and 11 February 1809.

CRO, Truro, Rashleigh Papers: DDR/5757/1/100
John Hawkins to Philip Rashleigh

No. 6 Crescent, Bognor, Sussex,
undated [but probably November 1806][1]

Allow me to console with you my dear Sir on your recent loss, which although long expected must be deeply regretted by yourself and your nearest relatives. It leaves however one consolation and that not a small one. I mean the retrospect of an exemplary life & reputation which adds another title of honour to your family that it may be proud of. In fact I hardly know a family, that in this respect has equal claims to your own, of a very few indeed is it the lot to be so beloved & respected.

. . .

I am sorry to say that the house is not yet quite fit for our reception, nevertheless we propose to remove thither in the course of a few days. My presence will then probably accelerate my workmen. I fear there will be no room for very few of my minerals until I build a room for that purpose which must be deferred. Although I still flatter myself you will see this collection, yet I must say the loss of it ought not to be much regretted, for except that it is pretty complete in any one Series,[2] there are few specimens in it of superior beauty. In fact my finances, when I form'd this collection did not permit any great expenditure of this sort & I found the prices of fine specimens every where extravagantly high. My Cornish specimens are by far the most valuable part of my collection and I owe the best of these to your goodness.

You will be surprised to hear that the Trustees of the young Duke of Dorset are expending great sums in attempts to discover coal mines in various parts of Ashdown Forest at the eastern extremity of this County. In the parish of Bignor is dug a hard grey limestone which seems to be the real basis of the chalk that forms the South down hills. I find no petrifications in it.

I beg you would inform Mr. Wm. Rashleigh with my best Compts. that our horticultural Society flourishes & that three papers are now printing.[3] Also that the first fascicules of Dr. Sibthorp's "Flora Graeca" containing 50 Coloured Plates is just publish'd. I am now improving my garden and Mrs. H. has already a pretty collection of Green house plants. I found the Campanula hederacea in my grounds & the Phyteuma orbicularis on the hills.

. . .

Notes

1. The date of this letter is after 31 October 1806, probably late November as the 'recent loss' referred to is the death Rashleigh's brother Jonathan Rashleigh, who died on that date (see Rashleigh's reply of 29 December (below)). This is supported by evidence in W. T. Stearn, 'The background and origin of the Flora Graeca', *Biological Journal of the Linnean Society*, 8, 4 (1976), 298, that records that the first fascicules of the *Flora Graeca* were published in November 1806.
2. The word 'some' is written above 'anyone'.
3. The Horticultural Society (now Royal Horticultural Society) was formed in 1804; Hawkins was one of the founder members and served on its committee.

CRO, Truro, Hawkins Letters: J3/3/323
Philip Rashleigh to John Hawkins
Menabilly, 29 December 1806[1]

There are many circumstances that require a quick correspondence
between Friends, such as Compliments of Condolence or subjects
for Rejoicing; I have – therefore taken my Pen soon after receiving
your kind Letter on Condolence on my late Brother's departure;
The manner of his Life & circumstances on his Death have been
duly considered by those who were nearest & dearest to him;
His Life was so Religious & in every respect so Honorable that
it ensured him Eternal happiness in another World; The prospect
of future life was dismal & not likely to produce ease to himself
or Comfort to his Friends; These circumstances being consider'd
& the Death not attended with great Pain gave all Friends less
distress than might have been expected. His latter moments were
as Calm & as free from Pain as if he was going into a great Sleep.
The present rector of Silverton has done every thing that was
Honorable Genteel to his Widdow [sic] & her near Relations.
  [comments on Hawkins' new house]
  I suppose you are out of the way from all Election Combats; we
had an attempt at Fowey to give us trouble, but after many attempts
to procure Candidates our opponents were obliged to put up with
a Person who was a late Book-keeper to a Stage Waggon; after
Polling a few Votes, their agent told us they would give us no more
trouble. So we gave them three Cheers for our Friends & retired to
Dinner. How your Brother[2] can delight in being troubled with so
many Boroughs, is beyond my conception. Unless he keeps a good
look out he may yet find himself in a very unpleasant situation.
  [remarks on managing Hawkins' new property]
  On Minerals I must say a few Words, & still lament my not
seeing Yours; I have lately purchased a great many of Mr. Fichtel
particularly Zeolites & many others: I have had a serious loss in a
very perfect & beautiful Spec. of the Cromate of Lead, by all the
Crystals being broke in carriage, I suspect by an Officer opening
the box & taking of it out & then returning of it with the Crystals
undermost. I have scarce seen any Collection where the Minerals
of this County are not superior to those of any other but they are
got to an Enormous price by an increase of Collectors.
  The price of Copper is fallen so much as to stop several Mines
in a short time: Our Fishery is likewise almost ruined, by the
threats of Bonaparte so detains many Ships from sailing that are

now loaded. Two serious things on this business is obtained, one that Bonaparte has succeeded in his endeavours to interrupt our Trade, which may encourage him to attempt others & to [illegible] Fishermen for want of Purchasers. Many [illegible] of last year are unsold, & I suppose would be only fit for Dressing.[3]

Note
1. Rashleigh's writing had become larger and spaced out.
2. Sir Christopher Hawkins (1758–1829); described as the 'Cornish borough monger' for his involvement with the boroughs of Tregony, Mitchell, Grampound, Helston, Penryn & St. Ives.
3. A postscript refers to Hawkins' comment in his previous letter about the publication of the *Flora Graeca* – see also J3/3/324 a letter from Wm. Rashleigh to John Hawkins, 30 December 1806: 'From selfish motives, I wish my Uncle Tom take in the *Flora Graeca* for which my purse is very inadequate, but his great dislike to Botany, nay contempt for it, prevents me from mentioning the subject'.

CRO, Truro, Rashleigh Papers: DDR/5305/37
Rev. William Gregor to Philip Rashleigh

Creed, 19 January 1807

I am very sorry to learn from your kind letter that you are not very well: The present damp foggy weather is neither favourable to bodily health nor animal spirits –

. . .

I have lately met amongst my specimens of Stenna Gwinn Fossils a variety of what I believe to be Hydrargillite.[1] It consists of crystals of a much larger size than those resembling Zeolite. They are transparent and consist of double four sided Pyramids – from an experim't. made upon a small portion, I believe that it consists of Clay united to fluat of Lime. – The fluoric acid is in greater quantity in this species than in the common Hydrargillite.

Note
1. Gregor commented in a letter to Sowerby (18 November 1807): 'the specimen is not such as to appear to advantage upon paper, but being new and exceeding scarce, I thought that it was worthy of your Notice'. Sowerby figured and described the specimen in the December 1807 number of *British Mineralogy*, Vol. 3, pl. 243,

85-6, using Gregor's own account of his analytical experiments; Sowerby's plate was referred to by Embrey and Symes, *Minerals of Cornwall and Devon*, 67, and reproduced there (75, fig. 78); Russell, 'The Rev. William Gregor', (1955: 620), explained that the material contained the mineral Fluellite.

NHM, Mineral Library, Russell Bequest, Hawkins Letters: 5/6
Rev. William Gregor to John Hawkins

Creed, 5 February 1807

I confess, that appearances are against me: I have received two very friendly letters from you, and I have suffered those letters to lie by me without any acknowledgements, for a considerable Time. – In short I may say '*Habeas confitentim reum*' – And what is worse – I have no just cause to bring forward to account for my apparent inattention & ingratitude. – I have long been intending to take up my Pen – But 'tis tomorrow, & tomorrow' – till one wonders at the interval of Time which has passed away in making good resolutions – I throw myself therefore upon your friendship & good nature. –

I was truly rejoiced to hear that you had at last obtained a place of Residence, which you could call your own. Circumstanced as you are you must feel great comfort in the contemplation of this.[1] – The act of settling oneself requires Time – and Time, with regard to improvements is peculiarly precious – I have no doubt but that your Mansion will combine Comfort with Elegance. – May you and Mrs Hawkins live long to enjoy Bignor Park! I do not know, whether or no you have hitherto been used to receive pleasure from Gardening & Agriculture; Now, however, at least you will learn to interest yourself in these pursuits. Since the progressive Improvements of a Place so much depends upon them. – You enjoy the great advantage of being at a commodious distance from London. We in this County are thrown too far off from that great source of information & entertainment. – However, I am contented where I am – I have struck my root: and could not bear to be transplanted even under a more genial sky without suffering inconvenience. – How happy a circumstance it is, that we are so much the Children of Habit!

. . .

My Brother & Sister are very well – The former indeed is more free from Gout than he has been for several Years. – He was induced by the frequent re-occurrence of that dreadful disease to ask medical advice; as to Regimen &c. and he has profited by it. – You are, of course informed that he has given up his honourable & labourious situation. –

I amuse myself occasionally with Chemical investigations. – Last year I published in the Philosophical Transactions an Analysis of a Cornish Fossil, wh. was supposed to be Zeolite – but wh. is the same as the Hydrargillite. I requested Mr. Hatchett to send a Copy of my Paper to you – but he could not then discover yr. address. – I have within a few months met with a variety of this substance in beautiful Crystals. double four-sided pyramid with truncated apex. But I have only one specimen. I have Klaproth's second Vol.

Note
1. Russell, 'The Rev. William Gregor', (1955: 619), referred to and quoted this letter congratulating Hawkins on at last, finding a suitable property for a home in Sussex. Although addressed to Bignor Park, there is a further indication of Gregor's uncertainty as to Hawkins' address for his use of '. . . Crescent, Chichester' suggests he had used this in an earlier attempt at communication.

CRO, Truro, Rashleigh Papers: DDR/5757/2/91-92
Henry Heuland to Phillip Rashleigh
London, 16 June 1807

[This rambling letter in Heuland's confused English demonstrates his intricate dealings in minerals]

In answer of Your much respected and agreable [sic] letter of the 10th inst. I have the honor to tell You Sir, that the name of the sulphur mine near Cadiz in Spain is Conilla /pronounced Conilliha/ that the cubic vitreous copper from Siberia is esteemed and rare, as when cubic the cristals are always of a beautiful ruby color and quite transparent, during the octaedral vitreous copper never possess this last quality in our Sybn. specimens. The arseniate wood-like copper ore I never saw or believe existing else where but in Cornwall, and the wood like tin I only know from Mexico next the Cornish, and possess one specimen of it, representing a very heavy brown round solid little pebble, intermixed with circular veines of a yellowish color, imitating by their various directions, those round [page torn with loss] Agathes, which come from Oberstein in the Palatinal. This wood tin was much admired, when the Company which I had the honor to explain to You Sir, came to see part of the great Collections and which I am much grieved I am unable to show to You Sir with that zeal duty a +[page torn with loss] where, as in gratitude of your kind correspondence I longed for.

I realy think Mrs Maw as she t[rades] Mineralogy only in a comercial view will be much dis[appoin]ted with her last purchases in Cornwall, because of Latham in Compton Street has got most beautiful arseniate of copper, and of which Mr. Greville bought a 20 pieces. I purchased 6 wonderful fine ones of the sort as the largest Specimen You was so kind Sir to send me for a Keep Sake, and I wonder where those things can have come from? Mr Latham says, that the box was packed up three years ago in Cornwall, and this is all he tells me, but I am very persuaded Sir, they must have been collected by an excellent judge, or met by great fortune and chance. There is likewise a piece of bel[l] metal ore, as large as a fist for which he asked Gs. 10 but I possess it already as fine. of tins there was nothing and it is only in that explained, and no other variety of the arseniate of Copper, that Mr. Latham's Specimens are so very exquisite, and which now are in the hands of Mr Greville and mine.

Before my leaving England, shall provide myself with all the newest & best mineralogical works, and shall procure that where mostly all the illuminated drawings are out of Your Collection Sir; my Aunt says she thinks I find that Mr Sowerby's de Bournon is a capital Cristallographer indeed, but he should Consider that Rome de L'isle was his master, laid the ground of the whole cristallography and being dead long ago, it is natural through the infinit late d+iscov,eries, that the living cristallographers have the advantage, and therefore de Bournon should not critize Rome de Lisle as he does now and then because if he was alife [sic], Bournon would always remain his Scholar. Abbé Huaÿ [sic] in Paris, is a far deeper Cristallographer, but is in want of seeing so many new products as the Count does from all quarters.

Now Sir do you like the said de Bournon's new System of arranging diamond – Spar, cats eyes, oriental and occidental rubies, topazes, sapphires, emeralds &c., all in one class, and to make one and the same Substance of them? I never shall follow it, though Cristallisation might induce to it, yet the knowledge of the colored stones, and the different treatment of them, under the lapidary's hands, which I studied particularly, and are qualities quite unknown to the learned Mineralogist, this knowledge I believe is too considerable and will overthrow all order and reason.

Last week I bought a new French work written by Mr Brongniart at Paris, the new names, some very barbarous have no end, and for this very reason the book is of use to me, as I must run with the rest. It gives a short explanation of almost every known [subs]tance and merely an extract of all the best authors. When Sir shall we See a mineralogical work, that the author does not copy his antecessors? I once, a 6 or 7 years ago thought to do something, and I had occasion to have things [page torn with loss] my hands, which no author ever saw and likely never will see, but trade became since the separation of my late Uncle so interesting for me, that all my ambition turned in its favor, and made me indifferent to the pretention of a learned man and the wish of immortality.

. . .

Mrs Forster Sir desires her respects. Mr Fichtel, nor I when in Spain, got any Sulphur from Conilla, and in the Spanish Collection they only have three specimens, but they are astonishing, and picked by late Mr. Clavijo the former Director, out of the party my Uncle was to have in payment of £4000 – and then the mine was shut up, not to make them common. Now you may judge, Sir, what a talking there was self [even?] at Madrid about my late Uncle's granted licence from the Court of Spain, to shut the mine, and certainly Mr. Fichtel's conversation with me on that head was a very just one, and I only could observe, that he should see, if they could open the mine, to let him take out of it, what he liked. I could have had in Madrid a very honourable employment of a £450 a year, house and living, besides, and nothing to do, but I preferred my liberty, besides I do better in my line likewise. Mr. Fichtel told me in Madrid he should be here for the last time at the beginning of the summer to dispose of what he had left here to Mrs Maw and Mr. Latham; but no body hears a word of him!

CRO, Truro, Rashleigh Papers: DDR/5757/2/161
Henry Heuland to Philip Rashleigh

London, 7 September 1807

I had the honour to receive your estimable letter of the 27th of last month, being as sensible Sir at your kind congratulation to see my property safe at hand, as I am glad to enjoy this benefit. Not being an Englishman, I at this time luckily run no risk to go to Paris, Sir. Till last year I was a Prussian subject, but through the Treaty of Tilsit a Bavarian now, as Bayreuth in Franconia to which I belong, was given to Bavaria. I learn, however, that she will loose it again, as whole Franconia will be formed in a new kingdom. All this Sir, is very indifferent to me, having no claims in Germany, and procuring only to get all my goods away from Paris. But there is now another new obstacle. Holland being the only country where to go to first from here, and no ships whatever being actually admitted there from any English port.

I was happy to learn Sir, that you would be so kind to give room for a box of my minerals, which I already sent off by Russell's waggon, Friday week the 28th of last month, so that there is a chance of [it] being soon at St. Austell, when you will be pleased Sir to send for, and run the expenses, till I shall be so lucky to make them good to you Sir at my arrival, thinking to set off myself Friday next, and to pass a few days at Bath, and Bristol, and to arrive at Menabilly some morning of the following week, in order of the favor and leave Sir, you honoured me with to render you a visit, and to see your fine collection Sir.

[omitted paragraph concerning specimens of 'blue lead'.]

I shall make another sacrifice Sir, of the various muriates, and [by] these means wish and hope to obtain the analysis of them for you, thinking Mr. Davy is the best apt for it. I was invited by Mr. Phillips to see his Collection and to [ex]change with him. I shall give myself the pleasure of seeing it at my return from you Sir, but the exchange I decline, as it seldom turns out to satisfaction on both sides, and not pretending that any Collector should part with products which he esteems most. I have not seen Sr. John St. Aubyn's Collection, which. I heard at Mr. Greville's was now a burden to him. I did not know that he possesses specimens of native lead, I doubt its existence, and if Count de Bournon made him believe to be such, I suppose he spoke against his conviction.

Supposing the box arrives before me, I leave it to your pleasure Sir, to open it, without waiting for me, and expect you will find yet many fine products, in particular I hope Sir, that you will be pleased seeing the 1st Chromate of Lead <u>existing</u>. By unpacking, be pleased Sir, to examine the tow with great care, as it commonly happens, and in particular with small specimens, that some fall out and mix themselves amongst the tow.[1]

Note

1. In a subsequent letter (6 October 1807) Heuland indicated that he had enjoyed his visit to Cornwall and the sight of Rashleigh's collection – afterwards he spent an entire day recording his observations. But he had to hasten back to London to deal with the arrival of his possessions from Russia and missed seeing the Williams collection.

CRO, Truro, Rashleigh Papers: DDR/5757/2/107
Rev. William Gregor to Philip Rashleigh

Creed 5 February 1808

I have to thank you for two very obliging letters and to beg your pardon for so long delaying to acknowledge them. I request that you also attribute my delay to particular engagements, which have prevented me from considering some of the subjects which you proposed to me.

. . .

I was much surprized at receiving a letter from the Secretary of the New Geological Society, which announced that I was chosen an Honorary Member. On looking over the List, I was glad to find that I was got into <u>good company</u> and amongst some of my friends. I was of course bound to thank the Society for the said honour – I wish that societies of this kind would stick more to facts than <u>Theories</u> – Whilst some are Neptunists and others <u>Volcanists</u>, Truth is distorted through the mist of party-prejudice and much labour and Ingenuity are expended to little purpose.

. . .

I believe that I mentioned to you, that I have discovered Arseniat of Lead in perfect and well-defined crystals of new sort in some specimens given me by Mr, Rogers. I have mentioned this to Mr. Sowerby: and he has informed me that he was unacquainted with any of this sort. I have no doubt that these <u>Arseniats</u> have been taken from <u>Phosphats</u>. . . . I made some experiments some months ago on a particular species of Carbon (seemingly an intermediate substance between Charcoal & Diamond) which accompany Culm – my experiments led me to some curious facts & combinations – But I have not had time to finish them.

RIC, Courtney Library, Truro, Rashleigh Papers: RASH/1/41
Rev'd. Wm. Gregor to Philip Rashleigh
Creed, 15 February 1808

. . .

I return you with many thanks the Paper relating to Professor Davy, which you kindly sent to me. – We have just reason to be proud of him as our Countryman. He has great sagacity & clearness of head, joined to steady & patient perseverance in his researches. The French will be mortified at Mr. Davy's discovery and I should not wonder if some after claims should be preferred as to the honour of priority.

My reason for thinking certain crystals contained in the Lead ores, which I mentioned as being <u>Arsenical</u> of Lead, is this that in the <u>gold spoon</u> when exposed to the heat of the blow pipe, they melt but are not reduced nor no arsenical vapour is extricated; but on the <u>charcoal</u>, the lead is reduced and arsenical vapours are extricated after continued digestion in nitric Acid, it is very slowly & sparingly acted upon. – These properties distinguish these crystals in a marked & decided manner, both from the Carbonats [sic] & Phosphats of Lead. I intend to send them to Mr. Sowerby soon and on their return,[1] if you have no specimens of them, they shall be much at your service. For you know I have no collection. My object being only, when I have leisure from other more important things to discover new substances or varieties.

. . .

Note
  1. Embrey and Symes, *Minerals of Cornwall and Devon*, 115, record that this rare mineral from Wheal Unity, near Gwennap – now named Mimetite – was given to Thomas Allan and is now in the Natural History Museum, London. Gregor subsequently wrote to Sowerby on 13 October 1808 and the specimen was figured in *British Mineralogy*, Vol. 3, pl. CCXCV that December using

Gregor's account of his experiments; see also Russell, 'The Rev. William Gregor', 622. Gregor published this himself in 1809: 'On a native arseniate of lead', *Philosophical Transactions*, Vol. 99:195-211.

NHM, General Library, Sowerby Archive: Rashleigh: 47/23
Philip Rashleigh to James Sowerby

Menabilly, 7 March 1808

. . .

Mr. William Gregor not keeping any Collection of Minerals has been kind enough to present me with his Capital piece of Hydrargillite that you have made such an accurate engraving of: The Cristals [sic] are so very small that I can not see them perfectly even with a high Magnifying Lens. I should not have deprived my Friend Mr. Wm. Gregor of this rare spec'm. if I had not known he did not make a Collection for his own Cabinet; and where a gentleman does not collect, my Conscience is not hurt by accepting Specimens I do not possess: for it very often happens that the rarest Minerals are obtained to exhibit on a Chimney piece, or some other exposed situation.

Your drawing of the Horn Silver, in the [? Cubes] is much greener than any I possess, or I think any I have lately sent to have the Silver extracted from to be made into a Candle-Stick this [sic] Mine has been abandoned for many Years, some few very good pieces were found in it when I was an Adventurer, for the sake of gaining fine Specimens; as such were generally broke to pieces for more accurate division, but in one of the Lots I desired the Parties concern'd would permit the pieces to be Valued without breaking, & I would either take the whole or my share according to valuation: One of these pieces was supposed to contain about five Guineas worth of Silver – which I thought it might, & gave it, but the form of the Cristals were not exposed in the outside: this I did not mind as I had some [illegible] small pieces very distinct, many of which I have given in exchange. I have one very large piece given me by the owner owner [sic] of the Mine, the late Viscount Falmouth, but it is not Horn Silver, & only shews the [? bigness] of the Lode.

CRO, Truro, Rogers of Penrose Autograph Album, Vol. 2:
RP/17/46
Phillip Rashleigh to Rev'd. John Rogers of Mawnan
Menabilly, 3 June 1808, 8 pm

[this accompanies a letter from William Rashleigh to Rogers]
You may suppose your kind Letter of the 25 May has been a
long time on the road, or that I have been very negligent in not
thanking you before for it; however when you hear the case you
will not think much neglect either in the Post or your Hble Servt.
Your Letter was recd. in due time, but I omited [sic] to thank you
for it until I received the parcel, which I have done within this hour
and now desire your acceptance of my thanks or both. I sent to my
Sister Gould to desire she would enquire for the parcel & bring it
with her to Trevarrick, where she was coming with Mrs Lakes &
her grandchildren; & from whence she has this afternoon sent it
here; As it is now Candlelight I can see but little of the Specimens.
I do not think I am a sufficient Judge of Acids to determine
what these Specimens contain, & I have now many Muriates of
Copper that have never been Analysed, and it is no easy matter to
determine what pieces Specimens of the seize [sic] those you have
just sent me contain; because it would be necessary to select a little
of every party, or it would never determine the general contents:
for it only a small sample was taken, that might contain a piece of
Native Metal & produce a great proportion of it, but that might
not give a certain knowledge of the whole.

The assayers of Copper in this County I believe are very
accurate in trying that Ore, & I think are as regular & exact as
any Chemist in any Country: But I do not think they are capable of
examining any other substance. Mr. Wm. Gregor is very diligent
in his Experiments, & I had much rather depend on his Judgement
– than I would Sowerby's, who I believe sometimes gets Count
de Bournon to assist him: but I should not depend much on the
Count neither. A Good Operator would be a very Valuable person
in this County. The Triers of Tin are tollerable [sic] but not half so
accurate as the Triers of Copper, who are very careful in selecting
their samples from every part of what is to be Assayed, if they
were not, the different offerers could not come so near to each
others Value.

Pray give my kind Respects to your father, & tell him, if he
should at any time come this way, as he is fond of Mineralogy, I
can show him some very Rare & Beautiful specimens I have lately

procured. I believe there never was such a sale before in London as
last Month & this, & yet not finished; I mean as to Numbers of
rare Specimens from distant Countries, as Chili, & the South Seas
in various places. My eyes are too Old for seeing the forms of fine
Cristals. Though you have seen most of my Cabinet I think when
you favor me with your Company another time I shall be able to
shew you some different.

RIC, Courtney Library, Truro, Rashleigh Papers:
RASH/1/76
Rev'd. Wm. Gregor to Philip Rashleigh
Creed, 3 September 1808

I intended to have sent a letter to you by the means of Mr. E.
Stackhouse's carriage and by the <u>same means</u> of conveyance to
have returned you the little Box and specimens contained in it,
of the curious ore from Huel Druid. The Nature of which I have
sufficiently ascertained without having injured the beauty of the
specimen. – As I detached a few fragments only from the extreme
end of it. – But I found that Mr. E. Stackhouse had already paid
his visit to you, when he came to us. – Your Specimen therefore
is set by, safely, until a safe opp'y. of returning it occurs. – I feel
much oblig'd to you for entrusting me with it & I hope that I shall
never on such occasion abuse your confidence. – That said mineral
from Huel Druid consists of <u>a peculiar combination</u> of <u>Oxide of
Iron</u> and Silex. It is probably not to be found in the systems of
Mineralogy. The Iron is completely separated from the silex by
Acids. The Silex is in a gelatinable state I had flattered myself <u>at
first</u>, that it was <u>G</u>adolinite. I wish it had been, for sake of the
value of the specimen.

I am not as yet able to send you the proportion of the constituent
parts of the new lead Ore of wh.you so kindly sent me a fine
specimen, and which will enable me, I trust, to ascertain its
nature. – I am in the midst of my analysis – and engagements
will prevent me for some days from weighing the results. – I have
proceeded slowly & warily on account of the rarity of the mineral.
I have, however, prepared an artificial <u>Arseniate of Lead</u> and
find some of the crystals to be compleat <u>six-sided Prisms</u>. I shall
communicate shortly with Mr. Sowerby. I shall take the liberty of
mentioning that I owe the ability of analizing this new Mineral to

your kindness. – The small specimen, which I shall send Sowerby for description contains one crystal which resembles a small Beryl. – Of course, I shall only send Mr Sowerby, this small specimen. – I have no doubt, but that this new Mineral will excite the attention of Mineralogists.[1]

I am sorry that you have a Fever in your House: but fortunately, your House is on as extended a scale that all ranges of Infection ways are cut off by a very little attention. – I had the Scarlet fever in my small dwelling, some years ago, and I am sure that I stopp'd the progress of the disease, by fumigating the passages & the sick rooms by the vapour of marine Acid extricated from common salt by means of vitriolic acid. A handful of common Salt may be placed in a water-glass or bason [sic] of Queen's-ware and a small quantity of vitriolic Acid (now called Sulphuric Acid) dropped upon it. The vapour, which arises will neutralize the contagious principle. . . . If the vessel containing the Salt &c be placed upon a <u>warm brick</u>, the vapour will be more fully extricated – fresh additions of Vitriolic Acid must be made from time to time.

Note
   1. See note to letter 15 February 1808; a further letter on 28 September
      provides details of his experiment and analysis.

CRO, Truro, Rashleigh Papers: DDR/5757/2/137
Rev. William Gregor to Philip Rashleigh
Creed, 18 January 1809

I am much obliged to you for your last kind favour. I am much indebted to yr. Kindness for the specimen of the Plumose Antimony which you sent me. It was a perfect novelty to me. I had not at [sic] recollected that you had given me any previous intimation of your intention of sending me any – and I was rather pleased with myself, that I had given to this mineral its proper title – when upon referring to a former letter of yours, I found that you had spoken of it before – [1]

The Quartz crystals, if they be pure Quartz are curious. They seem to me to be harder than the common – But this much I have been enabled to discover that the usual Chemical Analysis of Plumose Antimony is erroneous. As your specimen certainly consists of sulphuret of Antimony of Lead – I am obliged to you for your kind offer of sending me more fragments. I have already quite sufficient for my purpose.

I have not yet sent off my paper on the Arseniat of Lead. For I have reason to think that the Lead is united to the Arsenic Acid in two different proportions – which is the case of the Arseneats of Copper – The only difference wh. I can discover in the external aspect of this substance is that the crystals wh. contain the larger dose of acid are of a more delicate flaxen yellow, or Isabella colour and I think that the sides of the Hexa[h]edral Prism are not regular but two opposite sides are larger, the other smaller.

I wrote to Cap'n. Wm. Davy of Wh. Unity Mine to favour me with an account of the situation of the Lode &cc, which he has kindly done, & he has engaged to send me some of the different specimens found at the different depths & situations wh. he has described – I think it very probable that these different sorts may have been raised at different places. In about ten days I hope to get fairly rid of my paper – However, I do not grudge the pains, which I have taken with this fossil, as I hope to establish the fact of a new (or at least vaguely described) species of Lead Ore being found in our Native County.

The Pink coloured Stone from Liskeard is a very curious fossil – It may be called a New Ore of Manganese. As I believe that Manganese is about one half of the other Ingredients are chiefly Quartz and a small portion of Lime. But I speak not positively, as I have not had none to examine it fairly – Is this substance the Andalusite, or Handspath mentioned in the Appendix to the Second vol. of Jameson's Mineralogy Page 544? – I suspect that it is!

I am compelled to take a hasty trip to London this Spring – to see Mr. Williams Hope, whose health is in a very precarious state, and who also is about to return to Holland under the dominion of the Bonaparte upstart. His situation therefore is in every respect so critical, that if I see him not now, I shall not probably never see him again –

Note
1. This suggests that Gregor retained Rashleigh's letters.

CRO, Truro, Rashleigh Papers: DDR/5757/2/136
Henry Heuland to Philip Rashleigh

London, 11 February 1809

I was most happy to receive your most esteemed favor of the 2nd Instant and to learn Sir that you enjoy health, which after so long a silence I was anxious to know confirmed. Mr. Allan's book arrived some days ago, quite unexpected, not thinking Sir, you would return it.[1] I really was entertained at Mr. Walker's country seat (Arnos Grove, Southgate – 8 miles from London) though we were continually shut up in the house for the cold and then the rainy weather sake, he has some fine minerals indeed, and a beautiful collection of shells collected by his late mother.[2] His stay in Scotland was I suppose for the purpose of family affairs, as he collected no Scotch minerals whatever, except two polished topazine rock chrystals, which he bought from a lapidary at Edinburgh.

I learn that this Summer several Gentlemen of the Geological Society will examine Scotland in a mineralogical and geologic view. This society is new, Mr. Greville is the protector of, and all Collectors, Chimists and men of learning, or renown for interesting themselves in natural history are members of.[3] The two Philipp's[4] are amongst the number, so is the Count de Bournon. The work of the latter will not be published now, though 8 Gentlemen advanced each £50 for printing. He dedicated it to the Empress of Russia, which circumstance is the actual obstacle of its appearance. I should think he had enjoyed benefits enough in this country, to show his gratitude be the dedication of the work to some of his protectors.

Mr Lowry[5] when lately in Wales found beautiful groups of rock chrystals, like those found in France and with the same mixture of Adularia in chrystallized tables. I got 5 specimens of him for which I allowed £5. %. In case Sir you wish to possess one of them for £1.1.0 I can lay a specimen aside. He likewise found in Derby a rare and new chrystallization of calcareous Spar, which Sowerby has published. The latter Gentleman and his son have been with me yesterday, and took my scarcest Calcareous Spar with them for drawing, and I have the pleasure to have him and his son here at this hour. The father draws my first wonderful sulphur, and the son a most scarce group of berils, referring a thick chrystal with its pyramid.

I am sure Sir to have always considered your tins, coppers,

antimonies, leads and fluors &c. &c. with the esteem they so much deserve, and in particular do not think your Silvers superior to your Tins, which I am sure are the most fine in this and every other country. My late Uncle often spoke of to me, and never could forgive you Sir, that you had so many solitary chrystals of Tin in your Grotto, and which he had not in his Collection. You likewise possess Sir, some chrystallized golds, of which I have seen but one in Mr. Walker's collection, & your satin malachite with native gold is matchless.

When I said plumous Antimony, I could, or should have added the word Sulphuret, to distinguish the variety of the plumous from the chrystallized, or the needle sulphuret of Antimony. At Mr. Walker's I saw two specimens of triple sulphuret of antimony from South America,[6] at Mr. Greville's another, and at Mr. Lowry's the last, coming all from one specimen which Mrs Maw had sent by her husband and which, unfortunately, she broke up in small pieces to make the most of. Dr. Woollaston, a famous chimist, had analyzed it, and every Collector was eager for a specimen. Mr Lowry will be so kind to cede me his specimen, and he will contrive to get yet a smaller one for himself at Mrs Maw's. The specimen came much bruized. And is the only article Mr. Maw sent, saying he could get nothing, but means to settle at the Brazils, and it is talked of by Mrs Maw & family will follow him, as Mr. Maw gives to understand that the prince regent of Portugal makes him very flattering offers &c. I wish that they may turnout true. Supposing Sir, you will be anxious to see the triple sulphuret from the Brazils, I shall save it for you, at least, it was with this intention, that I begged Mr. Lowry for his.

Notes
1. Thomas Allan *An Alphabetical List of the names of Minerals ... with tables of Analyses* (Edinburgh, 1808).
2. Isaac Walker (1794–1853); wealthy brewer and mineral collector encouraged by Heuland.
3. The Geological Society was founded on 13 November 1807: H. B. Woodward, *The History of the Geological Society* (London, 1907), 10.
4. Richard Phillips (1778–1851); William Phillips (1775–1828); founder members of the Geological Society; Fellows of the Royal Society. Gregor and Rashleigh were elected members of the Geological Society in 1807 and Hawkins in early 1808, before Greville (and so prior to this letter).
5. Joseph Wilson Lowry (1762–1824) English artist and engraver,

pioneered steel engraving (see plate of Cassiterite in Wm Phillips (1814); he married Rebecca Delvalle, an accomplished mineralogist. Their substantial collection was used by Sowerby and admired by their contemporaries – see Wilson, 'The history of mineral collecting', 167, 181.

6. Bournonite – which was first figured by Rashleigh (1797), 34, pl. 19.

CRO, Truro, Hawkins Archive: J3/4/458
Rev. William Gregor to John Hawkins

Creed, 30 June 1813[1]

Upon my return from a Month excursion into Gloucestershire, I found your very acceptable letter. It was acceptable from the good account it communicated respecting your self & family, and for the interest & friendly disposition which it proves for me & mine. – I am sorry that there should be any drawback from your general Happiness in the tender health of Mrs Hawkins –

[Accounts of the health of his brother Francis Gregor[2] and his own family]

With respect to the Amusements which I suffer to fill up the intervals of my leisure from my business & my Duties: I draw occasionally and subject minerals to analysis, if I ever meet with such as appear worthy of it.

I have lately sent a paper to the Geological Society on a variety of Tremolite which I found in this County, and in a Rock of the <u>Serpentine</u> species; which has been strangely overlooked by Geologists, though it should seem to solicit attention. I am sorry that you have abandoned the study of Mineralogy & that your valuable collection has been suffered to be useless. – As you were qualified to be of service to others.

Although I have not lately written to you,[3] yet by means of the Chilcotts we have heard of you & yours and I shd. be exceedingly sorry if I were capable of suffering absence to efface from my recollection the ideas of passed obligations & old friends.

Notes

1. This letter has been used as an illustration in Cleevely, 'The contributions of a trio of Cornish geologists', 120, and in Cleevely and Bristow, 'Rev. William Gregor', 88.

2. Francis Gregor (1760–1815); Gregor's older brother, who became an MP in 1789 and served until ill-health caused his retirement in 1806.
3. Although Gregor mentions that he had '*not lately written*' this cannot refer to the apparent extensive gap of more than six years in the surviving letters. It is known that Hawkins' descendants did destroy material found at Bignor and it has to be assumed that the lack of any surviving letters from this period does not indicate a cessation in their correspondence.

NHM, General Library, Sowerby Archive: A23/139
Rev. William Gregor to James Sowerby
Creed, 10 December 1816

In answer to your letter of the 4th Inst. containing some queries respecting a mineral consisting of the oxides of Arsenic & Iron, which I sent you long ago, I am sorry to say that I have nothing satisfactory to say. As I find no Notes or Memoranda in my papers respecting it. I recollect my examination of it with a view to discover the constituent parts without regard to <u>the relative</u> quantities of them, and that I was led to the conclusion, which I drew from the few experiments, which I made upon the substance. I recollect, also that it was found in a mass of rock, which appears in a down in the Parish of Perran Arworthel.[1]

I have a specimen, or two somewhere, but I cannot put my hand upon them. – I have been prevented for a considerable time from paying much attention to subjects of this kind, both from want of leisure, & lately from want of health.

You have no doubt, seen the beautiful & extraordinary specimens of Carbonate of lead discovered in Pentre[2] Glaze mine in the North of Cornwall. Those Specimens must have found their way to the London Mineral Shops. If you have not seen this very singular ore it is well worth a place in yr. valuable work and if you wish to have a Specimen I will send you one.

<u>Pencil draft reply by Sowerby (undated)</u>
I very much thank you for your kind answers to Oxides of Arsenic & Iron.

Am sorry at your want of health. I hope you will soon be well again for your own ease & comfort and the good of mankind. I have seen of the Carbonate of Lead, but am not so good a Judge of them as you must be and should you find it convenient to <u>Send</u> or <u>Spare</u> me a spec'm, which in the former case shall be carefully returned and all expences cheerfully paid. I shall be [under] much obligation for such indulgence and a reciprocal endeavour, if you can command me to be in my turn usefull [sic]. Is it possible to get a [illegible] the spec'm. of Phosphate of Iron.

Shall regard any advice as [I] am now finishing Brit. Miner. the [illegible] with high regard and grateful rememberances of former kindnesses.

Notes
1. Sowerby figured this specimen in *Brit. Mineralogy*, Vol. V, (1817) pl. DXLVII, 275-6; it was one of the last plates published in this work (see comment in draft reply). It was Sowerby's habit to draft replies, or other matter, such as descriptions, on the letters he had received from his correspondents. The accompanying draft contains the substance of Sowerby's description of the specimen, but without exactly matching it in anyway. But in it Sowerby stated that he had received the specimen from Gregor in September 1808.
2. Russell, 'The Rev. William Gregor', 619, identified the specimen as Scorodite – a mineral first described by Bournon in 1801 and supposed to be a compound of iron, copper and arsenic. The formula given in Golley and Williams, *Cornish Mineral Reference Manual*, 56, does not include any copper; nor do they list the locality of Perran Arthowel amongst the Cornish locations at which scorodite has been found. However, the locality for the lead carbonate Cerussite (mentioned here in Gregor's letter) of the Pentire Glaze Mine, at St. Minver is included under that mineral.

CRO, Truro, Gregor Archive: DDG/1923/20
John Hawkins to Miss Gregor
        Warren's Hotel, Regent St., London, 8 March 1822[1]

In complying most readily with your wishes to appoint me one of the Trustees to your will I can not avoid expressing how much I feel gratified by your confidence in my friendship for your father, whom I sincerely loved & esteemed. His letters which I have preserved will shew that this regard was mutual although our intercourse was long interrupted. With your uncle too, tho some intimacy subsisted and I have always understood that the most friendly connexion had subsisted between our two families for some generations.

You may perceive therefore what a valid claim you possess to my best services.

I have forwarded by this day's post to Bignor a request which may possibly bring Mrs Hawkins to town to-morrow. . . . I have some doubts whether the state of her health at this instant will permit her to indulge her inclination so far, for the case will allow of no delay.

Beleive[2] me to be with great sincerity, My dear Miss Gregor, Your faithful friend, John Hawkins. P.S. My best Compts. to Miss Urquhart and thanks for her letter.[3]

Notes
  1. Annotated: '1822 – March From John Hawkins, Esqre. in answer to Miss Gregor's request to be one of her Executors'. There are three further letters during 1824 in this archive from Hawkins to Mrs Booker concerning the welfare of Gregor's daughter and her business interests.
  2. Hawkins always mis-spelt 'believe'.
  3. Miss Urquhart was Miss Gregor's companion.

CRO, Truro, Rashleigh Papers: DDR/5764-6
Charles Greville to Philip Rashleigh
Undated Memorandum

As my intention of establishing a Collection of Minerals took its rise on my visiting the Mines of

Hungary and Saxony, my Specimens all come from those Mines. I wish to Compleat my Collection of Tin from Cornwall. I am at a Loss to particularise the kinds not knowing any names by which Cornish Miners distinguish their ores – I have divided that Class of ores into the Following:

   Minera Stanni Vitrea Arsenicalis Amorpha –
   –   –   –   –   *Crystallina* –

answering to the Cornish Tin Stone & Tin Grains . . . *Stannium spatosum amorphum Crystallinum.* I should be glad to have a few specimens of all the sorts which are not numerous & ye different matrices on which they are & the Names of the mine from whence they come as I have been very fortunate in obtaining good

Specimens abroad a few good Specimens will be more acceptable than a great number of bad ones – as I do all I can to confine the Bulk of my Collection.

As to the other ores it would be abusing politeness to intrude a further List. My Collection of Copper is Good, likewise foreign. Any ores particullar [sic] to any of ye Mines will be highly acceptable. I have many Groups of Crystals – any particullarly [sic] good or Crystals of an uncommon colour or shape will be great addition to my Collection and if the person who will so obligingly undertake to assist me should be desirous of any particular foreign one, if I should not possess a Duplicate, [I] will undertake to acknowledge his politeness by getting them from abroad.

N.B. If on Chusing any of the Ores the matrix should differ I beg that particular may be attended to – It is a particular not much attended to by Collectors but makes one of the principal objects of my Collection after observing the appearance & structure of an Ore to collect the different matrices to see how far they influence their particular forms.

Bibliography

Adams, F. A., *The Birth and Development of the Geological Sciences* (New York, Dover Publications, 1938 and 1954).

Allan, T., *Mineralogical Nomenclature* (3rd edn., Edinburgh: A. Constable and Co., 1819).

Altick, R. D., *The English Common Reader: A Social History of the Mass Reading Public 1800–1900* (Chicago: University of Chicago Press, 1963).

Armstrong, P. H., *The English Parson-Naturalist: A Companionship between Science and Religion* (Leominster: Gracewing, 2000).

Ayling, S., *Fox: The Life of Charles James Fox* (London: John Murray, 1991).

Banks, R. E. R. (ed), *Sir Joseph Banks: A Global Perspective* (London: Royal Botanical Garden, Kew, 1994).

Bassett, D. A., 'James Hutton, the founder of modern geology: an anthology', *Geology*, 2 (1970), 5-76.

Bassett, D. A., 'Wales and the geological map', *Amgueddfa: Bulletin of the National Museum of Wales*, 3 (winter 1969), 10-25.

Berzelius, J., *An Attempt to Establish a Pure Scientific System of Mineralogy* (London: Black, 1814).

Berzelius, J., 'Des changemens dans le système de minéralogie chimique', *Annales de chimie et de physique*, 31 (1826), 34-5.

Borlase, W., *The Natural History of Cornwall* (Oxford: privately printed, 1758).

Brock, W. N., *The Fontana History of Chemistry* (Glasgow: Fontana Press, 1992).

Buffon, G. L. L., *Histoire naturelle* (Paris: 1749, 1779).

Burke, J. G., 'Mineral classification in the early nineteenth century', in Schneer, *Toward a History of Geology*, 62-77.

Campbell Smith, W., 'A history of the first hundred years of the mineral collection in the British Museum', *Bulletin of the British Museum (Natural History)*, (Historical Series), 3, 8 (1978), 137-159.

Carruth, N., R. Cleevely and D. I. Green, 'A Scorodite specimen figured by James Sowerby and analysed by William Gregor', *U.K. Journal of Mines and Minerals*, 28 (2007), 4-6.

Challinor, J., *The History of British Geology: A Bibliographical Study* (Newton Abbot: David & Charles, 1971).

Cleevely, R. J., 'Discovery of the 'Barnstaple Zeolite' – a minor geological controversy of the early 1800s', *Transactions of the Devonshire Association*, 2007 [2008], 133-67.

Cleevely, R. J., letter to editor, *The Linnean*, 21, 1 (2005), 12.

Cleevely, R. J., 'Carew and Rashleigh – a Cornish link during the "Age of the Curiosity Collector"; their association with Peter Pallas, the "Russian" German traveller-naturalist (1741–1811)', *Royal Institution of Cornwall Journal*, 2002, 9-29.

Cleevely, R. J., 'The contributions of a trio of Cornish geologists to the development of 18th century mineralogy' *Transactions of the Royal Geological Society of Cornwall*, 22, 3 (2000), 90-120.

Cleevely, R. J., 'A note on John Hawkins (1761–1841) and the Hawkins archive', *Archives of Natural History*, 27, 2 (2000), 261.

Cleevely, R. J., 'The Sowerbys and their publications in the light of the manuscript material in the British Museum (Natural History)', *Journal of the Society for the Bibliography of Natural History*, 7, 4 (1975), 345.

Cleevely, R. J. and C. M. Bristow, 'Rev. William Gregor (1761–1817): the contributions of a Cornish cleric and analytical chemist', *Journal of the Royal Institution of Cornwall*, 2003, 85-108.

Conklin, L. H., 'James Sowerby: his publications and collections', *Mineralogical Record*, 26 (4) 1995, 85-105.

Cooper, M. P., 'The Devonshire mineral collection in Chatsworth House', *The Mineralogical Record*, 36, 3 (2005), 251-4.

Cooper, M. P., 'Keeping it in the family: the Humphreys, Forsters and Heulands', *Matrix*, 9 (2001), 3-31.

Cooper, M. P., 'Letters from Henry Heuland (1778–1856) to Philip Rashleigh (1764–1811) in the Cornwall Record Office', unpublished transcription of 60 letters 1 April 1807 to 30 May 1809 (1999).

Cooper, M. P., *Robbing the Sparry Garniture: A 200-Year History of British Mineral Dealers* (Tucson, 2006).

Craig, G. Y., and J. H. Hull (eds), *James Hutton – Present and Future* (London: Geological Society Special Publication No. 150, 2002).

Crosland, M., *Historical Studies in the Language of Chemistry* (London: Constable, 1978).

Crump, J. (ed), *A Known Scribbler: Francis Burney on Literary Life* (London: Broadview Press, 2002).

Cunningham, A., and N. Jardine (eds), *Romanticism and the Sciences* (Cambridge: Cambridge University Press, 1990).

Daniel Clarke, E., *The Gas Blowpipe, or Art of Fusion by Burning* (London: T. Cadell and W. Davies, 1819).

Daunton, M., 'The Wealth of the Nation', in P. Langford (ed), *The*

Eighteenth Century, 1688–1815 (Oxford: Oxford University Press, 2002), 159-160.

Davies, G. L. H., *Sheets of Many Colours: The Mapping of Ireland's Rocks, 1750-1890* (Dublin: Royal Dublin Society, 1983).

Dawson, W. (ed), *The Banks Letters* (London: British Museum, 1958).

Dean, D. R., 'James Hutton and his public, 1785–1802', *Annals of Science*, 30, 1 (1973), 89-105.

Dott, R. H., 'James Hutton and the concept of a dynamic Earth', in Schneer, *Toward a History of Geology*, 122-141.

Eklund, J., 'The incompleat chymist: being an essay on the eighteenthcentury chemist in his laboratory, with a dictionary of obsolete chemical terms of the period', *Smithsonian Studies in History and Technology*, 33 (1975).

Embrey, P. G., 'Minerals', in J. M. Chalmers-Hunt, *Natural History Auctions 1700–1972* (London, Sotheby Parke Burnett, 1976), 39-44.

Embrey, P. G., and R. F. Symes, *Minerals of Cornwall and Devon* (London: British Museum (Natural History), 1987).

Eyles, V. A., 'The extent of geological knowledge in the eighteenth century, and the methods by which it was diffused', in Schneer (ed), *Toward a History of Geology*, 159-183.

Faraday, M., *Chemical Manipulation: Being Instructions to Students in Chemistry* (1827).

Flood, W. E., *The Dictionary of Chemical Names* (New York: Philosophical Library, 1963).

Ford, T. D., 'The growth of geological knowledge in the Peak District', *Mercian Geologist*, 14 (4), 1990, 161-190.

Gerhold, D., *Road Transport before Railways: Russell's London Flying Wagons* (Cambridge: Cambridge University Press, 1993).

Gerrard, S., *The Early British Tin Industry* (Stroud: Tempus, 2000).

Golley, P., and R. Williams, *Cornish Mineral Reference Manual* (Truro: Endsleigh, 1995).

Graham, A., *Catalogue of Meteorites* (Tucson, 1985).

Grant, J., *Hackh's Chemical Dictionary*, (3rd edn, Philadelphia: Blakiston, 1944).

Green, D. I., T. E. Cottrell, I. Jones, D. Cox and R. Cleevely, 'Wavellite: its discovery and occurrences in the British Isles', *U.K. Journal of Mines and Minerals*, 28 (2007), 11-30.

Gregor, W., 'Experiments on a mineral substance formerly supposed to be a Zeolite', *Philosophical Transactions of the Royal Society of London*, 95 (1805), 331-48.

Greville, C., 'Account of some stones said to have fallen on the earth in France; and of a lump of native iron said to have fallen in India', *Philosophical Transactions of the Royal Society*, 93, 1 (1823), 200-204.

Gruber, J. W. 'The Richard Owen Correspondence: An Introductory Essay', in J. W. Gruber and J. C. Thackray (eds), *Richard Owen Commemoration: Three Studies* (London: Natural History Museum Publications, 1992), 1-24.

Halliday, F. E., *A History of Cornwall* (London: Duckworth, 1959).

Harman, C., *Fanny Burney: A Biography* (London: HarperCollins, 2000).

Hibbert, C., *King Mob: The Story of Lord George Gordon and the Riots of 1780* (London: Longman, 1958).

Hill, C., *The House in St. Martin's Street, being Chronicles of the Burney Family* (London: John Lane, 1907).

Hony, T. L., 'The Rashleigh family', *Royal Cornwall Polytechnic Society, 106th Annual Report*, New Series IX, Part III (1939).

Hoskins, K. F. G., and G. J. Shrimpton, (eds), *Present Views of Some Aspects of the Geology of Cornwall and Devon* (Truro: Royal Geological Society of Cornwall, 1965).

Howard, E. C., et al., 'Experiments and observations on certain stony and metallic substances which at different times are said to have fallen on the Earth; also on various kinds of native iron', *Philosophical Transactions of the Royal Society*, 92 (1802), 168-212.

Hutchison, R, and A. Graham (1994) *Meteorites: The Key to our Existence* (London: Natural History Museum, 1994).

Hutton, J., *Theory of the Earth; or an Investigation of the Laws Observable in the Composition, Dissolution, and Restoration of Land upon the Globe* (Edinburgh: J. Dickson, 1788).

Hutton, J., *Theory of the Earth with Proofs and Illustrations* (Edinburgh: William Creech, 1795).

Izarn, J., *Des pierres tombées du ciel ou Lithologie Atmospherique* (Paris, 1803).

Jaggard, E., *Cornwall Politics in the Age of Reform 1790–1885* (London: Royal Historical Society, 1999).

Jaggard, E. (ed.), *Liberalism in West Cornwall: The 1868 Election Papers of A. Pendarves Vivian, M.P.* (Exeter: Devon and Cornwall Record Society, N.S. 42, 2000).

Jones, R. W., 'Philip Rashleigh and his specimens of British minerals (1797 & 1802)', *Mineralogical Record*, 26, 4 (1995), 77-84.

King, E., *Remarks Concerning Stones said to have Fallen from the Clouds, Both in these Days and in Ancient Times* (London: George Nicol, 1796).

Kingsbury, A. W. G., 'Some minerals of special interest in south-west England', in K. F. G. Hoskins and G. J. Shrimpton, (eds), *Present Views of Some Aspects of the Geology of Cornwall and Devon* (Truro: Royal Geological Society of Cornwall, 1965), pp.251, 252.

Kirwan, R., *Elements of Mineralogy* (London: 1784).

Klaproth, M. H., *Beiträge zur Chemischen Kenntniss der Mineralkörper* (Posen and Berlin: 1795).

Lack, H. W., *The Flora Graeca Story: Oxford's Finest Botanical Treasure. Sibthorp, Bauer and Hawkins in the Levant: An Exhibition at the Bodleian Library, Oxford 19 July 1999 – 25 September 1999* (Oxford: Bodleian Library, 1999).

Lack, H. W., *The Flora Graeca Story: Sibthorp, Bauer and Hawkins in the Levant* (Oxford: Oxford University Press, 1999).

Leibnitz, G. W., *Protogaea* (Göttingen: 1749).

Macgregor, M. A., *et al*, 'James Hutton 1726–1797', *Proceedings of the Royal Society of Edinburgh*, Sect B (Biology) LXIII (iv) (1950), 351-402.

Maton, W. G. *Observations Relative Chiefly to the Natural History, Picturesque Scenery & Antiquities of the Western Counties of England* (Salisbury: J. Eaton, 1797).

Mumby, A. N. L., *The Cult of the Autograph Letter in England*, (London: Athlone Press, 1962).

Namier, L. B. and J. Brooke *The House of Commons 1754–1790* (London: HMSO for the History of Parliament Trust, 1964), vol. 3.

Nicholson, N., *The World of Jane Austen* (London: Weidenfeld and Nicholson, 1991).

O'Brian, P., *Joseph Banks* (London: Collins Harvill, 1987).

Ospovat, A. M., 'Reflections on A. G. Werner's "Kurze Klassification"', in Schneer, *Toward a History of Geology*, 242-256.

Penhallurick, R. D., 'The mineral collection of the Royal Institution of Cornwall', *U.K. Journal of Mines & Minerals*, 18 (1997), 17-32.

Pillinger, C. T., and J. M. Pillinger, 'The Wold Cottage meteorite: not an ordinary chondrite', *Meteoritics and Planetary Science*, 31, 5 (1996), 589-605.

Porter, R., *English Society in the Eighteenth Century* (London: Penguin Books, 1982).

Porter, R., *The Making of Geology: Earth Science in Britain 1660–1815* (Cambridge: Cambridge University Press, 1977).

Porter, R., review of D. Stanfield, *Thomas Beddoes MD 1760–1808* (1984) in *British Journal for the History of Science*, 19, 1 (1986), 122.

Porter, T. M., 'The promotion of mining and the advancement of science: the chemical revolution of mineralogy', *Annals of Science*, 38 (1981), 543-70.

Raistrick A. (ed), *The Hatchett Diary: A Tour through the Counties of England and Scotland in 1796 visiting their Mines and Manufactories* (Truro: Bradford Barton, 1967).

Rappaport, R., 'The geological atlas of Guettard, Lavoisier and Monnet', in C. J. Schneer (ed), *Towards a History of Geology* (MIT Press, 1969), 272-87.

Ray, J., *Miscellaneous Discourses Concerning the Dissolution and Changes in the World* (London: 1692).

Ray, J., *The Wisdom of God Manifested in the Works of Creation* (London: 1691).

Reingold, N., 'On not doing the papers of great scientists', *British Journal for the History of Science*, 20 (1987), 29-38.

Roger, J., 'Les epoques de la nature: histoire naturelle', *Mémoire du Museum National d'Histoire Naturelle (Science de la Terre)*, 10 (1962).

Rose, G., *Das krystallo-chemische Mineralsystem* (Leipzig: 1852).

Rowse, A. L., *A Cornish Anthology* (London: Macmillan, 1968).

Russell, Sir A., 'John Hawkins, FGS, FRHS, FRS, 1761–1841: a distinguished Cornishman and early mining geologist', *Journal of the Royal Institution of Cornwall*, New Series, 2, 2 (1954), 97-106.

Russell, Sir A., 'Philip Rashleigh of Menabilly, Cornwall and his mineral collection', *Journal of the Royal Institution of Cornwall*, New Series, 1, 2 (1952).

Russell, Sir A., 'The Rev. William Gregor (1761–1817), discoverer of titanium', *The Mineralogical Magazine*, 30, 229 (1955), 617-624.

Schneer, C. J., *Toward a History of Geology* (Cambridge, Mass.: MIT Press, 1969).

Söderbaum H. G. (ed), *Jac. Berzelius Lettres: Correspondance entre Berzelius et Eilhard Mitscherlich (1818–1847)* (Uppsala: Almgvist, 1932).

Spedding, J., R. L. Ellis and D. D. Heath (eds), *The Works of Francis Bacon* (London: Longmans Green, 1868–90), vol. 4.

Stearn, W. T., 'The background and origin of the Flora Graeca', *Biological Journal of the Linnean Society*, 8, 4 (1976), 285.

Steers, F., *The Hawkins Papers: A Catalogue* (Chichester, West Sussex Record Office, 1962).

Steers, F., *I Am, My Dear Sir . . . A Selection of Letters Written Mainly to and by John Hawkins FRS, GS 1761–1841* (Chichester: West Sussex Record Office, 1959).

Steers, F., *The Letters of John Hawkins and Samuel and Daniel Lysons, 1812–1830* (Chichester: West Sussex Record Office, 1966).

Stevenson, J., *Popular Disturbances in England 1700–1832*, (Harlow: Longman, 2nd ed., 1992).

Thorne, R. G., *The House of Commons 1790–1820* (London: Secker and Warburg for the History of Parliament Trust, 1986), vol 4.

Thorne, R. G., *The House of Commons 1790–1820* (London: Secker and Warburg for the History of Parliament Trust, 1986), vol 5.

Tomkeieff, S. I., 'James Hutton and the philosophy of geology', *Proceedings of the Royal Society of*

Townson, R., *Philosophy of Mineralogy* (London: 1798).

Trengove, L, 'William Gregor (1761–1817) discover of titanium', *Annals of Science*, 29, 4 (1972), 361-95.

Uglow, J., *The Lunar Men: The Friends who made the Future, 1730–1810* (London: Faber and Faber, 2002).

Vincent, B. B., 'Mendeleev's periodic system of chemical elements', *British Journal for the History of Science*, 19, 1 (1986), 4-5.

Vincent, B. B., 'A view of the chemical revolution through contemporary textbooks: Lavoisier, Fourcroy and Chaptal', *British Journal for the History of Science*, 23, 4 (1990), 440.

Wedgwood, B., and H. Wedgwood, *The Wedgwood Circle 1730–1897* (London: Studio Vista, 1980).

Weindling, P., 'The British Mineralogical Society: a case study in science and social improvement', in I. Inkster and J. Morrell (eds), *Metropolis and Province: Science in British Culture, 1780–1850* (University of Pennsylvania Press, 1983), 127.

Werner, A. G., *Ausführliches und systematisches Verzeichnis des Mineralien-kabinets des weiland kurfürstlich Sächsischen Berghauptmans Herrn Karl Eugen Pabst von Ohain*. (2 vols., Freiberg: 1791).

Werner, A. G., *Kurze Klassification* (Dresden: 1785).

Whewell, W., *History of the Inductive Sciences* (New York: Appleton, 1884), vol. 2.

Wilson, W. E., 'The history of mineral collecting 1530–1799', *Mineralogical Record*, 25, 6 (1994), 46.

Wilson, W. E., 'Mineral books: five centuries of mineralogical literature', *Mineralogical Record*, 25, 4 (1995), 49-60, and 'Addendum 1800–1962', 60-64.

Full captions of colour Illustrations

Fig. 1   *Top left*   Rashleigh's letter to Pole Carew in St. Petersbourg (23rd Feb. 1781)
Giving details of his 'desiderata'; CRO, Antony, Carew papers – [CC/J/11/36].

             Top right   Gregor's letter to John Hawkins (8th Jan. 1791); CRO, Truro, Hawkins Papers – [J3/2/186], sent after his marriage and settling at Caerhays; [note the 'X' that Hawkins marked when he had replied.

             Bottom left   Letter sent to Rashleigh by R. Pole Carew from Angouléme (31st Dec. 1775) soon after beginning his European tour; CRO, Truro, Rashleigh papers – [5302/115] – Not selected.

             Bottom right   Letter from William Gregor to Rashleigh (25th July 1805) concerning specimens of Hydrargillite [= Wavellite] from Stenna Gwinn & Barnstaple; CRO, Truro, Rashleigh Papers – [5757/2/72].

Fig. 2   *Left*   Letter from the dealer Mrs Forster to Rashleigh (25th June 1805) with a list of specimens & their prices CRO, Truro, Rashleigh Papers [5757/2/44] – **not selected** but see her other letters on pp, 178 & 196.

             Right   Letter from Leopold Fichtel to Rashleigh sent after 19th July 1806 concerning the sale of specimens – CRO, Truro, Rashleigh Papers [5757/2/52] – **not selected** but see other related letters pp 192 & 194.

Fig. 3   Pages from Charles Hatchett's letter (19th November 1804) to Rashleigh on various mineral topics including Davy's analysis of the 'Barnstaple Zeolite' and establishing a mineral collection at the Royal Institution – CRO, Truro, Rashleigh Papers [5757/2/75]. **not selected**. Note the effects of and allowance for its wax seal.

Fig. 4   *Top*   19th century Illustration of the use of the Blowpipe – for further information see Ulrich Burchard., 'The History and Apparatus of Blowpipe Analysis', *The Mineralogical Record*, 25 Part 4, 1994: 251-277.

             Bottom   Drawing by Thomas Rackett in a letter to Dr. Pulteney (24th January 1793) that mentioned a simple improvement made by Hatchett [Pulteny letters No. 4, Linnean Society, London], but see letter here (p. 103) from Gregor to Rashleigh (24th November 1792) that refers to a similar modification.

Fig. 5 *Top*   Martin Klaproth's first volume of Mineral analyses
                              (1795) that included three Cornish minerals was
                              dedicated to John Hawkins in recognition of his
                              assistance (see p. xl) and letters (p, 51, 56, & 60).
                              His earlier analyses of tin and copper ores (1787) was
                              translated by J.G. Groschke as "*Observations relating
                              to the Mineralogical and Chemical . . . Fossils of
                              Cornwall*" and published in London that year (Cleevely,
                              2000: 112).

         Bottom   Catalogue of Mlle. Eleanore De Raab' Collection by
                              Baron von Born published in Vienna (1790).
                              Hawkins and Rashleigh sent specimens to her – (see
                              p. xxxiv & xxxvi) and letters sent between November
                              1790 to October 1791.

Fig. 6 Liroconite – Group of transparent crystals of Copper Ore in double
         4-sided pyramids from Wheal Gorland; specimen figured by Rashleigh
         (1802, pl. XI, fig. 3 – Truro Museum – Rashleigh Mss Catalogue No.
         1114.
         Left) –   NHM photo – see p. 154 and back cover of dust jacket
                              figured Embrey & Symes (1997) and (Russell (1952: 19
                              & 22).
         Right) –   original drawing by his sister Mrs J. Gould giving a
                              different view [in Russell Bequest, Mineralogy Library
                              archives, NHM].

Fig. 7 *Left*   Sowerby's figure of Gregor's 'new specimen of
                              Hydrargillite' with small pyramidal crystals of a
                              mineral later identified as Fluellite – pl. 243 in *British
                              Mineralogy*, vol. 3, 1st Dec. 1807.
         Right   Gregor's letter to Rashleigh (11th Feb. 1807) reporting
                              this as a new specimen of Hydrargillite where he stated
                              "As I wish Mr. Sowerby to notice it I have some thought
                              of lending him my specimen "– CRO, Truro, Rashleigh
                              Papers [5757/2/66] – **not selected**" – see also his letter
                              to Hawkins (5th February 1807) that mentions this
                              specimen [NHM, Russell Bequest 5/6].

Fig. 8 *Left*   Gregor's letter to Rashleigh (23 August 1804) that refers
                              to a possible "Thunderstone" falling at Saltash – CRO,
                              Truro, Rashleigh Papers [5757/2/35] – **not selected**; but
                              see his letter of (26th August 1804) and p. 167-169 for
                              other comments.
         Right   Sowerby's published print of the Yorkshire Stone (1812)
                              subsequently known as the 'Wold meteorite' – referred
                              to in various letters between Rashleigh, Sowerby and
                              Gregor during 1804–1807.

Name Index

Subject and Place Index

basalt 43, 50, 51, 75, 81, 107, 110
bournonite 123, 215 n6
'caak' 40
calamine 113
coal 143-4
cobalt 58, 65, 146, 158
corundum 152
copper 55, 64, 98,121, 134 , 164, 177, 200
  crystallization 56
  green copper ore 96, 98
  muriate of 166, 210
  price in 1790 65
  production 70, 135
  red /ruby copper 57, 98, 147
  white feather form 65
  wood copper ore 181, 182
'corneus' 44, 46
diamonds 168
elvan stone 102, 104, 105
erythrite (peach blossom efflorescence) 76, 77 n1
fire stone 102, 105
fluellite/'zeolite' 201-3
fluorite 58, 64, 69, 70 n1, 83, 113
frestone 104
gadoline/'gadolinite' 152, 186, 188, 211
ganges /'gangue' 20, 20, 21
gneiss 46
gold, native 7
Helstone earth 91
'hornetz' 74
horn silver 27, 29, 31, 57, 78, 89, 127, 209
hydrargillite 184 see also under wavellite
iron white ore 151
jargon 55
lead arseniate (mimetite) 207, 208, 213
lead chromate 207
lead molybdenate 168, 180
lead spar (white lead ore) 65, 68,

looking-glass iron ore 27, 30
luna-cornea 85
malachite 37
'manaccanite' 131
manganese 63, 66, 158
menackanite 66, 72, 84, 91, 92, 94, 111, 131
mica – green ore 96
mimetite 208, 211, 213
'peach' 104, 105, 146 see also under Erythrite
'Pierre de Corne' 60
pitchstone 194
'ponderous spar' 128
'regulus' 69, 74
'mundic' 164
Rotgiltig Erz 90
rubies 153
scorodite 217-18 n2
selenite 77, 111
selenite 'snow' 63
shirl: 43, 188
red 131
silver ore 12, 71, 74, 83, 91, 95, 104, 124, 127, 134-5, 158
'stone marrow' 60, 61 n2
strontian 128, 138
sylvanite 119 n 1, 121
sinopel 44
tellerium 143
terra ponderosa 42
thalite 153
thumerstein 152
'thunderstones' 167, 168
tin ore 57, 89, 93; 134, 191
  black tin 61
  'rash' tin ore 61
  refining 76, 89
  'ruby tin' 147
  stannary matters 91
titanium 151
toadstone 47, 53
tourmaline 44
tungsten 30, 69, 83, 84, 89, 117
tungstate of lime 194
uranglimmer 185

DEVON AND CORNWALL
RECORD SOCIETY

(Founded 1904)

Officers 2008–9

The Devon and Cornwall Record Society promotes the study of history in the South West of England through publishing and transcribing original records. In return for the annual subscription members receive the volumes as published (normally annually) and the use of the Society's library, housed in the Westcountry Studies Library, Exeter. The library includes transcripts of parish registers relating to Devon and Cornwall as well as useful genealogical works.

Applications to join the Society or to purchase volumes should be sent to the Assistant Secretary, Devon and Cornwall Record Society, c/o Devon and Exeter Institution, 7 Cathedral Close, Exeter EX1 1EZ.

DEVON AND CORNWALL
RECORD SOCIETY PUBLICATIONS

The following New Series titles are obtainable from the Administrator, Devon and Cornwall Record Society, 7 The Close, Exeter EX1 1EZ

Unless otherwise indicated, prices are: £15.00 UK, £20.00 overseas (surface mail). All prices include p/p.

At joining, new members are offered volumes of the preceding 4 years at current subscription prices rather than the listed price.

Fully-paid members are offered a discount on volumes older than 5 years if the remaining stock exceeds 20: please enquire.

ISSN/ISBN 978-0-901853-

New Series

2 *Exeter in the Seventeenth Century: Tax and Rate Assessments 1602–1699*, ed. W G Hoskins, 1957 - **05 4**

4 *The Diocese of Exeter in 1821: Bishop Carey's Replies to Queries before Visitation*, vol. II Devon, ed. Michael Cook, 1960 - **07 0**

6 *The Exeter Assembly: Minutes of the Assemblies of the United Brethren of Devon and Cornwall 1691–1717*, as transcribed by the Reverend Isaac Gilling, ed. Allan Brockett, 1963 - **09 7**

12 *Plymouth Building Accounts of the 16th & 17th Centuries*, ed. Edwin Welch, 1967 - **14 3**

15 *Churchwardens' Accounts of Ashburton 1479–1580*, ed. Alison Hanham, 1970 - **01 1**

17§ *The Caption of Seisin of the Duchy of Cornwall 1377*, ed. P L Hull, 1971 - **03 8**

19 *A Calendar of Cornish Glebe Terriers 1673–1735*, ed. Richard Potts, 1974 - **19 4** *£18.00*

20   *John Lydford's Book: the Fourteenth Century Formulary of the Archdeacon of Totnes*, ed. Dorothy M Owen, 1975 (with Historical Manuscripts Commission) - **011 440046 6**

21   *A Calendar of Early Chancery Proceedings relating to West Country Shipping 1388–1493*, ed. Dorothy A Gardiner, 1976 - **20 8**

22   *Tudor Exeter: Tax Assessments 1489–1595*, ed. Margery M Rowe, 1977 - **21 6**

23   *The Devon Cloth Industry in the 18th Century*, ed. Stanley D Chapman, 1978 - **22 4**

24, 26   *The Accounts of the Fabric of Exeter Cathedral 1279–1353*, Parts I & II, ed. Audrey M Erskine, 1981 & 1983 - **24 0, 26 7** *£15.00 individually, £20.00 the pair* (UK)

25, 27   *The Parliamentary Survey of the Duchy of Cornwall*, Parts I & II, ed. Norman J G Pounds 1982 & 1984 - **25 2, 27 5** - *£15.00 individually, £20.00 the pair* (UK)

28   *Crown Pleas of the Devon Eyre 1238*, ed. Henry Summerson, 1985 - **28 3**

29   *Georgian Tiverton, The Political Memoranda of Beavis Wood 1768–98*, ed. John Bourne, 1986 - **29 1**

30   *The Cartulary of Launceston Priory* (Lambeth Palace MS.719): *A Calendar*, ed. P L Hull, 1987 - **30 5**

31   *Shipbuilding on the Exe: The Memoranda Book of Daniel Bishop Davy (1799–1874) of Topsham, Devon*, ed. Clive N Ponsford, 1988 - **31 3**

32   *The Receivers' Accounts of the City of Exeter 1304–1353*, ed. Margery Rowe and John M Draisey, 1989 - **32 1**

33   *Early-Stuart Mariners and Shipping: The Maritime Surveys of Devon and Cornwall 1619–35*, ed. Todd Gray, 1990 - **33 X**

34   *Joel Gascoyne's Map of Cornwall 1699*. Introduction by W L D Ravenhill and O J Padel, 1991. *£25.00 UK, £32.00 overseas* - **34 8**

35   *Nicholas Roscarrock's 'Lives of the Saints': Cornwall and Devon*, ed. Nicholas Orme, 1992 - **35 6**

36   *The Local Port Customs Accounts of Exeter 1266–1321*, ed. Maryanne Kowaleski, 1993 - **36 4**

37   *Charters of the Redvers Family and the Earldom of Devon 1090–1217*, ed. Robert Bearman, 1994 - **37 2**

38   *Devon Household Accounts, 1627–59, Part I: Sir Richard and Lady Lucy Reynell of Forde House, 1627–43, John Willoughby of Leyhill, 1644–6, and Sir Edward Wise of Sydenham, 1656–9*, ed. Todd Gray, 1995 *£17.00 UK, £22.00 overseas* - **38 0**

Extra Series

Shelf list of the Society's Collections, revised June 1986. *£2.30 UK, £3.50 overseas.*
http://www.devon.gov.uk/library/locstudy/dcrs.html.

New Series out of print:
1 *Devon Monastic Lands: Calendar of Particulars for Grants 1536-1558*, ed. Youings, 1955; 3 *The Diocese of Exeter in 1821: vol. I Cornwall*, ed. Cook, 1958; 5 *The Cartulary of St Michael's Mount*, ed. Hull, 1962; 8 *The Cartulary of Canonsleigh Abbey*, calendared & ed. London, 1965; 9 *Benjamin Donn's Map of Devon 1765*. Intro. Ravenhill, 1965; 11 *Devon Inventories of the 16th & 17th Centuries*, ed. Cash, 1966; 14 *The Devonshire Lay Subsidy of 1332*, ed. Audrey M Erskine, 1969; 7, 10, 13, 16, 18 *The Register of Edmund Lacy, Bishop of Exeter 1420–1455* (five volumes), ed. Dunstan, 1963–1972

Extra Series out of print: *Guide to the Parish and Non-Parochial Registers of Devon and Cornwall 1538–1837*, compiled: Peskett, 1979 & supplement 1983